LINCOLN'S EXCAVATORS
The Ruston-Bucyrus Years
1945 - 1970

First published in 2010 by Roundoak Publishing,
The Old Dairy, Perry Farm, East Nynehead,
Wellington, Somerset, TA21 0DA. United Kingdom

Tel. +44 (0)1823 461997

email: info@nynehead-books.co.uk
www.nynehead-books.co.uk

Origination: Roundoak Associates
Printed in Great Britain by Amadeus Press,
Cleckheaton, West Yorkshire

ISBN 978-1-871565-52-2

Front cover picture and this page: 38-RB Shovel
working for Sir John Jackson at the Treforgan
contract, Crynant, Neath in September 1955.

Half title picture: 38-RB Shovel working on the
Breadalbane Hydro-Electric Project, February 1956.

ACKNOWLEDGEMENTS

As with the previous volumes of Lincoln's Excavators, the bulk of the material in this book
is derived from my own collection of original documents and photographs.
However, I am grateful for the following, some of whom are former colleagues from my
RB days, for their offer of personal photographs or material in the compiling of this third
volume of Lincoln's Excavators.

Keith Bradshaw, Derek Broughton, Dennis 'Snowy' Clawson, Michael Everitt, David and
Arthur Fatchett, Carl Halliwell, Peter Odam, Michael Parker, John Selby, Bert Suthrell and
Family, John Turner, Peter Wyatt.

Peter Robinson B.Ed. (Hons.) Fillingham, Lincolnshire

LINCOLN'S EXCAVATORS

The Ruston-Bucyrus Years
1945 - 1970

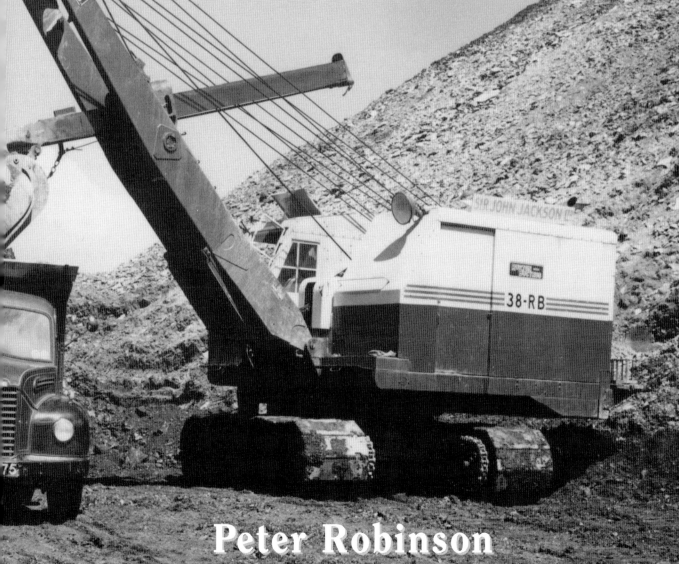

Peter Robinson
Roundoak Publishing

Contents

Introduction	6
The Relationship between	7
Ruston-Bucyrus Ltd.	
and Bucyrus-Erie Co.	
Post War Recovery	9
Ruston-Bucyrus Board of Directors	11
The 1947 Floods	12
Factory Extensions 1949	19
The Big Move	19
1,000 Excavators in a Year	21
The Festival of Britain	22
RB Excavators to the Rescue	22
The Great Flood of 1953	24
Excavators at the Coronation	26
History Repeats Itself	28
The Excavator Works in the 1950s	29
Changes to the Ruston-Bucyrus	30
Board of Directors 1954-57	
The Apprentices	32
It's a Small World	37
On the Theme of 'Strange Bed-Fellows'	37
Ruston-Bucyrus Annual Open Day 1956	40
Difficult Times 1956-58	44
End of the Line for Some	45
The 10-RB Goes On	48
Drainage	48
The 54-RB	53
The 54-RB Shovel / Dragline	54
Truck Frame and Revolving Frame	55
Main Machinery - 54-RB	56
Diesel / Single Motor Electric	
54-RB Dragline	61
Pontoon Mounted 54-RB Dragline	64
54-RB Folding A-Frame	66
54-RB Long-Boom Stripping Shovel	68
54-RB Ward-Leonard Electric Excavator	70
Ward-Leonard System	70
The 38-RB	75
The 38-RB Excavator	76
38-RB Basic Design	80
38-RB Single Motor Electric	82
38-RB Dragline	83
38-RB Series Two	84
38-RB Series Two Standard and	94
Heavy Duty Crane / Dragline	
The 22-RB	95
22-RB Excavator	96
22-RB Single Motor Electric	100
Development of the 22-RB	109
Lifting Crane	
The 22-RB Two-in-One	110
'An Absorbing Entertainment'	
22-RB Wrist-Action Dragshovel	112
The Improved 22-RB Wrist-action	115
Dragshovel	
Wrist-action on the M18 Motorway	116
22-RB with Air Controls	119
The 22-RB Air Assist Control System	121
1981, the 10,000th 22-RB	122
The '100' Series	123
110-RB / 150-RB Mining Shovels	124
and Draglines	
110-RB Crawler Mounting	127
The '100' Series Shovel Front End	128
Equipment	
110-RB Long Range Mining Shovel	129
110-RB Excavators at Barrington Quarry	130
110-RB Diesel-Electric Shovel / Dragline	134
Pressurised Cabs	135
'Operation Century'	137
The One Hundredth 110-RB	
150-RB Ward-Leonard	138
Electric Shovel / Dragline	
The 150-RB on Show	139
150-RB Demonstration at Amberswood	140
150-RB Electric Shovel in Opencast	142
Coal Operations	
150-RB Shovel - Further Improvements	144
150-RB Shovel with Live Boom	144
Suspension	
Towards a 110-RB / 150-RB Lifting Crane	146
Static Control	148
Uprating for the 150-RB	150
150-RB Shovels in Spain	152
A New Look	153
A New Look for Lincoln's Engines	154
A New Livery	155
Customised Liveries	156
Excavator Engines	157
Excavator Engines - Freedom to Choose	158
A New Bay for the Mining Shovels	159
Ruston-Bucyrus - 'A Family Firm'	160
A Welding Challenge	162
The 30-RB	165
30-RB Universal Excavator	166
30-RB Full Air Controls	172

30-RB Continued:
Innovations - Involute Splines and Cut-Hardened Gears 174
'Christmas Island' and Problems with the Hardening Process 176
The Swing Brake and an Alarmed Ship's Captain 177
Logging Cranes for New Zealand 178
30-RB Dragline / Crane / Grabbing Crane
Piling & Special Applications 181
Drop Hammer Pile Driving 182
Power Hammer Application 182
Sand Drain Piling 190
Bored (Non-displacement) Piling 191
Continuous Flight Auger (CFA) 195
Types of Piling 196
Diaphragm Walling 197
The Carriers - Part Two 199
An Island Works 200
Ruston-Bucyrus Conventions for Road Transportation 202
Suthrell Haulage Contractors 204
Wynns 212
Pickfords 216
Hallett Silbermann Ltd 220
Excavators for Sweden 222
George Wimpey 226
'A Bridge Too Far' 228
Two New Products 229
A New Chairman for Ruston-Bucyrus Ltd 231
A New Chairman's Concerns 232
Tower Cranes 233
The 12/52 and 34/80 Tower Cranes 240
Basic Design 240
12/52 Operating Machinery 246
34/80 Tower Crane 249
34/80 Tower Crane Hydraulic System 253
Ruston-Bucyrus 15/50 Tower Crane Prototype 256
Summary - Ruston-Bucyrus Tower Cranes 256
Hydraulic Excavators Part One - The 3-RB 257
3-RB Hydraulic Excavator 258
3-RB Series One Hydraulic Excavator 259
Basic Design - Hydraulics - Power Unit 260
Working Dimensions - 3-RB Series One Hydraulic Hoe Excavator 264
3-RB Clamshell Grab Equipment 268
3-RB Wheel Mounted 1965 270

Working Dimensions of the 3-RB Wheel Mounted Excavator 272
3-RB Series II (Intermediate Stage) 274
3-RB Series II (Final Version) 275
The Ruston-Bucyrus 3-RB; 'A Missed Opportunity' 278
Changes at the Excavator Works 279
Change to the Company's Articles of Association 280
Bucyrus-Erie Co. Increases it's Control 281
"The Future has Never Been Brighter" 281
Expansion of the Ruston-Bucyrus Plant 282
The Spike Island Foundry Development 282
"You Shall Go To The Ball" 287
The Firth Road Factory Development 289
Hydraulic Excavators - The 'H' Range 291
The European Surveys 292
German Market Survey - 1965 292
Report by J.H. Page and R.C. Chevassut 292
The B.E. 'H' Range of Hydraulic Excavators 293
'A Strange Animal' - Hydraulic Hoe with Rotating Boom 302
Problems with the 20-H 303
20-RBH 303
20-RBH Hoe with Two-Piece Pin Connected Boom 1969 305
20-RBH Parallel Action Loading Shovel 1970/71 306
15-H / 15-RBH Hydraulic Excavator 308
Ruston Bucyrus 30-H / 30-RBH 310
Hydraulic Excavators - Success at Last 311
A New Range of RB Hydraulic Excavators 312
RBH-1 Hydraulic Excavator (The Test Mock-up) 313
The RBH-1 Prototype Hydraulic Excavator 1971/72 313
RBH-1 Success at Last 314
A Sudden Departure 315
The Ruston-Bucyrus 150-RH 316
Expanding the Range - 150-RW / 175-RH / 220-RH 322
375-RS Hydraulic Quarry Shovel 324
A Summary of Ruston-Bucyrus Hydraulic Excavators 330
Types of Excavators 332
Excavator Terminology 333
Machinery Index 334
General Index 335

Introduction

Volume Three of Lincoln's Excavators picks up the story in the early post World War Two years when nations around the world were facing the task of repairing the ravages of war and restoring their economies to meet the challenge of an uncertain peace time future.

Excavator manufacturer Ruston-Bucyrus Ltd., established in 1930 at the height of the depression, was a successful company at the outbreak of the war and like other British industries the consequences of its war effort had furthered the company's financial status and led to improved and expanded manufacturing facilities at the Excavator Works.

With the war over the Lincoln company could face the future with confidence and the only cloud on the horizon was the shortage of raw materials necessary for the factory to satisfy the world wide demand for its Excavators.

In 1951 a significant milestone was reached when Ruston-Bucyrus celebrated the production of 1,000 Excavators at the Lincoln works in that one year alone and by 1954 the company was described as being in "the most favourable competitive and financial condition of its existence".

Despite a temporary recession in the late fifties, the story of Lincoln's Excavators in the two decades after the war was one of continual growth - in the range and quantity of products and in the size of the works and workforce. It was a time of much optimism at the Excavator Works generated by full order books and a seemingly endless line of customers for excavators and a wide range of specialized cranes that formed a large part of the company's output.

Like the Ruston Navvies of an earlier age Ruston-Bucyrus Excavators epitomized the quality of engineering for which Lincoln has become famous throughout the world and within its three thousand strong work force there was the unspoken belief that the company, like their excavators, could go on forever. It is understandable, therefore, that there are those who describe the 1950s-1960s era as the 'Golden Age' of Lincoln's Excavators; this book charts the history of Ruston-Bucyrus and its products through that period reflecting its success and possibly the seeds of its eventual decline.

The 1970s, to be recorded in Vol. IV of Lincoln's Excavators, would see a massive expansion of the Ruston-Bucyrus factories and a wide range of new products designed for markets at home and abroad, but it would also see ever increasing competition from other manufacturers. So an old RB Sales Representative can be forgiven for looking back with some affection to the days when the machines 'sold themselves', and his business could be conducted in the relaxed atmosphere of a golf course.

The author, Peter Robinson

The Relationship between Ruston-Bucyrus Ltd. and Bucyrus-Erie Co.

The circumstances of the creation of Ruston-Bucyrus Ltd. (described in more detail in earlier volumes of 'Lincoln's Excavators') resulted in the Lincoln Company having two parent companies - Ruston & Hornsby Ltd. of Lincoln and the Bucyrus-Erie Co. of America, each with equal share-holding and equal representation on the Ruston-Bucyrus Board of Directors. The Chairman of the Board, appointed from the American parent company had the additional casting vote in any Board decisions, though in W.W. Coleman's time (chairman of Ruston-Bucyrus Ltd. until 1957) the necessity to use it had never occurred.

The Products;

Though Ruston-Bucyrus products were in the main based on B.E. designs, the Lincoln company had the autonomy to

"modify, develop, or incorporate changes to these designs as required to meet their own markets and to design and develop new models to meet the requirements of their own markets when no suitable BE model was available."

As a matter of policy it was also agreed from the outset that Ruston-Bucyrus would use only Ruston engines in their products.

The Sales;

Since both RB and Bucyrus-Erie were manufacturing the same or similar products it was established at the creation of Ruston-Bucyrus in 1930 that each would have their own designated sales areas. The triangular relationship between Ruston-Bucyrus Ltd. and its two separate parent companies, Ruston & Hornsby Ltd. and Bucyrus Erie Co. became a highly successful one founded upon a dedicated British management supported by W.W. Coleman, RB's experienced and understanding American founder Chairman. This success was reflected in the speech made by 'Ernie' Everett, RB's Managing Director, at a meeting of the Lincoln Junior Chamber of Commerce in 1952.

Extracts from the speech by E.S. Everitt to the Junior Chamber of Commerce, 20th January 1952;

Referring to RB/BE Sales Territories -

"The world's markets for excavators is divided between RB/BE into three territorial classifications - broadly the Bucyrus Erie share of influence is Canada, South and Central America, Japan and China. Then there is the so-called 'open' territories where either company can sell as they wish without reference to the other, namely U.S.S.R. and the U.S.A. Thirdly, there is the Ruston-Bucyrus sphere of influence which is the rest of the world, including Europe, the African Continent, and the British Commonwealth. If, however, there are good reasons such as exchange problems, or customer requirements, each company can and does obtain orders from the other's territory. Our prices are identical for all export markets whether in our so-called territory or B.E.'s."

Referring to the Relationship between the two companies;

"A question we are frequently asked is whether we are a subsidiary of Ruston-Hornsby or Bucyrus Erie; we are neither, we are an independent private limited company with, in effect only two share holders who each own 50% of the total shares."

"Another remarkable feature is that despite B.E.'s holding and interest in the company, for the last 12 years there has been only one American on the Ruston-Bucyrus pay-roll and he is our Chairman, Mr. Coleman. This would seem a remarkable expression of confidence by the Americans in their British counterparts. There is of course close liaison at all times between the two companies."

Mr. Everitt went on to list some company statistics for Ruston-Bucyrus Ltd. for the years up to that time that reveal company growth over the past decades.

Employment Records;

1930	-	687
1939	-	1350
1952	-	2250

Output per annum of Machines;

1930	-	220
1939	-	518
1951	-	1024

Annual Production in Tons;

1930	-	3850
1939	-	9834
1951	-	24,700

Total Wages and Salaries;

1930	-	£115,000
1939	-	£250,000
1952	-	£ 1,140,000.

A 10-RB Dragline in the new maroon and cream livery introduced in 1956 is pictured under test at the Excavator Works in the late 1950s. It also features a more rounded style of cab introduced around that time to modernise the range and soften the 'boxy' look of the superstructure. The 10-RB first went into production in 1934 with the last machine leaving the Excavator Works in November 1969 by which time 7625 examples had been built.

LINCOLN'S EXCAVATORS

POST WAR RECOVERY

10-RB working on pre-fab construction site, Bristol, 1947

POST WAR RECOVERY

The optimism with which Ruston-Bucyrus Ltd. faced the future at the end of World War II was not misplaced for between 1945 and 1953 the output from the Excavator Works more than doubled, rising from an annual output of 500 small to medium size excavators in the war years to 1,200 by 1953. This reflected the massive demand for machinery and equipment to repair the ravages of war, both in the U.K. and overseas; a demand which was met by the Lincoln company's post-war expansion plans and which led in 1954 to Ruston-Bucyrus establishing itself as a world leader in small to medium excavator production, shipments of which, by 1954, constituted 50 per cent of all industry sales for domestic and overseas markets.

Comparing RB's production figures with those of the Bucyrus Erie Company, the number of machines built by Ruston-Bucyrus in the 3/8 cu.yd. to 2½ cu.yd. category rose from 70 per cent of Bucyrus Erie's volume in 1945 to 140 per cent of the American firm's shipments in 1953. This indicates not only the Lincoln company's growth but the fact that the post-war years had not gone so smoothly with the American parent company which was beset by serious labour problems and a long succession of strikes that had begun in wartime and continued into the early 1950s.

For the products of Ruston-Bucyrus, the years from the end of the war to the mid-1950s marked a period of change; the Tractor Equipment production that had proved such a successful and lucrative addition to the excavators effectively came to an end in 1953/54 when International Harvester took over the manufacture of their own equipments, and the production of Blast Hole Drills at Lincoln ceased with RB's decision not to follow the parent company in the manufacture of Rotary type drills. (Though the Lincoln company continued to manufacture percussion type Well Drills, they were increasingly regarded by the management as a side line to the main business and given low priority.)

For the company's main excavator business, however, the decade after the war was one of rising production figures, increase in factory capacity to meet this, and a phasing out of older models to be replaced by machines some of which, with improvements along the way, remained in production throughout the life of Ruston-Bucyrus Ltd.

19-RB Shovel, Mc.No. 11201, at the works ready for transportation to the Olympia Exhibition, November 1948 courtesy of one of E.W. Rudd's low loaders.

It was a measure of the return to some degree of normalcy in the aftermath of World War II, that in 1948 the Lincoln company resumed their practice of exhibiting at a major international trade show.

For the first time since 1938 Ruston-Bucyrus products were on display to the public and the show was the Public Health & Municipal Engineering Exhibition at Olympia. The central exhibit, a 19-RB Shovel taken out of the Lincoln production line, was Machine No. 11201 scheduled for delivery to Sir Robert McAlpine, contractor and owner of a large number of Ruston-Bucyrus Excavators.

For the Lincoln company, this was a time of full order books and long waiting lists of customers, signalling a need for greater production capacity and raw materials.

Ruston-Bucyrus Board of Directors in the Post-War Years

By the early 1950s, almost a complete change had taken place in the composition of the Ruston-Bucyrus Board of Directors and only W.W. Coleman, founder Chairman, and J.S. Ruston remained of the original 1930 Board.

In 1941 W. Savage, the company's first Chief Engineer and C.J. Hyde-Truch, Works Manager, were appointed 'S' Directors to the board; Hyde-Truch resigned in 1945 but Bill Savage went on to become Works Director and Chief Engineer until his retirement in 1954. In 1944, H.B. Rigall, already a Director of R&H, was appointed to the RB board and in 1949 G.R. Sharpley, R&H representative on the original board, died and was replaced by W. J. Ruston who was currently Chairman of the Board for R&H. Also in 1949, V.W. Bone resigned due to ill health from his position on the board and was replaced by V.R. Prehn, at that time the Works Manager of R&H.

In 1950, J.H. Pawlyn, another R&H representative on the original board resigned and his place was filled by E.R. Jones, a Director of R&H. In the post-war period a further 'S' type Directorship with responsibility for sales and commercial activities was created for G.E. Savory.

Of the Bucyrus representatives on the board; P. Ionides resigned in 1951 and E.A. Watson in 1954 and they were replaced by J.C.P. Brunyate, partner in a London law firm, and W.L. Litle, President of Bucyrus-Erie.

W.W. Coleman

William W. Colman (pictured below) was the dynamic founder Chairman of Ruston-Bucyrus Ltd. and held that office until 1957 when he was made honorary chairman for life and he remained on the board of Ruston-Bucyrus until 1964. He was born in Baltimore, Maryland, in 1873

and graduated as metallurgical engineer eventually joining the Bucyrus Company at the age of thirty-two. Within two years he was works manager and he became President of the company, a position he held for thirty-two years. Following the creation of the Bucyrus-Erie Co. he held the post of Chairman of the company from 1943 to 1957.

On his visits to Lincoln he showed a keen interest in every aspect of the company and those at the Excavator Works who new him personally and professionally described him as - "an outstanding personality whose contribution to the company is beyond measure". W.W. Colman died in December 1965 at the age of ninety-two.

E.S. Everitt

E.S. 'Ernie' Everitt had succeeded Victor Bone as Managing Director in 1943 and would prove to be a worthy successor, steering the company through the next two successful decades until his resignation in December 1965 after thirty eight years with the Bucyrus and Ruston-Bucyrus companies.

Ernest Everitt (pictured above), whose father was chairman of Edgar Allens of Sheffield, graduated in mechanical engineering at Sheffield University in 1925 and after an apprenticeship with a diesel engine manufacturer he joined the London office of the Bucyrus Company in October 1927. Along with other members of that office he took up residence in Lincoln in January 1930 when Ruston-Bucyrus was formed and successively held positions of asst. commercial manager, export manager, and sales director with the new company before taking up duties as Managing Director on the 1st January 1944.

Ernest Everitt became a leading figure in Lincoln and in the excavator industry, and the success of the company was due in no small part to the team spirit which he created and fostered during his years as Managing Director.

The 1947 Floods

Life at the Excavator Works immediately after the war was not without its problems; the shortage of raw materials was expected but a factory under water could not have been foreseen.

In early 1947 severe flooding affected large areas of Lincoln including the New Boultham district in which the Excavator Works was situated. Beevor Street leading to the works and several of the workshops were flooded, all production ceased and the only direct access to either factory or offices was by boat.

Above: Beevor Street and the Excavator Works under water in 1947. During the floods hire-boats were commandeered from a Lincoln park for those needing to gain access to their office at the Excavator Works, one such is seen in the left foreground moored up awaiting passengers. Also in the above photograph Maurice Lambert, Section Leader in charge of RB Tractor Equipment and one of the few employees with his own boat, is seen ferrying himself and colleagues to the Ruston-Bucyrus Admin. and Canteen building on the left where on its upper floor the Engineering Drawing Office was located. In the distance can be seen a 100-RB standing in water outside No.2 Bay, apparently fairing better than a 33-RB that needed rescuing from the waves after the Foreman had bravely attempted to drive it out of the flooded works.

Left: A heavy work bench complete with vice is forlornly swept along by the rising flood waters. Through the main entrance to the Excavator Works can be seen Dawson's Leather Works, fellow victim to the city's inadequate flood protection.

The 1947 floods were no respecter of persons - these two photographs show members of the RB management caught on camera attempting to reach their respective offices at the Excavator Works. Chief Engineer Bill Savage (fourth from left in upper photo) appears puzzled, the others slightly embarrassed by the situation. Only Bob Lawson of the Electrical Dept. rowing the boat seems comfortable while beyond him at the works entrance a wader-clad Maurice Lambert of the Engineering Dept. views the proceedings with obvious amusement.
The 'no parking' sign in the lower picture might well be changed to 'no mooring'.

Flooded workshops at the Excavator Works in 1947; the workers were laid off, with the exception of the
Plant Department whose task it was to save as much of the machinery as possible from the rising flood waters.
However, it was the apprentices who, with youthful enthusiasm, gained access to the back of the works via the high
level railway and across the rooftops, with the allotted task of removing the motors of the machine tools from under
the waters of the flooded machine shops and drying them out.

The Excavator Works Recovers. By October 1947 when these two photographs were taken - Heavy Machine Bay (above),
Light Machine Shop (below) - all evidence of that year's floods had disappeared and production had resumed.
The restored workshop clutter, however, masked a problem for the Lincoln company less easy to resolve than nature's
flood waters - a serious lack of raw material. That year a new rationing scheme had been introduced by the
Government allocating Ruston-Bucyrus far less steel than they required for full production.

No.2 Fitting and Assembly Bay of the Excavator Works in 1949; under construction is a
5-W Walking Dragline, a 100-RB Quarry Shovel, and two 54-RB Excavators. Despite a shortage of
raw materials, rising production figures in the immediate post-war years led to overcrowded
workshops at the Excavator Works and pressure for more factory space. The above photograph,
and that on the opposite page (upper), give some indication of the congestion in the assembly
shops which led to a planned expansion of the war-time facilities.

Above: Photograph of the 10-RB assembly section at the Excavator Works
taken in the late 1940s; in 1949 the assembly of the 10-RB was transferred to
a new purpose-built workshop in new Bay 14.

Below: Completed 10-RB and 19-RB machines lined up outside the
Excavator Works' Packing Shop in July 1950.

Ruston-Bucyrus Excavator Works photographed in 1947, with ten workshop Bays along Beevor Street.
The Test Ground can be seen beyond the workshops on the extreme right of the picture and the still unfinished
new Administration Office Block is in the foreground.

Factory Extensions 1949

When Ruston-Bucyrus Ltd. took over the former Ruston's Navvy Works in 1930, the factory comprised four adjoining workshops, or bays, with their north ends facing on to Beevor Street. Bays 2 and 3 of these were high bays, so built to accommodate the assembly of Ruston's large steam navvies. In succeeding years further workshops were added to the line along Beevor Street until by the time the photo on the page opposite was taken in 1947 the number of workshop Bays had reached 10, at the end of which was a further open-gantry Bay and beyond this the Test Ground. The new Ruston-Bucyrus Admin. Building seen in the photograph remained unfinished. In April 1949, the Rt.Hon. G.R. Strauss, Minister of Supply, visited the Excavator Works, where he congratulated the employees on the remarkable contribution they were making to the national recovery.

This visit served to highlight the need for more workshop space, and further expansion quickly ensued; the existing open-gantry Bay being covered to create a new workshop Bay 11, a new open-gantry Bay 12 was created, and next to this a new workshop Bay 14 was added. Bay 11 would be used for the manufacture of cabs and light fabricated components, and all the plate burning machines were installed in one section of the Bay. Bay No.14 was used for the assembly of 10-RBs including 10-RB and 19-RB engines and the assembly of all types of equipments up to and including 43-RBs. Such was the layout of 14-Bay that assembly of the 10-RBs could be a continuous flow from the bare truck frame to the completed machine at a rate of one per eight hour day, seven days per week.

The Big Move

A milestone was reached in the history of the Excavator Works in 1951 when the construction of the new Ruston-Bucyrus Headquarters and Admin. Offices was completed and ready for occupation. Hardly 'new', the building was begun before the war and its skeleton structure was used throughout the war years as a temporary store and workshops. The different departments were soon moved from the top floor of the old Ruston Canteen block that had served as their home since Ruston-Bucyrus was formed in 1930, leaving only the Engineering Dept. Drawing Office and Publicity Dept. to follow three years later.

In the Summer of 1953, amid great confusion and some hilarity, the clerical staff and fifty draughtsman that formed the personnel of the Ruston-Bucyrus Engineering Dept., (including the author, a young student apprentice draughtsman) personally transported the whole of their equipment the three hundred yards or so down the road to their new offices. Each had responsibility for their own equipment, including desks, drawing boards, etc., and all manner of wheel barrows and trolleys were put to use. Mr. Lambert of the Tractor Equipment section once again proved popular as one of the handful of RB employees who came to work in a motor car and who had a small trailer.

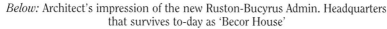

Below: Architect's impression of the new Ruston-Bucyrus Admin. Headquarters that survives to-day as 'Becor House'

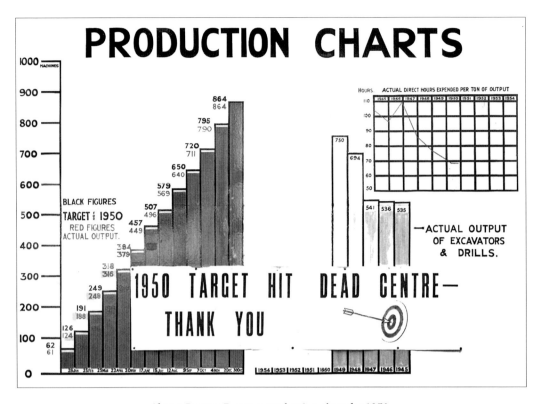

Above: Ruston-Bucyrus production chart for 1950.

Below: The 1000th Ruston-Bucyrus machine to be built in one year is proudly displayed in 1951.

1,000 Excavators in a Year

On Monday 17th. December 1951 Mr. Everitt, Managing Director of Ruston-Bucyrus Ltd., addressed an assembly of works and staff personnel at the Excavator Works, the purpose of this gathering was, in Mr. Everitt's own words "to acknowledge a very special record, namely, the 1000th machine to have been produced in one year".

He described his workforce as a first class and enthusiastic team working in a factory which was the finest of its type in the world and thanked them for their individual efforts. The achievement warranted a second celebration with the 1000th machine (not the same one as that above) to be dispatched to a customer from the Excavator Works in 1951. This was Mc.No.14771, a 19-RB Dragshovel delivered to customer W. Llewellyn on the 28th December 1951.

Referring to the target for 1952, Mr. Everitt said every effort was being made to obtain as much steel as possible but until this was known he couldn't say what the target would be.

Right: Mr. Everitt addresses the workers on the occasion of the 1000th machine completed in 1951.

Below: The 1000th machine to be dispatched from the Excavator Works in 1951 is ready to leave bound for Walter Llewellyn & Sons Ltd of east London on one of Pickfords' low-loaders.

The Festival of Britain

British industry's optimism and belief in the future was expressed in the staging of the 1951 Festival of Britain and its preparation gave impetus to the clearance of much of London's remaining areas devastated by the war.

A large number of Lincoln's excavators were put to this work; in the photograph below taken in the Spring of 1950, 54-RB and 19-RB machines owned and operated by London contractor Willment Brothers, who had their own crushing plant on the site, are excavating foundations on the Festival site on the south bank of the Thames.

The 54-RB Dragline, Mc.No.7990, had been purchased by the contractors in 1943 and was only the second of these models to leave the Excavator Works; the 19-RB Shovel, Mc.No.12669, was supplied new to Willment Bros. in December 1949 and this was one of its first applications.

In the background is the historic Shot Tower where lead shot for pistols and muskets was once produced for long forgotten armies by tipping molten lead from the top of the tower where its fall through the air formed the lead ball which was cooled and hardened in water below. The Tower, spared in the site clearance to become a popular attraction of the Festival though like other Festival buildings, was later demolished leaving only the Royal Festival Hall as a reminder of a unique celebration of British industry.

19-RB and 54-RB machines excavating the site for the 1951 Festival of Britain;
in the background can be seen the Shot Tower and in the distance Waterloo Bridge.

RB Excavators to the Rescue

On the 15th August 1952 disaster struck the North Devon coastal village of Lynmouth and surrounding area when the West and East Lyn rivers, swollen by torrential rain, flooded. A wall of water surged down from Exmoor onto Lynmouth, uprooting trees and destroying buildings; thirty four people were killed in Britain's worse flood disaster since the War.

The photographs on the opposite page taken after the disaster show a 22-RB Shovel helping to clear the river bed in the centre of Lynmouth. After the machine was left standing in three inches of water the river rose again with the result seen in the lower picture, remarkably the 22-RB continued to work.

The Great Flood of 1953

Just as the nation was reeling from the events at Lynmouth, the services of Ruston-Bucyrus excavators was once more called upon in a state of emergency. On January 31st and February 1st 1953, high tides swept along by hurricane force winds created exceptional conditions, breaching sea defences along the east and south-east coast of Britain and leaving a trail of death and destruction. The floods caused damage over a length of 1,000 miles of Britain's coastline, claiming 307 lives, devastating 200,000 acres of farmland and leaving 21,000 people homeless. Over 100 more lives were lost at sea and Holland suffered even worse than Britain with 1,800 lives lost.

During and in the aftermath of this tragic event manpower and machinery was quickly on the scene and Ruston-Bucyrus excavators began rescue and repair work in conditions hitherto only experienced in wartime. The eventual cost in monetary terms to Britain's industries and agriculture amounted to £50 million at 1953 prices - equivalent to over £850 million at today's prices.

19-RBs repairing sea defences on the Lincolnshire coast in August 1953.

Above: A 19-RB Dragline at work repairing damage caused to Sutton-on-Sea on the Lincolnshire coast during the January and February floods of 1953.

Below: Britain was not the only country whose coast-line suffered the effects of the gales of February 1953; in this photograph a more ambitious task faces a 10-RB Dragline as it attempts to rescue a German tanker that had run aground on the Dutch coast near Noordwijk as a result of the storms.

Excavators at the Coronation

The Queen's Coronation on the 2nd June 1953, provided a much needed lift to the spirits of a Britain still recovering from traumas of the earlier east coast floods, and Lincoln was ready and eager to enter into the Nation's celebrations of this historic occasion.

Numerous events were arranged throughout the city and, not surprisingly, its world famous engineering industries were invited to take part. Prominent among these events, and beginning Lincoln's civic Coronation Celebrations, was an exhibition mounted in the city's Usher Art Gallery entitled 'Lincoln Illustrated'. One of the five rooms set aside for the exhibition depicted the industrial history of Lincoln and local manufacturers each had their own display stands reflecting their company and its products.

Another popular event was the Lincoln Coronation procession, and again the city's engineering industries were represented with each company creating their own float or floats which, with much flag waving were paraded through the city streets. Ruston-Bucyrus, in keeping with this happy occasion, was represented by two floats expressing the company's products in a more picturesque and humorous light than was usual in their public displays.

Ruston-Bucyrus display at the 'Lincoln Illustrated' exhibition in celebration of the Queen's Coronation, 1953.

Photos Opposite: One of the RB floats in the Coronation procession was a light-hearted presentation of their latest excavator, seen here at the works with its builders, RB employees G. Hunter, E. Brackenbury, H. Jones and R. McClelland. The second RB float, seen parading along Lincoln's High Street, advertised the company's products with enlarged photographs.

History Repeats Itself

In 1936, a 10-RB was employed in the re-construction of the airfield at RAF Scampton, just north of Lincoln. This was part of a major programme of preparing Lincolnshire's many airfields for the Lancasters and Wellingtons that were soon to play a major role in the Second World War (as detailed in Lincoln's Excavators Vol. II).

In 1955, with the nation involved in another kind of war - the 'Cold War' - the 10-RB was called back to RAF Scampton. The airfield had been temporarily closed for runway extensions to accommodate the new Vulcan aircraft the base was about to receive in the re-formation of its famous 617 Squadron.

The 10-RB's task was the diversion of the A15 which ran alongside the airfield to provide room for the longer runway. Once the Roman 'Ermine Street', this road running straight as an arrow north out of Lincoln would, for the first time in its history, depart from its 2000 year old course in a two and a half mile loop round the end of the new runway.

The construction of this by-pass began in June 1956 and involved the blasting of 5,000 tons of rock and the excavation of 90,000 tons of earth before its completion seven months later, on the 28th January 1957. Although by today's standards only a minor road work, the achievement is remarkable for the absence of the mass of large scale equipment that would be brought in for a similar project today, and it is tempting to consider how the Excavator and its application had not changed at all in the twenty years that had seen the Lancaster evolve into the Vulcan.

Pictured here and below left is the lonely 10-RB Dragshovel putting the finishing touches to the Ermine Street by-pass. Note Scampton's hangers in the far distance.

The 10-RB's work and the Vulcan aircraft are both recognised in the present day badge of R.A.F. Scampton which incorporates the symbol of a bow and arrow. The string represents the original Roman Ermine Street; the bow, the 1956 diversion; and the arrow, the new Vulcan runway.

LINCOLN'S EXCAVATORS

THE EXCAVATOR WORKS
IN THE 1950s

Changes to the Ruston-Bucyrus
Board of Directors 1954-57

The photograph below was taken in the Summer of 1954 on the occasion of a visit to the Lincoln works by three Americans - W.W. Coleman, Chairman of B.E. Co. and of Ruston-Bucyrus Ltd.; W.L. Litle, President of B.E. Co. and recently appointed RB Director; and R.W. Newberry, Vice President of Bucyrus-Erie.

The group of Ruston-Bucyrus Ltd. Directors in the photograph indicates significant changes to the Board - in 1954, W. Savage had retired as Works Director and Chief Engineer though continuing on as a Director, and in addition to Mr. Litle, other recent appointees to the Board are J.H. Page who had been appointed technical assistant to the Managing Director in 1953 and was by now Technical Director, and F.T. Hartland, as Secretary of RB., (a future Ruston-Bucyrus Managing Director). Three years after this photograph came the biggest change when, in the Summer of 1957, Mr. Coleman retired from his position as Chairman of Ruston-Bucyrus Ltd., to be replaced by Mr. Litle.

Back row (left to right): W. Savage (Director), G.E. Savory (Sales Director), V.R. Prehn (Director), H.B. Riggall (Director), J.C.P. Brunyate (Director), E.R. Jones (Director), F.T. Hartland (Secretary), J.H. Page (Technical Director).
Front row: R.W. Newberry (Vice-President, Bucyrus-Erie), W.J. Ruston (Managing Director), W.W. Coleman (Chairman, Bucyrus-Erie and Ruston-Bucyrus), W.J. Ruston (Director), W.L. Litle (President, Bucyrus-Erie).

Mr. Everitt greets Mr. Litle the new RB Chairman.

Mr. Litle replaces Mr. Coleman
as Chairman

Founder Chairman Mr. Coleman had occupied this position with the Lincoln company for twenty-seven highly successful years, during which time his keen perception, great knowledge of engineering, and his sense of humour endeared him to all who met him on his visits to the Excavator Works. Although also President and Chairman of Bucyrus Erie Co., Mr. Coleman's excellent relationship with the Lincoln management stemmed from his recognition of the particular needs of Ruston-Bucyrus and the markets that it served.

Mr. Everitt, in appreciation of Mr. Coleman at his retirement said; "Few companies could have been as fortunate as ours in its founder Chairman and in the inestimable value of his services over the years." Mr. Coleman was invited to accept a life appointment as Honorary Chairman.

There was sadness when Mr. Coleman retired as Chairman, but the true loss to the company of his departure can only be fully realised in hindsight and in the light of later events. At the time, Ruston-Bucyrus had more immediate problems for by the Winter of 1957 falling demand for smaller size excavators had led to a decrease in production and shorter working hours, though there was confidence that this was only a temporary situation and there was much optimism at the Excavator Works.

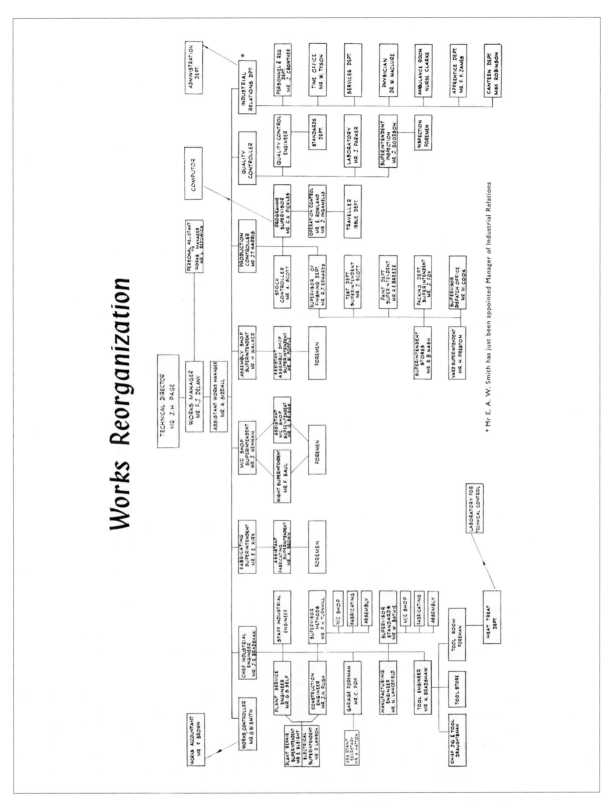

Works Reorganization

TECHNICAL DIRECTOR MR J.H PAGE

WORKS MANAGER MR F.J DELANY

ASSISTANT WORKS MANAGER MR A. SIDDALL

PERSONAL ASSISTANT TO WORKS MANAGER MR J. SEDGWICK

COMPUTOR

ADMINISTRATION DEPT.

INDUSTRIAL RELATIONS DPT. *

PERSONNEL & REG DEPT. MR J. CROWTHER

TIME OFFICE MR W. TYSON

SERVICES DEPT.

PHYSICIAN DR W. MACLURE

AMBULANCE ROOM NURSE CLARKE

APPRENTICE DEPT. MR F. F. JAMES

CANTEEN DEPT. MISS ROBINSON

QUALITY CONTROLLER

QUALITY CONTROL ENGINEER

STANDARDS DEPT.

LABORATORY MR J. PARKER

SUPERINTENDENT INSPECTION MR J. GOODSON

INSPECTION FOREMEN

PRODUCTION CONTROLLER MR J.T HARRIS

PROGRAMME SUPERVISOR MR C.K. PICKLES

OPERATION CONTROL MR E. ROWLAND MR J. INGAMELLS

TRAVELLER ISSUE DEPT.

STOCK CONTROLLER MR A. SCOTT

SUPERVISOR OF FINISHING DEPT MR R.J EDWARDS

TEST DEPT SUPERINTENDENT MR J. SCOTT

PAINT DEPT SUPERINTENDENT MR A.E.BREEZE

PACKING DEPT. SUPERINTENDENT MR J. FOX

SUPERVISOR DESPATCH OFFICE MR M. COOK

ASSEMBLY SHOP SUPERINTENDENT MR H. WALKER

ASSISTANT ASSEMBLY SHOP SUPERINTENDENT MR W. CHAPPEL

FOREMEN

SUPERINTENDENT STORES MR R.B NASH

YARD SUPERINTENDENT MR H. PRESTON

M/C SHOP SUPERINTENDENT MR J. KENNAN

NIGHT SUPERINTENDENT MR F. GAUL

ASSISTANT M/C SHOP SUPERINTENDENT MR G. BRIGGS

FOREMEN

FABRICATING SUPERINTENDENT MR E.E. KIRK

ASSISTANT FABRICATING SUPERINTENDENT MR A. BROWN

FOREMEN

CHIEF INDUSTRIAL ENGINEER MR J.R BRADSHAW

STAFF INDUSTRIAL ENGINEER

SUPERVISOR METHODS MR P. W. TUNNILL

M/C SHOP

FABRICATING

ASSEMBLY

SUPERVISOR STANDARDS MR W. BATHIE

M/C SHOP

FABRICATING

ASSEMBLY

WORKS CONTROLLER MR G.W.SMITH

WORKS ACCOUNTANT MR F. BROWN

PLANT SERVICE ENGINEER MR G.D SELF

CONSTRUCTION ENGINEER MR C. FOX

GARAGE FOREMAN MR C. FOX

MANUFACTURING ENGINEER MR N. LANGFIELD

TOOL ENGINEER MR K. BRADSHAW

PLANT REPAIR SUPERINTENDENT MR E. B.EIGHT

ELECTRICAL SUPERINTENDENT MR E. LAMBON

ASSISTANT SUPERINTENDENT MR A. HATTON

CHIEF JIG & TOOL DRAUGHTSMAN

TOOL STORE

TOOL ROOM FOREMAN

HEAT TREAT DEPT.

LABORATORY FOR TECHNICAL CONTROL

* Mr E. A. W. Smith has just been appointed Manager of Industrial Relations

In 1954 Bill Savage, who held the dual role of Works Director and Chief Engineer, retired from the company. His functions as Works Director was taken over by J.H. Page under the newly created title of Technical Director. Assistant Chief Engineer Philip Durand assumed the separate position of Chief Engineer. This was to pave the way for a reorganisation of the Ruston-Bucyrus Works Management. The above chart shows a new structure which came into effect on the 1st November 1958. (Note that this chart does not include the Engineering Department and Drawing Office which was under the charge of the Chief Engineer directly responsible to the Technical Director.)

The Apprentices

Ruston-Bucyrus, like most U.K. engineering companies, traditionally depended greatly upon its own apprentice scheme for its skilled factory workers and technical staff.

Apprenticeship has its origin in the 11th century and become established as the period of training required by craftsmen in almost every trade. During this period the apprentice was indentured to a master, and although the guild of his particular trade supervised the apprentice system, an apprentice was bound to his master.

By Act of Parliament in the 16th century it was laid down that no person should exercise a trade in England unless he had served a seven year apprenticeship under an indenture. Despite abuses of the system, it was a privilege for a boy to serve an apprenticeship, the Guilds imposing their own restrictions of entry in order to make sure that only efficient craftsmen were trained.

When the new company of Ruston-Bucyrus took over the Excavator Works from Ruston & Hornsby in 1931 it inherited a company apprentice scheme with on the job practical training in engineering crafts. In 1939, by Act of Parliament, new regulations came into force regarding the working hours of all young persons under 16, and on June 5th 1939 Ruston-Bucyrus opened its first purpose-built Apprentice Workshop. By the end of World War II, an apprentice scheme had developed at the Excavator Works along traditional lines but in a dual system formalising the distinction between the 'crafts' and the 'professions'. The five year Apprentice Scheme beginning at age sixteen was divided into two streams, the Craftsman Course and the Student Course, which were described in the 1950 Apprentice Handbook as follows;

Craftsman Course - for boys coming from elementary or secondary modern schools, who have not attained School Certificate standard. They are taught one of the following trades - Turner, Fitter, Inspector, Millwright, Electrician, Plater.

Student Course - for boys coming from technical, secondary or public schools, who are of School Certificate or Matriculation standard. In addition to practical workshop training, this group receives training in specialised departments to enable them to obtain appointments as Draughtsmen, in Planning, in Production, or as Service, Sales or Commercial Engineers.

In addition to the above training, all apprentices were committed to part-time Technical College courses leading to Ordinary National Certificate in Mechanical or Electrical Engineering at age 18 followed by the Higher National Certificate at 20 years of age.

Ruston-Bucyrus apprentice workshop established in 1939 at the end of one of the Bays at the Excavator Works.

By the end of the war the Ruston-Bucyrus Apprentice Department had been moved into a separate room at the north end of No.2 Bay of the Excavator Works. These two photographs taken of the department in October 1947 reveal its basic nature and antiquated machinery.
In the picture below Apprentice Supervisor Charlie Walker is addressing a group of apprentices.

RUSTON-BUCYRUS APPRENTICESHIP SCHEME
STUDENT COURSE

AGE	16	16½	17	17½	18	18¼	19	20	21	PROFESSION
	THEORY, EVENING SCHOOL & PART TIME DAY COURSE				ORDINARY NATIONAL CERTIFICATE	COURSES IN SPECIALISED SUBJECTS AS FAR AS TECHNICAL COLLEGE OFFERS				
SCHOOL CERTIFICATE STANDARD OR EQUAL, OR MASTERS' REPORTS IN SPECIAL CASES	FULL REVIEW OF PROGRESS TO DETERMINE FUTURE TRAINING									
	ENG. DEPT. DRAWING OFFICE	MACHINE SHOPS	MARKING OFF	ASSEMBLY & WELD	FITTING SHOPS	TEST	ENGINEERING DEPARTMENT DRAWING OFFICE			DRAUGHTSMAN—MECHANICAL
	JIG AND TOOL DRAWING OFFICE	MACHINE SHOPS	MARKING OFF	ASSEMBLY & WELD	TOOL ROOM		PLANNING DEPT.	JIG AND TOOL DRAWING OFFICE		DRAUGHTSMAN—JIG & TOOL
	PLANT DRAWING OFFICE	MACHINE SHOPS	MARKING OFF	ASSEMBLY & WELD	PLANT DEPARTMENT		PLANNING DEPT.	PLANT DRAWING OFFICE		DRAUGHTSMAN—PLANT
	JIG & TOOL DRAWING OFFICE	PLANNING DEPT.	MARKING OFF PLATE SHOP	PLATE AND WELDING SHOP				PLANNING DEPT.		PLANNER & RATE-FIXER—FAB. SECTION
	JIG & TOOL DRAWING OFFICE	PLANNING DEPT.	MARKING OFF	MACHINE SHOPS		METHODS ENGINEERS		PLANNING DEPT.		PLANNER & RATE-FIXER—MACHINE SECTION
	JIG & TOOL DRAWING OFFICE	PLANNING DEPT.	MARKING OFF	FITTING SHOPS		SERVICE FITTING	DISMANTLING SHOPS	PLANNING DEPT.		PLANNER & RATE-FIXER—FITTING SECTION
	MACHINE SHOPS	FABRICATING SHOP	FITTING SHOPS	INSPECTION DEPT.	JIG & TOOL DRAWING OFFICE	STOCK CONTROL	PLANNING DEPT.	PRODUCTION DEPT.		PRODUCTION ENGINEER
	MACHINE SHOPS	INSPECTION	ERECTING AND DISMANTLING SHOPS			RUSTON-HORNSBY ENGINES	TEST	DRAWING OFFICE	FIELD DEPT.	SERVICE ENGINEER
	MACHINE SHOPS	INSPECTION	FITTING SHOPS	RUSTON-HORNSBY ENGINES	TEST		ENGINEERING DEPT. DRAWING OFFICE	SALES & COMMERCIAL DEPTS.		SALES OR COMMERCIAL ENGINEER

RUSTON-BUCYRUS APPRENTICESHIP SCHEME
CRAFTSMAN COURSE

AGE	16	16½	17	17½	18	18¼	19	20	21	TRADE
		CAPSTAN	SHAPER OR SLOTTER	BORER OR MILLER	MARKING OFF	INSPECTION	LATHE	LATHE		TURNER
		CAPSTAN	SHAPER OR SLOTTER	MILLER	TOOL ROOM BORER OR GRINDER	T.R. MARKING OFF AND INSPECTION	LATHE (TOOL ROOM)	LATHE (TOOL ROOM)		TOOL ROOM TURNER
SHOP AND OFFICE BOYS	WORKS	CAPSTAN	SHAPER OR SLOTTER	BORER	MARKING OFF	SALVAGE	10, 19 or 24 RB. MACHINE ERECTIONS / EQUIP. OR SUB-ASSEMBLIES	DISMANTLING OR 54 AND 100 R.B.	TEST	FITTER
	SCHOOL	CAPSTAN	SHAPER OR SLOTTER	MILLER	TOOL GRINDING	T.R. MARKING OFF AND INSPECTION	FITTING BENCHES	FITTING BENCHES		TOOL ROOM FITTER
		CAPSTAN	SHAPER OR SLOTTER	SALVAGE	MARKING OFF	INSPECTION TURRETS	INSP. LATHE & DRILL OR FITTINGS / INSP. HEAVY M.C. SHOP OR SERV. REPAIR	INSPECT. FAB. DEPT.	INSPECT. FINAL	INSPECTOR
		CAPSTAN	SHAPER OR SLOTTER	MILLER OR BORER	MARKING OFF	BENCH PLANT DEPT.	MAINT. CRANES, COMPRESSORS, etc.	MAINTENANCE MACHINE SHOPS AND MACHINE TOOLS FAB. DEPT.		MILLWRIGHT
		CAPSTAN	SHAPER OR SLOTTER	MARKING OFF	BENCH ELEC. DEPT.	INSTALLATION AND ELECTRICAL MAINTENANCE		EXCAVATOR WIRING	TEST	ELECTRICIAN
		RIVET HEATING	MARKING OFF	ROLLS AND FOLDING MACHINE	HAND BURNING	ASSEMBLY AND WELD	LIGHT PLATING	HEAVY PLATING	TEMPLATE MAKER	PLATER
BELOW SCHOOL CERTIFICATE STANDARD	FULL REVIEW OF PROGRESS TO DETERMINE FUTURE TRAINING				ORDINARY NATIONAL CERTIFICATE	ATTAINMENT OF NATIONAL CERTIFICATE COUPLED WITH SATISFACTORY WORKS RECORD MAY QUALIFY FOR TRANSFER TO STUDENT COURSE				
	THEORY, EVENING SCHOOL AND PART TIME DAY SCHOOL									

Extract from the Ruston-Bucyrus 1950 Apprentice Handbook
two-tier Student / Craft structure.
(There is suggested in this traditional apprenticeship certain underlying assumptions
(a) It is selective in its distinction between trades and professions, assuming suitability for
one or the other based upon formal academic qualifications.
(b) It is boys only, with no provision for a girl who might wish to take up engineering in
any of its categories. This despite the fact that women successfully replaced men at lathe or
milling machine at the Excavator Works during the war years.)

CURRENT WAGES FOR APPRENTICES

AGE	% of Fitters District Rate	RATE		National Award Bonus		TOTAL	
		s.	d.	s.	d.	s.	d.
15	22½	14	10¼	9	2¾	24	1
16	27½	18	1¾	11	3¼	29	5
17	32½	21	5½	13	4	34	9½
18	45	28	8½	18	5½	48	2
19	52½	34	7¾	21	6¼	56	2
20	62½	41	3	25	7½	66	10½
21	Adult Wage					Adult Wage	

These are the guaranteed day-work wages payable for a 44 hour 5-day working week. At intervals in his training, an apprentice may find he has to work on piecework, in which case the National Award Bonus is slightly reduced, this is however counterbalanced by his piecework earnings. Although a boy may at times be on piecework, he is guaranteed the normal daywork wages, as the minimum, whatever happens.

Above: Extract from the Apprentice Handbook of 1950 showing the Craft Apprentice wage structure; the Student Apprentice wage was equivalent to the flat rate wage of the Craft Apprentice.

Below: The Ruston-Bucyrus Apprentice Department continued in its No. 2 Bay location, as this photograph taken in 1959 shows, and remained there until entirely new training facilities were created at the Excavator Works in 1968.

Above: New Training Facilities

When Ruston-Bucyrus enlarged the Excavator Works by the purchase of the old Ruston & Hornsby Spike Island Foundry in 1968, part of the foundry complex - the Heavy Core Shop - was converted into a specialised centre which combined the re-training of adults with the basic training of apprentices.

The centre was opened by Sir Arnold Lindley, Chairman of the Engineering Industry Training Board on 18th July 1968. It was the first Adult Training Centre in Lincolnshire and was fitted out with the latest equipment enabling the training of over 50 setter/operators per year on a six months course giving new opportunities for workers as well as providing up-to-date workshop training for Ruston-Bucyrus apprentices.

Left: Adult re-training in the new Training Department.

It's a Small World

The Excavator Works, like all large manufacturing plants, was a 'world apart' in which its many participants from all walks of life and different personal backgrounds shared a common goal - the success of the company. Occasionally, along the way, this can give rise to unexpected and surprising 'bed-fellows'.

Over the years the Excavator Works had its share of those 'characters'  whose force of personality and singular code of behaviour earned them the respect of their fellow workers; such a figure was Denis Marlow (pictured left). In 1923, the twenty year old Londoner Marlow joined the American Bucyrus Co. as one of only three representatives of that company based in London. When Ruston-Bucyrus was formed in 1930, he left the direct employ of the American company to become manager of RB's Continental Sales Division. After war service, he returned to RB and from 1945 to his semi-retirement in 1966 carried the responsibility of Ruston-Bucyrus Export Manager, travelling widely through Europe, Asia and Africa, representing RB and BE machines.

A native of London and like his father a hereditary Freeman of that city, Denis Marlow was confident, yet softly spoken, and in manners and appearance fitted everyone's idea of a 'true English Gentleman'. Always impeccably dressed, with bowler hat, furled umbrella, and 'British Warm' top-coat, his upright figure could be seen striding to his office every day from his adopted home in the shadow of Lincoln Cathedral (rarely was he seen in a motor car). The Americans respected Marlow's professional expertise but his many visits to Bucyrus-Erie gave rise to much wonderment at this eccentric Englishman who waved away the chauffeured limousine to actually walk from his hotel to their office or factory.

Denis Marlow's quiet confidence was matched by his bravery when, in World War II, he joined the Lincolnshire Regiment to serve in France, Norway, and Iceland, then in the Parachute Regiment in West Africa, France, Greece and Italy. Involved in special missions behind enemy lines, the story goes that on one occasion Captain Marlow was parachuted with his unit into Italy at night and landed in what seemed to be a quarry. He searched around and found a 100-RB Shovel, whereupon he checked the nameplate serial number with hooded flashlight, then exclaimed "Now I know exactly where we are".

On the theme of 'Strange Bed-Fellows'

At the Excavator Works in the years following the war, in the works garage that could be seen from Dennis Marlow's office, worked fitter Bert Polligkeit. He shared with Marlow a working life in the cause of Lincoln's Excavators, but it was arrived at in a very different way. Bert came to Britain in 1946 after his capture by the Allies in France and eventually found his way to Lincoln and employment with Ruston-Bucyrus.

He had been a member of the German anti-aircraft detachment defending the Mohne Dam and although he was on leave at the time of the famous 'Dambuster' raid he risked security to take a number of unique photographs of the immediate re-building that went on round the clock. He recalled

"It was a year before the dam was completely re-built, the defences were strengthened many times afterwards and we had some of the heaviest firepower in Germany but never had to use it."

Bert said that there was considerable doubt whether the bouncing bombs in fact functioned correctly and

"at least one bounced clear over the dam."

There is no record that Corporal Polligkeit and Captain Marlow ever met to 'chew over' their war experiences and consider what twist of fate had brought these two former enemies to Spike Island, and in Bert Polligkeit's case to live and work a mile or so from the home of the 'Dambuster' squadron base from which the aircraft flew on that fateful raid, and which it was his duty to shoot down.

Above: Bert Polligkeit at the Mohne Dam in 1943.

The Excavator Works in 1955.
At the beginning of 1955 Ruston-Bucyrus Ltd. celebrated twenty-five years of its existence. In this time the number of employees had risen from about 500 to 2,570. The total area of the works was now 35 acres, with 20 workshop bays, the longest of which were 550ft long, 66ft wide and 48ft high. The company's policy had always been to buy the most up-to-date equipment and machine tools, and since the war the continual expansion and re-equipment had resulted in a factory as modern as any in Britain.

During 1954, Ruston-Bucyrus had dispatched a greater number of new machines from the Excavator Works than ever before and despite the steel shortage, the company entered its twenty-fifth year with optimism. These two photographs taken in August 1955 of the new 18-Bay assembly shop for the 10, 19, and 22-RBs, show (above) the erection and paint section and (below) the dispatch section.

Ruston-Bucyrus Annual Open Day 1956

In today's security conscious Britain the practice of an annual works open day when the general public have free access to every corner of a large manufacturing company may seem surprising. Yet, once a year, it was the tradition for Ruston-Bucyrus to proudly throw open the gates of the Excavator Works to all-comers, a tradition broken only during the war years.

On that day special Corporation buses were laid on to carry hordes of visitors from the centre of town to the works where they were received by unofficial guides recruited from the work force (including apprentices), and where refreshments were available throughout the day for the tired and hungry visitors.

The following photographs were taken on the occasion of the Ruston-Bucyrus annual Open Day on Saturday 27th October 1956, when some 3500 members of the public of all ages visited the works. There they saw the production processes in action including various machining and fabricating operations, as well as the test ground where different excavators, including a 110-RB, were put through their paces.

Today's obligatory 'hard hats' and safety glasses for all workers and works visitors were unheard of at the Excavator Works, and the extent to which the general public were allowed to roam the factory and test grounds right up to the 1980s suggests fewer safety regulations and a more relaxed attitude to the dangers from heavy machinery. Yet over the years even minor accidents to the public on Open Day were thankfully rare.

Above: Visitors to the Ruston-Bucyrus 1956 Open Day marvel at the size of the 110-RB's 4½ cu. yd. dipper.

Left: Young visitor viewing through a piece of dark glass the process of welding a crawler frame. One of the hazards for visitors to the Fabricating Bays was the danger to eyesight from staring directly at welding flashes.

Above & below: The machine shops are of great interest to the majority of visitors, but the marking-out table offers riches for more thoughtful youngsters like this couple.

Always the star attraction was the excavators themselves, and for the visitors to the Excavator Works
on Open Day the most exciting spectacle was the display on the test ground.
Here, a range of machines from the smallest to the largest (in 1956 from the 10-RB to the 110-RB)
would be put through their paces.

The 1956 Ruston-Bucyrus Open Day has come to an end and by bus and on foot the last of the 3500 visitors are seen leaving the works. Since 9.30 a.m. the factory has been on show, and though few ever doubted the value of this proud demonstration of Lincoln's engineering, for the workers there was some small relief that for the Excavator Works it would be business as usual in the morning.

Difficult Times 1956-58

In 1955, Ruston-Bucyrus Ltd. had experienced one of its best years yet for shipments and earnings, though new orders fell off towards the end of that year as a result of severe credit restrictions imposed by the Government and unsettled conditions in the Middle East which affected their export market. Further problems arose from the fact that since the war a considerable portion of the company's sales outlets had been in respect of the U.K.'s opencast coal industry which due to the Government's curtailment of these operations had largely dried up.

By 1957, the country's economic difficulties had resulted in a falling demand for excavators, particularly in the home market and drastic action was needed by the Lincoln management if they were to survive the crisis; between 1957 and 1958 the Excavator Works was put on a 'four day' week and 400 employees were made redundant.

Some two years later in 1959 British industry was showing signs of recovery with spectacular successes abroad by British construction firms earning £114 million in contracts. In 1960, with the upsurge in industrial construction at home and abroad, and a steel output greater than ever before with a corresponding demand for iron-ore and ironstone, the Lincoln company's production was soon back at its pre-depression level. The harsh measures had paid off and they had ridden the crisis - Ruston-Bucyrus would now benefit from its earlier investment in new manufacturing techniques and processes which would enable more efficient production.

During these difficult times for Ruston-Bucyrus, their parent Bucyrus Erie Co. were experiencing their own problems - more serious and more difficult to resolve. In 1955 there was general euphoria in the American company, business was booming and despite the warning signs B.E. embarked upon massive expansion plans.

At the Erie plant two expansion and modernization programmes costing $4 million had been completed; Bucyrus-Erie Co. of Canada, a wholly owned subsidiary started operating in a new $3.5 million plant in Ontario; and at Evansville an expansion and modernization programme costing $2 million was in progress. However, the largest commitment was the building of a new plant for the manufacture of Drills and Drill Equipment at Richmond, Virginia, at a cost of $12 million.

Though B.E. shipments were high in 1956, inflation was under way and the American company had not developed a programme of protection against a downward spiral of ever increasing production costs and declining markets. The problems were compounded by the company's indebtedness to six major banks for the capital required for their expansion plans.

By 1958, the industry was in its most serious recession for 20 years and it brought B.E.'s first net loss in 28 years.

Since Coleman, as Honorary Chairman, was no longer involved in active management of Bucyrus Erie Co., the company's problems were in the hands of Chairman and President Litle and Vice President Robert Allen. Outside consultants were brought in, redundancies ensued at all levels of management and it was no surprise to anyone that the new Drill Manufacturing Plant at Richmond was to be closed down and sold off before ever going into full production. Litle retired from the company through ill health in 1959 and the many strategies to recover the company's fortunes such as reorganisation, the disposing of excess plant, etc. was now in the hands of Allen who had been appointed the company's Chief Executive Officer.

With a gradual increase in the demand for large machines and an effective cost reduction programme, matters slowly improved but a significant factor in B.E.'s recovery was the appointment in 1960 of Eugene P. Berg as Executive Vice President. It was apparent to all that he had been brought in to 'save the company', and by December 1962 Berg had replaced Allen as President.

Left: The newly appointed Chairman of the Board of Ruston-Bucyrus Ltd. R.G. Allen is greeted by Ruston-Bucyrus Managing Director E.S. Everitt on the former's visit to the Lincoln Works. Allen joined Bucyrus-Erie in 1957 as Vice President from an illustrious career in politics and in December 1958 he became the fourth President of the American company. Upon Litle's resignation as Chairman of Ruston-Bucyrus Ltd in 1959 he also filled that vacancy. The strain of being at the helm of the mighty Bucyrus-Erie organisation in those troubled times took its toll and Allen retired from active business duties in December 1962. His sudden death at the age of 60 on the 9th August 1963 was a shock to colleagues on both sides of the Atlantic.

LINCOLN'S EXCAVATORS

END OF THE LINE FOR SOME

END OF THE LINE FOR SOME

With the exception of the 38-RB, 54-RB, 110-RB, and 120-RB all the models in the product range of Ruston-Bucyrus Excavators shown listed for 1954 / 55 had their origins before World War II and although some, like the 10-RB and 19-RB, would continue well into the future, for others the mid 1950s marked the end of their production at the Excavator Works. Of the models phased out, the 43-RB 1¾ cu.yd. Universal Excavator had enjoyed the longest life, with a remarkable production run in the Lincoln factory dating back to 1931. The production of this successful, though by this time dated machine, came to an end in September 1955.

The 24-RB and 33-RB Universal Excavators were not so long-lived, their dates were 1939-1957 and 1938-1956 respectively and these two elderly models were phased out in 1956 to be replaced by the 30-RB. These models were identical in their basic design which had changed little from the first range of B.E. designed Ruston-Bucyrus Excavators introduced in 1931/32. They were consistent with B.E.'s general practice with the small to medium Universal Excavators of taking one basic design and scaling it up to create a larger machine with a greater digging capacity. Both the 24-RB and the 33-RB were true Universal Excavators in that they were capable of operating different front end equipments which included Shovel, Dragline, Dragshovel, Crane and Grabbing Crane. Both models could also be supplied powered by either diesel engine, petrol engine, or where external electricity supply was available, as a single motor electric machine.

In the large mining shovel category the 110-RB Shovel had already replaced the 100-RB when in 1958 the 120-RB was replaced by the 150-RB.

Like the crawler excavators referred to above, the Ruston-Bucyrus 3-W and 5-W walking draglines were also of early vintage. Based upon the old Bucyrus-Monighan design, which had its origins in the first practical 'walking excavator' developed by the Monighan Machine Company in the early 1900s, these machines had provided excellent service stripping overburden in the U.K's open-cast coal and iron-ore mines. However, by the mid 1950s new concepts in walking dragline design led to the phasing out of these two models from the RB production line with what should have been the last 5-W in September 1962.

24-RB Shovel operated by the Chinnor Cement Co.; with a standard ⁷/₈ cu.yd dipper this machine was driven by a 77 h.p. Ruston 4-cyl. VPHN diesel engine and had a bucket capacity of ⁷/₈ cu.yd.

Above: 24-RB Dragline operated by the Avon & Somerset River Board on river widening. For dragline duty optional lengths of boom on the 24-RB ranged from 40' - 60', with a range of buckets respectively of ¾ cu.yd. to 1½ cu.yd.

Below: 33-RB Single motor Electric Shovel digging clay for brick-making; the 33-RB had a nominal 1¼ cu.yd. capacity dipper and though positive chain crowd was standard on both the 24-RB and 33-RB Shovels, the option of rope crowd was available for both models. The trailing cable of the external power supply for this electric machine can be seen. For diesel powered 33-RBs the standard engine was the Ruston 110 h.p. 5-cyl. VPBN.

The 10-RB Goes On

The 10-RB was introduced by Ruston-Bucyrus in 1934 and it is testament to its design that this most successful of small excavators enjoyed a long life spanning thirty-four years. Unlike the other early Ruston-Bucyrus models of small to medium excavators derived from 1930s B-E models all of the same design of which the 24-RB and 33-RB were typical, the 10-RB represented a radical departure.

Making use of the new production techniques and materials becoming available by that time, the 10-RB / 10-B became, not only a highly successful excavator in its own right, but the standard design for other excavator models of the future. The fact that the 10-RB went through very few changes during its lifetime attests to the strength of its design and its popularity with customers all over the world.

The peak period for 10-RB production was 1954, when no less than 485 were completed at the Excavator Works. However, with increasing competition from hydraulic excavators, the demand for small rope machines dropped steadily and production of the 10-RB gradually declined until, in 1968, it was phased out of the Lincoln production line. By its end, a total of 7585 10-RBs had been built

at the Excavator Works, serving the need for a versatile, easily transportable excavator, at home and abroad, in peacetime and in war.

The origins and development of the 10-RB are covered in Volume II of 'Lincoln's Excavators'; with rear end and counterweight changes, engine changes, further cab styles, and the incorporation of air-assisted steering as standard, the 10-RB continued into the 1960s, a remarkable survivor from the early days of the Lincoln company.

Drainage

Though the domestic sales gradually declined as a consequence of the competition from hydraulic excavators, the 10-RB continued to find work in its traditional role as a drainage machine, finding a particular niche of its own among the Fenland and other Drainage Boards.

This work needed a crawler mounted dragline which offered a low ground pressure to cope with the very soft ground conditions and this led to the introduction of a wide crawler version. The 10-RB proved ideal for clearing the narrow drainage channels that were such a vital feature of the low-lying eastern counties of England.

A 10-RB Dragline photographed in June 1955 with 35' boom and wide
crawlers excavating fen drains at Deeping Fen, Lincolnshire.

The clearance of narrow drainage channels in fen land is an ongoing requirement and the difficulties of using a Dragline Excavator for this work is all too apparent. The machine cannot operate on the line of the dig in the normal way and this has led to the idea of some form of attachment that deflects the Excavator's drag rope enabling the machine to operate sideways on to the line of the excavation. Commercially, Priestman manufactured a side dragline attachment for their Cub Excavator but may operators developed their own ideas using whatever materials came to hand.

The photographs show a 10-RB Dragline operated by Fen Drains & Excavations Ltd. of Whittlesey clearing drains in the fens near Peterborough to which is attached a 'home made' side deflecting arm bolted to the crawler frame whose main component is a section of rail track. This Dragline (Mc.No.10687) was supplied new to Fen Drains in October 1947 and the photograph taken in the early 1950s shows it fitted with a 'continental' cab which confirms the fact that this type of cab was not exclusive to machines shipped abroad.

Left & below: 10-RB Dragline with side attachment.

Apart from being highly popular in the U.K., the 10-RB found ready export markets and could be found employed on a great variety of applications world-wide.
Above - Photograph taken in January 1955 of a 10-RB shovel engaged on arduous quarry work for the Lian Hup Granite Company, Malaya. *Below* - A train-load of five 10-RBs destined for Yugoslavia is ready to be dispatched from the Excavator Works in March 1955.

Although undergoing few major changes over the years, the 10-RB enjoyed several changes
of cab style, culminating in the American style seen in these photographs; among other
changes was the introduction of a hydraulic wrist-action version of the 10-RB Dragshovel
(seen in the above photograph) and the replacement of the standard straight-boom
dragshovel by the cambered-boom version (seen below in July 1963). This example
reflected the policy of replacing as standard all models of Ruston-Bucyrus straight-boom
dragshovels with the much more efficient cambered-boom equipped type.

THE STANDARD RANGE OF RUSTON-BUCYRUS EXCAVATORS

Machine designation and rated capacity (cu. yds.)	Specification	Approximate working weight		Diesel engine*		Equipments			Available boom lengths for bucket service	Maximum weight of bucket and contents		Lifting crane (see footnote on extension jibs)		
		Shovel	Dragline	Horse-power	Approx. fuel con-sumption per hour	Shovel: Cutting height and radius at 45°	Dragshovel: Maximum digging depth	Skimmer: Maximum digging radius		Dragline	Grabbing crane	Available boom lengths	Maximum British rating and minimum radius	
		tons	tons		gallons				ft.	lb.	lb.	ft.	tons	ft.
10-RB ⅜	Standard	9¼	9½	34	1	16′ 6″ 19′ 0″	12′ 0″	20′ 0″	30 to 40	2150	2900	30 to 40	3	11
19-RB ⅝	Standard	17¾	18¼	55	1½	22′ 9″ 26′ 6″	Straight boom 18′ 6″	25′ 0″	40 to 50	3600	4500	40 to 70	5¾	12
22-RB ¾	Standard	20¾	20¾	66	2	22′ 9″ 27′ 3″	Cambered boom 20′ 3″		40 to 50	4250	5400	40 to 70	7¾	12
	Widespread mounting	22	21¾										10	11
	Heavy-duty machine	—	22¼			—	—	—	35 to 50			35 to 70	10¾	12
	Transit machine	28½	29¼			24′ 7″ 27′ 3″	Cambered boom 18′ 5″	—	30 to 50		6400	30 to 80	22¼	10
30-RB 1	Std. mounting, ctwt. B	29¾	29¼	98	3	25′ 3″ 31′ 6″	26′ 9″		40 to 60	7200	8300	40 to 90	13¾	12
	L & W mounting, ctwt. C	31½	32¼									40 to 100	16½	12
38-RB 1½	Std. mounting, std. ctwt.	46½	42	132	4	27′ 9″ 33′ 0″	18′ 0″ to 22′ 0″		45 to 80	9100	11,000	45 to 100	14½	15
	L & W mounting, max. ctwt.	—	50¾										19½	15
54-RB 2½	Std. mounting, std. ctwt.	74½	64½	210	6½	29′ 0″ 37′ 9″			60 to 100	15,800	17,000	60 to 100	17½	20
	L & W mounting, max. ctwt.	—	77									50 to 120	41½	15
				Ward-Leonard electric control										
	Std. mounting, std. ctwt.	74½	67	**Motor** Hoist Swing Crowd	**h.p.** 60 23 23	26′ 0″ 37′ 3″				15,500	—	60 to 100	17½	20
	L & W mounting, max. ctwt.	—	81									60 to 100	27¼	20
110-RB 4½	Standard	152	162¼	Hoist Swing Crowd	125 44 35	34′ 9″ 46′ 3″			80 to 120	27,000	—	Available with full electric or diesel-electric power		
150-RB 6	Standard	201½	206¾	Hoist Swing Crowd	187½ 2 at 35 44	36′ 0″ 48′ 9″			90 to 130	31,000	—			

* Alternative power unit may be a single electric motor of suitable power and characteristics

Lifting cranes—extension jibs up to 30′ in length normally available

WALKING DRAGLINE

Size	Boom length	Bucket capacity	Maximum operating radius	Diameter of circular base	Approximate working weight	Diesel engine: Horse-power	Diesel engine: Approx. fuel consumption per hour	Ward-Leonard electric control	
					tons		gallons	**Motor**	**h.p.**
5-W	Boom lengths 150′, 135′ and 120′ with corresponding buckets according to duty			24′ 0″	170 diesel 171 electric	320	7½	Hoist Swing	125 40

Ruston-Bucyrus standard product range of Excavators 1956

LINCOLN'S EXCAVATORS

THE 54-RB

THE 54-RB SHOVEL / DRAGLINE

The first 2½ cu.yd. 54-RB left the Lincoln production line in 1942 having taken two and a half years in its development and it was to join the group of Ruston-Bucyrus excavators that enjoyed a long and successful production life.

Originally offered by RB as a Diesel or Single Motor Electric powered excavator, the 54-RB was intended to replace the 55-RB as a medium size quarry shovel / dragline in the Ruston-Bucyrus product range, but there was some overlap and the 55-RB continued to be produced well into 1945. In the States, Bucyrus-Erie had introduced the 54-B in 1939 to replace the older design 48-B of which Ruston-Bucyrus only ever built four machines, (due to limited space the 48-RB was not included in Vol. II of Lincoln's Excavators).

The 54-RB shovel weighed 72½ tons with a standard crawler mounting 15ft 1in. overall length with cast steel side frames. There was an alternative longer 20ft. 3in. crawler mounting for Dragline application using fabricated crawler side frames. The original power unit was a Ruston four-stroke 202 h.p. diesel engine or alternatively a 125 h.p. continuous rating electric motor.

Over the years, the 54-RB continued to be offered with Diesel, Single Motor Electric, or Ward-Leonard Electric power and apart from the introduction of the Ward-Leonard version, the 54-RB changed very little. Engine changes occurred; a long boom stripping shovel version was developed; the lifting crane performance was increased and improved by features such as power-controlled load lowering; and in 1946 a simple low pressure hydraulic-assist system was added to centralise control of the machine at the operator's position. Yet, despite such relatively few changes the 54-RB maintained its popularity with RB customers; this popularity was proven when the time came to replace it with the new 61-RB which came into production at the Excavator Works in 1967.

Despite the new machine, orders for the 54-RB were still coming in to the extent that the Lincoln firm was obliged to retain the 54-RB in their product range alongside the 61-RB. The last 54-RB Ward-Leonard excavator left the factory in March 1973, by which time a total of 582 had been built at the Excavator Works.

An early diesel powered 54-RB Shovel on the test ground at the Excavator Works.

Truck Frame and Revolving Frame

Above: Underside of revolving frame.

Below: Underside of truck frame and crawlers showing propel machinery.

The steel casting forming the truck frame houses the bearings for the horizontal drive shaft and the double-flanged roller path for the hook rollers. Onto the upper face of the truck frame is welded the separate alloy steel swing rack casting with its internal gear teeth. The truck frame unit is bolted to the crawler axles. The revolving frame casting which is mounted onto the truck frame to form a platform for the main machinery also provides the support for the vertical propel shaft, vertical swing shaft, and on its underside the supports for the conical hook rollers. The internal swing rack and use of these conical hook rollers, two sets of two at the front and two single rollers at the rear eliminates the need for a centre pintle which would have been necessary on earlier machines with external swing rack such as the 55-RB.

The crawler drive is taken through bevel gears from the vertical shaft to a single horizontal shaft in the truck frame. A single chain drive at each end of this shaft connects to sprockets on the right hand and left hand crawler drive tumblers. Both the drive tumblers and the take-up tumblers which are mounted at opposite ends of the crawler side frames are arranged to slide laterally enabling adjustment of the track tension.

Main Machinery - 54-RB Diesel / Single Motor Electric

Primary transmission from the drive unit to the main transmission shaft of the hoist pinion and swing / propel reversing clutches is by multi-strand roller chain. The 36" diameter, internal expanding swing clutches are directly hand-set. The main hoist drum with its booster-set hoist and crow-out clutches are mounted on the main drum shaft, along with the hoist and crowd brakes. (For dragline operation this shaft carries a second drum required for the drag rope operation.)

The rope operated boom hoist is independent of other motions; the boom hoist rope drum is set in the underside of the revolving frame and is driven by roller chain, through an intermediate shaft, from the main transmission shaft. A booster-set clutch is provided for raising the boom hoist and a brake for stopping, lowering and holding. An automatic ratchet and locking pawl is fitted into the boom hoist for lowering the boom at machine speed.

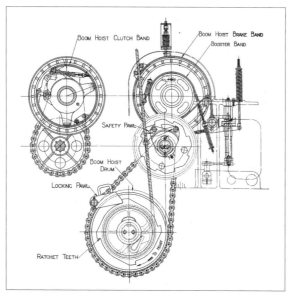

Left: Diagram of boom hoist assembly and rope drum. Located in the revolving frame, the chain - driven boom hoist drum can just be seen in the picture of the underside of the revolving frame on Page 55.

Below: Main machinery of the 54-RB Diesel excavator with the shovel chain crowd drive and machinery removed. The original engine, seen here, was the Ruston 5VCBN diesel engine, many of which were supplied, and it wasn't until 1956 that the Paxman 6RPHN six-cylinder engine replaced it as the chosen alternative to electric power on the 54-RB.

Above: 54-RB Diesel Shovel in the assembly shop with the crowd sprockets mounted on revolving frame.

Below: Diagram of the bolted on chain crowd machinery which was standard on the 54-RB Diesel / S.M.E. Shovel.

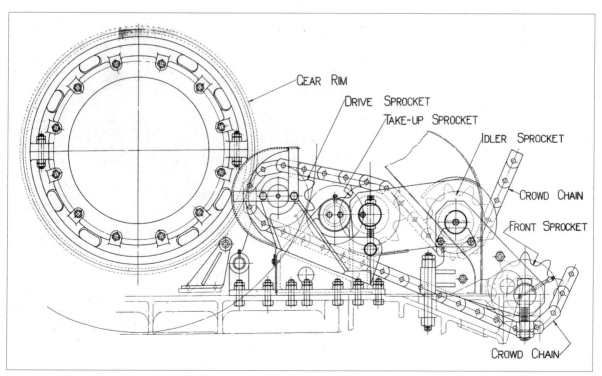

Operator's controls for the original 54-RB Diesel and Single Motor Electric machines.

A   Operates the transmission clutches for swinging and propel, depending upon which selector is engaged.

B   Controls the R.H. or drag clutch on draglines, and the L.H. and backhaul clutch on shovels.

C   Controls the hoist on both shovel and dragline equipments.

D   Operates the main engine clutch - (set when pushed into forward position).

E   Operates the brake locks, locking one or both brakes in the 'Hard-on' position when pushed forward.

F   Operates the boom hoist locking pawl - (pulled up to release, pushed down to engage).

G   Operates the steering clutches on the lower propel shaft.

H   Operates the transmission brake.

J   Operates the crowd brake on shovels and drag drum brake on draglines.

K   Operates the hoist brake on both shovels and draglines.

L   Four-position selector lever for the digging lock - (Top notch - machine free to move forward; Second notch - machine held in both directions; Third notch - machine free to travel backwards; Bottom notch - machine free to travel in either direction).

M   Operates the swing jaw clutch (when moved to top notch) and propel jaw clutch (when in lower notch).

N   Operates the independent boom hoist clutch and brake - (Centre notch - booster band released and brake spring set; Top notch - raises boom; Lever moved downwards, with Lever 'F' released, lowers boom).

Two photographs taken in July 1942 of the first 54-RB Diesel Shovel on the test ground at the Excavator Works; as Mc.No.6997 this first 54-RB was purchased by the Oxfordshire Ironstone Co. who went on to purchase a second similar machine, No. 8647, in 1944. The 54-RB Shovel's welded box section boom was 26ft. long and the 'twin-stick' dipper handle designed for lightness with strength was typical of medium to large quarry / mining shovels. The need for boom side braces to stabilise the boom as in the case of the 54-RB was dispensed with on modern shovel excavators with wider boom foot.

Two photographs taken in October 1948 of Oxfordshire Ironstone Company's 54-RB Diesel Shovel Mc.No.8647 at work in the company's ironstone quarries.

54-RB Dragline

The early 54-RB Draglines used the basic 60ft. two-piece butt-jointed lattice boom made up by 30ft. lower and upper sections, with inserts of 10ft. and 20ft. intermediate sections available to provide boom lengths up to 100ft.

Different capacity buckets were offered to match the boom length as follows;

60ft.	(2½ cu.yd.)
70ft.	(2 cu.yd.)
80ft.	(1½ cu.yd.)
90ft.	(1¼ cu.yd.)
100ft.	(1 cu.yd.)

For maximum ratings as a dragline the long mounting with wider 36" track links was required, and machines sold specifically for dragline use were equipped with this. The long crawler mounting had tapered ends to prevent the tracks 'digging in' at the front from the downward loading when operating as a dragline. However, when a standard convertible machine was sold for contract work requiring alternate use of shovel and dragline equipment, the machine could be used as a dragline on the standard crawler mounting, though with some reduction in the operating radii.

By 1950, changes to the 54-RB included the replacement of each of the two single rollers by a pair so that the 54-RB now had four pairs of equalized hook rollers in the swing circle. This provided additional stability and enabled larger counterweight to be fitted with the consequent increase in performance for Crane / Dragline operation. Further improvements at Lot 21, involved a redesigned rear end casting and operator's cab.

Above: 54-RB Dragline operated by Shephard Hill & Co., November 1955.

Left: 54-RB Dragline fairlead.

The photographs on this and the opposite page were taken in June 1954 and though nine years after the war, Britain's major cities at this time still showed evidence of bomb damage. Reconstruction was at full force, and no more so than in the capital city; here a 54-RB diesel Dragline and 19-RB Shovel operated by the large and well-known contractors Willment Bros. Ltd. of London is at work in the heart of the city preparing the ground for the new London.

The third 54-RB to leave the Lincoln production line, this machine (No. 7990) was delivered to Willment Bros in 1943; powered by a Ruston 5VCBN diesel engine and equipped with basic 60' boom and 2½ cu.yd. bucket, the machine was used extensively on bomb site clearances in the London area.

Pontoon Mounted 54-RB Dragline

In March 1953, an enquiry was received by the Ruston-Bucyrus Sales Department from the Crown Agents for the Colonies concerning the suitability of mounting and operating a 54-RB Grabbing Crane from a pontoon dredger. In response to this enquiry the RB Engineering Department drew up a specification for a 54-RB mounted on long wide-track crawler base, equipped with 80ft boom and clamshell bucket.

The task facing the 54-RB was the underwater excavation of Malayan tin mining deposits from the stern well-deck of a floating pontoon, the area in which the machine was to be mounted measuring 100ft x 30ft with the excavator's tracks 3ft 6in. below deck level. When operating with the 80ft boom at its maximum radius it was important that the counterweight tail radius of 15ft should clear all the pontoon deck equipment.

It was assumed by RB that the machine was intended to be used only as a clamshell from the pontoon, though the Ruston-Bucyrus Engineering Dept. saw no reason why the dragline equipment should not be used, provided the limited clearance of the drag rope over the pontoon was sufficient to meet the particular digging depth conditions and suitable anchorage could be obtained for the vessels anchoring lines. In order to secure the 54-RB to the well deck of the pontoon, lugs were welded to the crawler side frames to which chains could be attached.

Satisfied that the project would be successful, an order for the machine was confirmed and it was duly dispatched to the customer through Harper Gilfillan & Co. Ltd., RB agents in Malaysia.

Below: The 54-RB Grabbing Crane / Dragline mounted in the aft well of the pontoon dredger 'Perak'. Though not used when these photographs were taken, the dragline fairlead can be seen fitted and a dragline bucket was supplied with the machine in addition to the clamshell.

54-RB Dragline / Grabbing Crane operating with clamshell bucket from the pontoon dredger 'Perak'. With its 80ft boom and mounted on its long / wide crawlers the machine had an operating radius between 50ft to 75ft. At the maximum operating radius of 75ft. its clamshell rating was 6830lbs.

54-RB Folding A-Frame

Mobility on and around a working site is an important factor in the profitability of a crawler crane or excavator and sometimes on a particular site restricted headroom, either by bridge or permanent overhead structure, can be a problem. The standard 54-RB with its high A-Frame was open to problems of headroom so the idea of a folding A-Frame was an answer to customers experiencing such site problems, as well as providing a quick and easy way of reducing height when necessary for transportation of the machine by road.

The folding type A-Frame could be supplied with the standard machine at customer's request and the photos below and opposite taken on the Excavator Works test ground show stages in the folding sequence.

Above: The first stage seen above shows the rear legs of the two-piece A-Frame disconnected and the supporting ropes temporarily reeved to the machine's drag drum.

The main members are folded down and
locked into place and the gantry frame
partially lowered.

Travelling with the A-frame lowered.

54-RB Long-Boom Stripping Shovel

The 54-B / RB's inherent strength and power coupled with the extra stability afforded by the long / wide crawler mounting developed for the dragline, made it possible to convert the standard shovel to a long-range stripping shovel.

The standard shovel boom is replaced by a longer fabricated boom consisting of two widely spaced box sections and the standard dipper handle is replaced by an extra long tubular dipper handle which is free to revolve in the saddle block, thus preventing torsional stresses in heavy digging conditions.

The 54-RB stripping shovel was equipped with a twin-grooved hoist drum and two hoist lines controlled by a single clutch and brake. The twin hoist connected to each side of the dipper replaces the single hoist and dipper bail of the standard shovel, resulting in even pulling force on the dipper which not only increases digging efficiency but prolongs cable life.

Replacing the chain crowd system used on the standard 54-RB shovel is a positive twin-rope crowd/retract system driven from a twin-cable crowd drum mounted at the foot of the boom. Described in the Section on 110-RB / 150-RB Mining Shovels, this type of shovel front-end with twin hoist and tubular dipper handle, has became the accepted system on the larger shovel excavators where front-end lightness with strength has become to this day a necessary characteristic.

Long-boom stripping shovels existed in the days of Ruston Steam Navvies (Lincoln's Excavators Vol. I), and in addition to overburden stripping duties in opencast mining, they could be found operating in the U.K's limestone quarries and the clay pits of the brick making industry. The 54-RB Diesel Stripping Shovel pictured above was photographed in 1966 whilst excavating clay in the quarries of the Ketton Portland Cement Co.

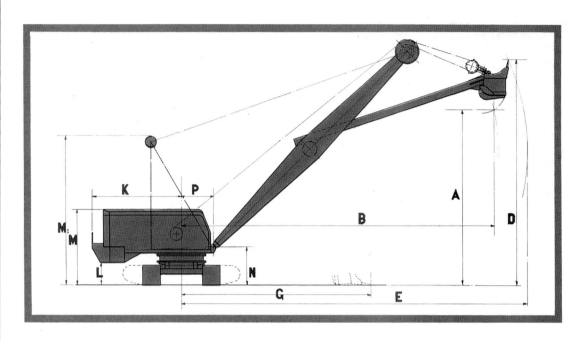

WORKING RANGES

Capacity of dipper, cubic yard		2
Length of boom		45'-0"
Length of handle		32'-0"
Angle of boom		45°
A — Dumping height, maximum		36'-0"
A1 — Dumping height, at maximum radius (B1)		24'-0"
B — Dumping radius, at maximum height (A)		48'-0"
B1 — Dumping radius, maximum		53'-0"

D — Cutting height, maximum		45'-0"
E — Cutting radius, maximum		57'-0"
G — Radius of level floor		30'-9"
K — Clearance radius of revolving frame		14'-8"
L — Clearance under frame to ground		4'-0"
M — Clearance height, boom and A-frame lowered		12'-7"
M1 — Clearance height, A-frame		25'-4"
N — Height boom foot pin above ground		6'-7"
P — Distance boom foot pin to center of rotation		5'-3"

CATERPILLAR MOUNTING

	Stripper Standard
Width of treads	36"
Overall width, working	12'-9"
Overall width, shipping	10'-6"
Overall length	20'-3"
Bearing area, square feet	94.5

MACHINERY

Hoist drum, grooved, dia.	30"
Hoist rope, twin (2-part)	7/8"
Hoist bail pull, max.	60,200 lbs.
Hoist bail speed (engine speed)	98 FPM
Crowd rope, twin	1⅛"
Boom point sheaves, dia.	42"
Padlock sheaves, dia.	20"
Boom guys, two, dia.	1½"
Boom hoist rope, 8-part	¾"
Travel speed, level ground	0.84 MPH

Specification of the 54-RB long-boom Stripping Shovel

54-RB Ward-Leonard Electric Excavator

Following the introduction of the Diesel and Single Motor Electric versions of the 54-RB, thoughts at Lincoln turned to the production of a Ward-Leonard Electric version, thus following a similar path to that taken with the earlier 52-RB. By 1946, the 54-RB Ward-Leonard Electric Shovel / Dragline was well into production at the Excavator Works, and it soon became available as an alternative to the Standard 54-RB Diesel / Electric machine. A Ward-Leonard Electric version of the 54-RB Stripping Shovel was also produced at this time.

The Ward-Leonard system of electric drive had been applied to excavators in America as early as the 1920s and its application on the 54-RB as an alternative to the Diesel / S.M.E. versions contributed greatly to the machine's long and successful production life at the Excavator Works. Unlike the Single Motor Electric machine, which largely involved the straight forward replacement of diesel engine with electric motor to drive the same basic machine, the development of the Ward-Leonard 54-RB resulted in a radically different excavator, with new revolving frame and little more than the crawler mounting remaining unchanged.

Ward-Leonard System

The essential feature of the Ward-Leonard system is that instead of the whole panoply of mechanical levers, clutches and brakes to operate the machine, the different functions of the excavator are powered by individual electric motors, with the operator controlling the speed, power and direction of rotation of each motor by small controllers at the operator's position. An incoming A.C. current is supplied to the machine which is converted to direct current, the voltage of which is controlled according to the requirements of the D.C. motors; a separate generator and motor are used for each motion and all control is obtained by varying the current in the field windings of the generator.

A separate source supplies the separately excited field winding of the generator, and it is by varying the resistance in series with this winding that the excavator operator can vary at will the motor speed, torque, and direction of rotation.

The motors on a Ward-Leonard machine, in addition to their digging function also act as powerful electric brakes. When a motor is running, it is brought to rest by throwing the controller handle right over into the position for reverse running. The motor then acts as a generator and converts the kinetic energy of the moving parts into electrical energy which is returned to the generator, thus saving power.

Dock Machinery & Electrical Equipment - 54-RB Ward-Leonard Electric Excavator

(Key to Illustration on opposite page)

A	SWING GENERATOR		M	CROWD CONTROLLER
B	MAIN INDUCTION MOTOR		N	SWING CONTROLLER
C	HOIST GENERATOR		P	HOIST MOTOR
D	CROWD GENERATOR		Q	SWING MOTOR
E	EXCITER GENERATOR		R	SWING UNIT
F	AUXILIARY TRANSFORMER		S	HOIST SHAFT ASSEMBLY
G	AUTO TRANSFORMER		T	TRANSMISSION SHAFT ASSEMBLY
H	MAIN MOTOR STARTER		U	UPPER PROPEL UNIT
J	CONTACTOR CONTROL CUBICLE		V	HYDRAULIC CONTROL UNIT
K	RESISTANCE UNIT		X	PROPEL INTERLOCK SWITCH
L	HOIST CONTROLLER		Y	HYDRAULIC ACCUMULATOR

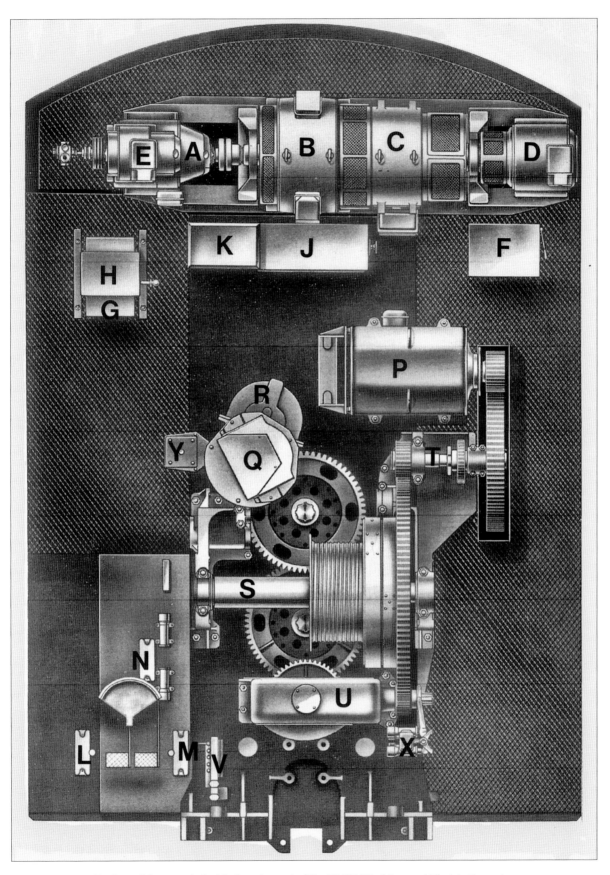

Deck machinery and electrical equipment of the 54-RB Ward-Leonard Electric Excavator.

Above: Two 54-RB Ward-Leonard Electric Shovels ready for testing at the Excavator Works.

Below: View of the 54-RB Ward Leonard Shovel's crowd motor mounted on the boom and reduction gear drive from motor to shipper shaft replacing the chain crowd mechanism which was the standard system on the 54-RB Diesel / S.M.E. machines.

Above: To meet conditions where operating space was too restricted for a standard machine to operate a 54-RB Ward-Leonard Tunnel Shovel was developed which went into production at the Excavator Works in 1952. It was fitted with a 22ft. boom, 15ft dipper handle and carried a 3 cu.yd. dipper. With less counterweight required it had a reduced rear end radius and a special low A-Frame reduced overall height. This photo of a 54-RB Tunnel Shovel on the test ground was taken in January 1953.

Below: In 1964 the 54-RB received a new style cab; this photograph taken in November 1964 shows a 54-RB Ward-Leonard Electric Shovel on the test ground in its 'new clothes'.

54-RB Ward-Leonard Electric Shovel (Mc.No.30670) handling hot slag for the
Appleby - Frodingham Steel Co., Scunthorpe, in January 1966.
The machine is fitted with additional boom safety pendants.

LINCOLN'S EXCAVATORS

THE 38-RB

38-RB Series One Shovel on the Excavator Works test ground

THE 38-RB EXCAVATOR

The Bucyrus-Erie 1½ cu.yd. 38-B Excavator was introduced in the States in 1945 and it was based upon the 54-B and earlier models in its basic single drum shaft design. In 1948 production began at the Excavator Works of the Ruston-Bucyrus version and by the end of that year the first two 38-RBs were being put through their paces on the Lincoln company's test ground.

Manually controlled and powered by a Ruston 6VPHN diesel engine rated 132 h.p. at 1,000 r.p.m. (later replaced by a 4-cylinder Ruston-Paxman 4RPHN II), the 38-RB was also offered in a single-motor electric version. Typical of the medium size RB/BE excavators the equipments available for the 38-RB were shovel, cambered boom dragshovel, and for lattice boom operation dragline, lifting crane and grabbing crane.

With a total working weight of 46½ tons, the 38-RB was to prove a successful and popular medium size excavator with a long production life. However, its longevity was largely due to its subsequent resurrection as the greatly improved air-controlled 38-RB Series Two.

The 38-RB Series Two was still in production when the Ruston-Bucyrus company closed in 1985, by which time the combined total of 38-RB and 38-RB Series Two excavators built at the Excavator Works had reached 1,800 machines.

The first 38-RB (Mc.No.11156) on the test ground in January 1949.

A major improvement incorporated on the 38-B/RB was the replacement of the narrow footed shovel boom with its necessary supporting side-stays typical of earlier BE designs by a wide-footed boom which greatly improved the strength and rigidity of the front end equipment.

To this was added the further benefit of a positive twin-rope crowd-retract system which replaced the direct chain-driven crowd of earlier models. This reduced the front-end weight enabling the machine to swing quicker and also had the effect of absorbing harmful digging shocks so reducing wear and maintenance costs.

The square box-like cab characteristic of the 38-RB is a necessary design to accommodate the Ruston & Hornsby 6VPHN engine.

The first 38-RB (Mc.No.11156) was purchased by Clugston Cawood and was delivered to them at Scunthorpe in February 1949. These two photographs taken in May 1949 show the machine digging and loading slag at the Scunthorpe steel works.

Above: In addition to its mining and quarrying duties, the 38-RB, with larger capacity than the 22-RB yet still reasonably transportable, proved popular with the U.K. construction industry and could often be found on the larger construction sites. This 38-RB Shovel of Western Excavating was photographed in December 1957 whilst loading a 15-ton Euclid dump truck on the Falmouth Dock construction.

Opposite page: Two photographs taken in November 1963 of a 38-RB Shovel operated by Messrs. G. Wimpey & Co. loading rubble on a building site in Euston Road, London. In the background is a 22-RB Dragline.

38-RB Basic Design

The 38-RB belongs to that group of excavators whose main machinery and general operation is based upon a single main drum shaft; other medium size Ruston-Bucyrus machines based upon this 'one-drum-shaft' design included the 54-RB, 71-RB and 61-RB, (but not the 30-RB which operated with two main drum shafts).

Primary transmission to the main machinery is by multi-strand roller chain and the main machinery layout of the 38-RB is almost identical to that of the 54-RB. The only main difference in machinery and operation of these two machines is that on the 38-RB an extra crowd-rope drum is fitted on the deck plate in front of the main machinery when it is operated as a shovel, signifying the change from the direct chain-driven crowd of the 54-RB Shovel to a chain-driven rope-operated crowd on the 38-RB. In other respects such as swing machinery, hoist machinery and chain driven independent boom hoist, the two models of excavator are identical.

The basic principle on machines with a single main drum shaft is that only one drum is required on the shaft for shovel hoist operation, but for all other equipments a second drum is mounted on the same shaft. This standard side-by-side drum arrangement provides rope drives as follows;

    Shovel   . . . . .Hoist (right drum)
    Dragline . . . . . .Hoist (left drum) Drag (right drum)
    Clamshell . . . . . .Hoist / closing (right drum) holding / lowering (left drum)
    Crane   . . . . .Hoist (right drum) Aux. Hoist (left drum)
    Dragshovel . . . . .Hoist (left drum) Drag (right drum)

The design of the lower works on the 38-RB is also identical to the 54-RB; there is the same set of hook-rollers mounted on the underside of the revolving frame which travel in the double-flange roller path of a single steel truck frame casting within which is located similar swing-propel machinery.

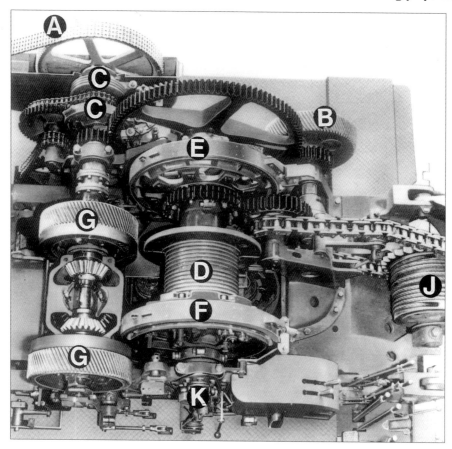

Main machinery layout for the 38-RB Diesel and Single Motor Electric Shovel
A. Primary Transmission Chain **B.** Back Haul Clutch **C.** Boom Hoist Clutches **D.** Hoist Drum
E. Crowd Clutch **F.** Hoist Clutch **G.** Reverse Clutches **J.** Crowd Drum **K.** Dipper Trip

Above: 38-RB diesel shovel assembled in the factory awaiting the crowd drum unit to be mounted.

Below: 38-RB diesel dragline assembled in the factory with the second drum fitted to main shaft.

38-RB Single Motor Electric

As an alternative to diesel power the 38-RB could be supplied with a single electric motor. This power unit depended on the availability of an on-site external electric power source and was best suited for work where extensive travelling of the machine was not necessary.

The electric motor supplied for the 38-RB S.M.E. was a 75 h.p. continuously rated squirrel cage induction motor specially designed for excavator work with a synchronous speed of 1000 r.p.m. Current is supplied to the machine by trailing cable, and led from the truck frame to the revolving superstructure through collector gear consisting of cast-iron shoes running on steel rings.

Above: 38-RB S.M.E. under assembly in the factory with electric motor mounted in place of diesel engine.

Below: Revolving frame of the Single Motor Electric machine in the factory showing the collector rings.

38-RB Dragline

The 38-RB was of a size that lent itself to successful use as a dragline and the long wide crawler mounting developed for dragline, crane, or grabbing crane work provided increased stability for maximum performance. To provide a climbing angle that gives increased manoeuvrability for dragline work on soft ground this mounting could be readily changed from flat to tapered ends by the insertion of bearing blocks between the side frames and the idler roller pins.

From the basic 45' lattice boom, additional sections could be inserted to a maximum length of 80' for dragline service. Continuous suspension between 'A' frame and boom point is fitted for booms below 60' in length; pendant suspension with mast is required for all boom lengths over this, but can be fitted for shorter booms when specified.

Bucket capacities for the 38-RB Dragline ranged from $5/8$ cu.yd. to $1^1/2$ cu.yd. depending upon boom length and mounting but for normal operation weight of bucket and contents must not exceed 9,100 lbs. and boom angle of less than 30° was not recommended for dragline service.

Left & below: 38-RB Dragline on the test ground with long wide crawlers, mast suspension and 60' boom with 1½ cu.yd. bucket.

38-RB Series Two

In July 1966 a significant event occurred in the history of the 38-RB with the announcement of the proposed introduction of the 38-RB Series Two to replace the popular but ageing current model.

The Series Two was a full air-controlled machine, as against the mechanical controls of the 38-RB Series One, of which 1100 had been built by then.

This was not, however, the simple up-rating of the earlier model, for in addition to the full air-control operation of all the main functions with air-assist drum brakes, there were many other new features and improvements incorporated in the 38-Series Two which led to increased performance and almost a complete new model. Improvements to the basic machine included;

1. Choice of Diesel Engines; Ruston-Paxman 4RPHN III (150 net h.p. at 1180 r.p.m.) or Ruston 6YEXN II turbo charged with Clark A.K.C. 16.1 torque converter (220 net h.p. at 1800 r.p.m.).
2. Complete new revolving frame casting.
3. Special attention of the operator's air console to enhance operator efficiency.
4. Eight adjustable conical hook rollers in the swing circle.
5. Swing pinion of forged steel hardened and tempered with machine cut teeth.
6. Alloy steel for the transmission shaft to a superior specification. Shaft re-designed to withstand the higher loading requirements of the Series Two.
7. 'V' block type spring-set air-released swing brake with air assist setting.
8. Air controlled quick shift from swing to propel.
9. Complete new design truck frame with integral line bored mounting holes for horizontal propel shaft bearings. Flame hardened swing rack teeth.
10. Reinforced upper roller path in the truck frame.
11. Improved crawler mounting specification with flame-hardening of roller path on the links, rims, and lugs of drive tumblers and rim of take-up tumbler.
12. Air-controlled steering jaw clutches.
13. 'V' block type propel brakes, spring-set air-released with air assist setting when required.
14. 33" crawler links as standard.

The first 38-RB Series Two, Mc.No.30718, seen here in the assembly
shop was fitted with a 4RPHN III engine

Development of the 38-RB Series Two required a complete new revolving frame to
accommodate all the changes. The revolving frame for the first machine (No.30718) is
here in the factory ready for mounting onto the lower works.

Above: Underside view of the 38-RB Series Two truck frame. The new one-piece cast-steel truck frame with integral double flanged roller path ensured strength and accurate alignment of horizontal and vertical propel shafts. There is a separate renewable swing gear ring of heat-treated alloy steel with machine-cut hardened internal teeth. Like the Series One, power is transmitted via driving chains to the horizontal propel shaft, but a feature of the Series Two is the easy manoeuvrability by spring-set, air-released steering jaw clutches and 'V'-block propel brakes. Brakes have air-assist for extra holding power and also serve as digging locks.

Opposite (Top): Main Machinery of the 38-RB Series Two Diesel Excavator. The incorporation of full air-control on the Series Two radically changes the appearance of the main machinery of the 38-RB. The reversing clutches are fully air-operated two-shoe internal-expanding type and the drum clutches are fully air controlled internal-expanding band-type with air-assisted external-contracting band type brakes.

Opposite (Bottom left): Air-operated swing clutch.

Opposite (Bottom right): Boom hoist unit with single-lever control. The independent boom hoist has full power control for raising and lowering by air-controlled clutches and incorporates a spring-set air-released brake with air-operated safety pawl. Clutches and brake control is inter-connected for safety in operation.

An early 38-RB Series Two shovel photographed at the works in April 1967 with cab
removed and equipped with 6YEXN engine.

A second photograph of the 38-RB Series Two shovel taken at the Works in April 1967
shows the right hand side of the machine with operator's controls. It also offers a
view of the twin-rope crowd system with chain-driven double rope drum at the boom
foot and rope drum mounted on the shipper shaft over which runs the single rope
that operates the retract (inward) movement of the dipper handle. From the underside
of this runs the twin ropes that operate the crowd (outward) movement
of the dipper handle.

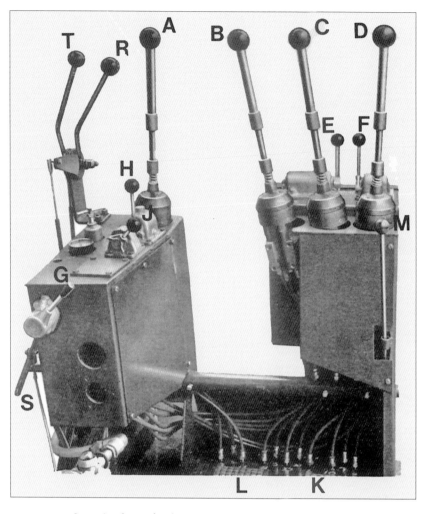

Operating levers for the 38-RB Series Two (6YEXN engine).

REF.	CONTROL	FUNCTION CONTROLLED
A	HAND LEVER	SWING AND PROPEL REVERSING CLUTCHES
B	HAND LEVER	CROWD AND RETRACT CLUTCH, ETC.
C	HAND LEVER	HOIST DRUM
D	HAND LEVER	BOOM HOIST
E	HAND LEVER	DIGGING AND STEERING BRAKES
F	HAND LEVER	STEERING JAW CLUTCHES
G	HAND LEVER	SWING BRAKE
H	HAND LEVER	SWING AND PROPEL JAW CLUTCHES
J	HAND LEVER	MAIN ENGINE CLUTCH
K	FOOT PEDAL (R.H.)	HOIST DRUM BRAKE
L	FOOT PEDAL (L.H.)	SECOND DRUM BRAKE
M	LOCK ROD	BRAKE PEDAL LOCK (LOCKS EITHER OR BOTH PEDALS)
R	HAND LEVER	ENGINE GOVERNOR CONTROL
S	HAND LEVER	ENGINE STOPPING CONTROL
T	HAND LEVER	TORQUE CONVERTER OUT-PUT SHAFT SPEED CONTROL

This photograph taken in November 1965 shows the first 38-RB Series Two shovel excavator
(Mc.No.30718) being tested at the Excavator Works. Fitted with a 4RPHN III diesel engine
it was purchased by the Amalgamated Roadstone Co. and delivered to them in December 1965.

A Note on 38-RB Series Two Engines

Ruston-Bucyrus production records show that in the choice of Ruston-Paxman 4RPHN or Ruston & Hornsby 6YEXN, both engines were supplied for the 38-RB Series Two in equal measure in the first year or so. Gradually, sales showed the 6YEXN to be the preferred choice.

The 1970s saw a change of policy in which cost largely determined the choice of engine in RB machines, and since the company had long been free from the constraints of having to fit only Ruston engines, the available engines on the 38-RB Series Two became a choice between Cummins or Dorman, with the General Motors (Detroit Diesel) 6-71 also available at customer request.

Two more photographs of the first 38-RB Series Two excavator on test; with its revised crawler mounting and increased counterweight it was equipped with longer boom and dipper handle than the Series One and had the ability to carry a general duty 1¾ cu.yd. dipper or 1½ cu.yd. rock dipper, with the further option of a 2¼ cu.yd. coal dipper. Another new feature on the shovel was the replacement of the Series One's reel-type dipper trip by an air-operated dipper trip mounted on the boom.

38-RB Series Two Shovel, Mc.No.31241, equipped with 1½ cu.yd. rock dipper loading blasted limestone at Bolsover Moor quarry for Hoveringham Stone Ltd. in August 1966. Equipped with a 4RPHN engine, this machine, and a second 38-RB Series Two shovel, Mc.No.31242 with a 6YEXN engine, were delivered to the customer in April and June 1966.

38-RB Series Two Standard and Heavy Duty Crane / Dragline

Already at Lincoln there was an on-going design and development programme in the Engineering Department headed by Bob Chevassut (who was later to become RB's Chief Engineer) to increase the crane performance of Ruston-Bucyrus machines to suit both its Domestic and Export markets. The ultimate aim of this programme at Lincoln was to develop the crane beyond its status as an optional equipment and produce a range of specialist high-performance lifting cranes in their own right.

Unlike other models in the RB product range the 38-RB was never selected for development towards 'Supercrane' status but the emergence of the 38-RB Series Two provided the opportunity for special crane development which would both increase its lifting crane capacity and meet the crane regulations applying to Domestic and Export markets.

New lattice booms and special new crane features resulted in two lifting crane versions of the 38-RB Series Two - the Standard machine for lifting crane service having a rating of about 30 tons with increased maximum allowable load for dragline of 13,500 lbs., and for grabbing crane 16,200 lbs - and the Heavy-Duty lifting crane version on long crawlers with maximum counterweight having a maximum rating of about 40 tons.

38-RB Series Two Heavy Duty Lifting Crane with basic 40' boom on test at the Excavator Works. The hydraulic counterweight lifting device seen at the rear of the machine at first optional became a standard feature of the Ruston-Bucyrus range of purpose-built lifting cranes. (A section in 'Lincoln's Excavators Vol. IV' is devoted to the development of the Ruston-Bucyrus high-performance Heavy Duty lifting cranes and 'Supercranes'.)

LINCOLN'S EXCAVATORS

THE 22-RB

22-RB Shovel in Kelengwa Copper Mine, Zambia

22-RB EXCAVATOR

In its time the 10-RB, familiar to the general public in town or country became, like the JCB today, synonymous with all small excavators. Yet it was the slightly larger 22-RB that enjoyed the greatest popularity of all Ruston-Bucyrus Universal Excavators as evidence by the total of 7585 built during its long production life at the Excavator Works.

A favourite on small building and constructions sites as well as drainage schemes and road works, the 22-RB proved the perfect compromise between digging performance and the need to be easily and quickly transported from one working site to another. The 22-RB was the maximum size of Ruston-Bucyrus excavator that could be transported by the roads without prior notice to the police.

The ¾ cu.yd. 22-RB was one of the group of RB/BE excavators whose proven design was based upon the mould-breaking 10B / 10-RB. Introduced in the latter part of 1950, the 22-RB joined the 17, 19, and 20-RB having capacities of ½, 5/8 and ¾. respectively, but of these only the 19-RB was retained in production alongside the new 22-RB, and these two, together with the 3/8th cu.yd. 10-RB formed the Ruston-Bucyrus standard range of small Universal Excavators.

The first two 22-RBs, machine number 13485 and 13486, were sold to two well known large contractors, Balfour Beatty and John Laing in December 1950. The following year, only sixteen machines were sold, but this leapt to 133 in 1952, and by 1956 production of the 22-RB at the Excavator Works was running at twenty two machines a week, and it was difficult to move in No.1 Bay without stepping on a 19-RB or 22-RB truck frame awaiting machining.

The newly introduced 22-RB had the 'continental' version of the traditional 'Lincoln' style cab seen above which had become standard on the 19-RB, though by 1956, consistent with the company's policy for all their small to medium excavators, both the 19-RB and the 22-RB acquired the American style cab.
(In 1964 a continental version of the new-style was provided for those 22-RB machines required to be transported complete on continental railways.)

Two photographs taken in September 1955 of 22-RB Mc.No.17827 owned by the
Stirlingshire County Council working in a quarry; the machine was supplied new to the
S.C.C. as a universal excavator on 13th June, 1954.

22-RB base machine showing the main machinery mounted on the
standard crawlers and equipped with a Ruston 4YEN diesel engine.

Steel castings were used extensively in the construction of the 22-RB, including both the truck frame and the revolving frame. The box-section cast steel revolving frame runs on conical shaped rollers to avoid slip in the double flanged roller path which is integral with the truck frame. With the rollers disposed as four unit taking both upward and downward loading, stresses are distributed efficiently through-out the truck frame eliminating the need for a heavy centre post. There are two pairs of large diameter twin rollers mounted in equalizing frames at the front where the heaviest loads are concentrated, and two single rollers fitted at the rear.

On the original 22-RBs the crawler mounting, comprising welded steel unit side frames, was fitted with 26" wide track links and had an overall width of

9' 4" over the links and 12' 0" overall length; this was standard for all the front-end equipments.

The first 22-RB models were powered by a 4 cylinder, 66 hp. Ruston 4YEN diesel engine with an alternative electric driven version powered by a 40-hp. electric motor. Operation of the early 22-RBs was entirely through mechanical controls to the friction clutches and brakes, and this remained the case until 1966 when air-control was introduced on to the machine.

*Opposite page: (*Above) Mounting the 22-RB upper works with Ruston 4YEN engine in the Lincoln factory. (Below) View of the assembled base machine showing the conical hook swing rollers.

22-RB base machine in the factory fitted with B.T.H. single electric motor.
The machine was ordered by customer United Africa with a delivery date of 20th
January 1958 (which was not going to be met, since the photograph was taken on
the 22nd with assembly to be completed and machine still to be tested).

22-RB Single Motor Electric

From its inception, the 22-RB was offered with electric drive as an alternative to the standard diesel powered machine where an external electricity supply was available. In such cases the diesel engine was replaced by a single electric motor.

The standard equipment, suitable for 3 phase, 50 cycles, 400/440 volts comprised;

Motor
40 h.p., 1000 r.p.m. synchronous, continuously rated, protected type, squirrel cage induction motor with end-shield ball and roller bearings.

Motor Starter
Oil-immersed, 'deep tank' type star-delta starter with under-voltage release and time-delay overload relays. Separate heavy-duty 'stop' button at operator's controls.

Collector Gear
Power is transmitted from the truck frame to the revolving frame through a collector gear comprising a collector ring assembly mounted on the truck frame, and corresponding brush gear mounted on the revolving frame. The brushes being spring-loaded to ensure efficient contact with the rings. An earthing device is also fitted.

Approximate Power Consumption
0.3 to 0.7 kWh per cubic yard solid
80 kW average momentary peak load
32 kW average 15 min. max. demand
40 kVA transformer capacity.

22-RB upper works with Ruston 6YDAN engine being
mounted on long and wide crawler base.

In 1963, an alternative to the 4YEN diesel engine
was offered in the form of the Ruston air-cooled
6YDAN diesel engine with six cylinders and an
excavator rating of 66 h.p. at 1275 r.p.m. The choice
of the two different engines continued until by 1967
it became apparent that there had built up a greater
proportional demand for the air-cooled engine at the
expense of the water-cooled.

This reached the stage where the continued
production of the 4YEN version was no longer
justified and from July 1967 the company ceased to
build 22-RBs with 4YEN engines.

Within a year or so of the 22-RBs introduction, the
alternative option of long and wide crawler mounting
seen in the above photograph was made available for
crane/dragline service; wider 30" track links were
fitted and the crawler base had been increased to an
overall width of 11' 0" and overall length of 13' 7".
This 'swamp' mounting as it was called increased
the ground bearing area from standard 45.60 sq.ft. to
60 sq.ft. and enabled the application of longer booms
for crane and dragline service.

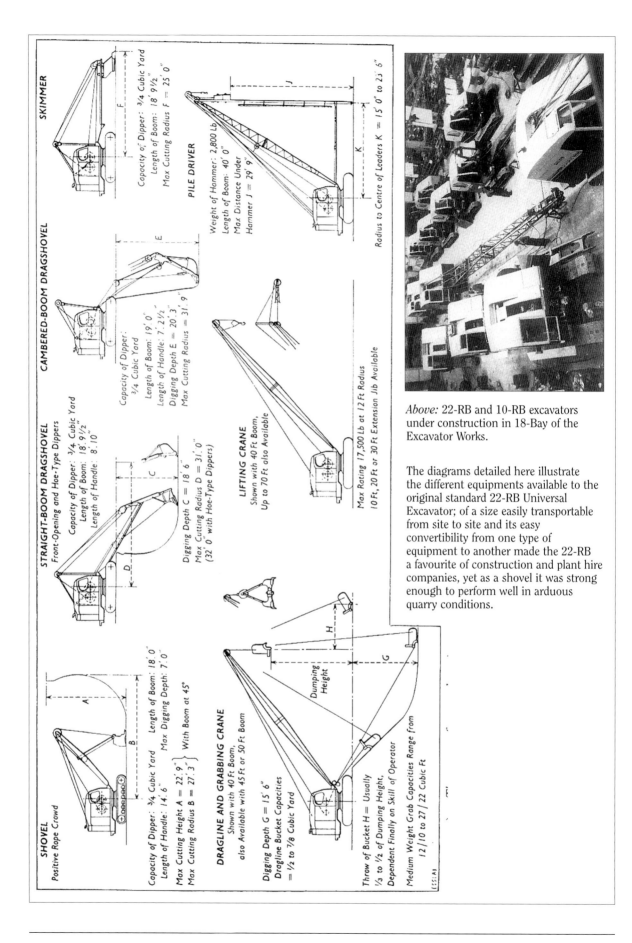

Above: 22-RB and 10-RB excavators under construction in 18-Bay of the Excavator Works.

The diagrams detailed here illustrate the different equipments available to the original standard 22-RB Universal Excavator; of a size easily transportable from site to site and its easy convertibility from one type of equipment to another made the 22-RB a favourite of construction and plant hire companies, yet as a shovel it was strong enough to perform well in arduous quarry conditions.

22-RB Shovel with ¾ cu.yd. dipper loading
blasted limestone in a Lincolnshire quarry.

Though highly popular in the construction industry due to its mobility and versatility as a Universal machine, the long-lasting success of the 22-RB was in no small measure due to the fact that as a shovel it could also stand up to rigorous conditions of quarry work.

Maximum load capacity of the 22-RB, including the dipper itself, was achieved through the use of special alloy steels. The revolving frame was a steel casting of great strength and the conical hook swing rollers used instead of the traditional centre pintle which greatly reduced the stresses on the truck and revolving frame in hard digging conditions.

The shovel front-end equipment followed the design of previous Ruston-Bucyrus excavators in which the torsional stresses imparted through the handle are carried by the full box-section lower half of the boom, while the dual arm upper boom which carries no torsional stress, has plenty of strength to withstand digging loads. The faster swing obtainable from light yet strong front-end, resulted in more power being available for other operations, less stress on machinery and better balance for the entire machine.

Twin crowd drums located at the foot of the boom chain-driven from the main machinery controlled the twin-rope crowd/single-rope retract of the dipper handle which added to the speed of operation and a also provided a shock-absorbing effect during digging that reduced wear and minimised stand-down time.

Peter Stevenson, product training engineer of the Ruston-Bucyrus Product Training Dept.,
is pictured on the left greeting the driver of a 22-RB on the occasion of his visit to Longwood
Quarries, Blankney, with quarry site manager Mr. Mitchell looking on.

The Ruston-Bucyrus Product Training Section, not to be confused with the company's Works Training Dept. was part of the Sales Promotion Department and was set up to provide courses at the Excavator Works designed to improve and increase knowledge of the company's products.

The courses included instruction on the machine's capabilities, on maintenance and recommended servicing etc. The recipients of these courses were operators, maintenance engineers, foremen and mechanics from Ruston-Bucyrus product users around the world. Such courses included the use of training films produced by the department, often using convenient local quarries and working sites for their subject matter, which explains Peter's visit to Longwood Quarries.

Longwood Quarries was founded by Mr. Parker the present owners' grandfather, a member of the local farming community, and came about when in the 1930s he purchased the area of land at Blankney near Lincoln known as Longwood. Mr. Parker discovered among the trees an ancient lime kiln signifying the presence of limestone in the area and a former lime-making industry. Aware of the importance to farmers of lime and the government subsidy received by farmers for its purchase, Mr. Parker decided to resume lime-burning and the necessary quarrying at Longwood., though on a relatively small scale.

The lime-making business at Longwood declined through the 1950s and 60s, ending in 1970 with the end of farmers' subsidies, but the quarrying business thrived and continued to expand to become the present successful family concern.

In 1952, a 10-RB Shovel was employed at Longwood Quarries to load hardcore, this was followed by the 22-RB Shovel (MC.No.27806) seen above which was equipped with a 6YDAN engine and delivered new to the quarry in April 1963 at a cost of £7,166-16s-4p. In 1974 Longwood Quarries purchased a second-hand 10-RB Dragline for £225 followed in 1979 by a works re-built 38-RB Diesel Shovel with 2 cu.yd. dipper costing £54,250.

Two more photographs on the occasion of the RB Product Training Dept. visit to Longwood Quarries in May 1963 showing Machine 27806 loading blasted limestone. In the 1960s until the early 1970s explosives were used and the RB machines loaded stone into Shawney Pool dumper loaders. Increased production at Longwood, however, led to the use of Volvo loading shovels - a Volvo BM4600 purchased in 1984, a Volvo BM2160 in 1986 and a second BM2160 in 1987. Since that time two Volvo loading shovels have been used, one to load stone off the rock face to the primary crusher with a second example to load the graded stone into the lorries.

Above: 22-RB Skimmer. The outward travel of the dipper is controlled by the drag rope from the front drum and the boom is raised and lowered by three-part hoist over the auxiliary 'A' frame to the rear shaft drum. Backward movement of the dipper and lowering the boom is by gravity and both movements are controlled by the brakes fitted on the drum shaft.

Below: 22-RB Straight-boom Dragshovel. This equipment could be fitted with either a front-opening type dipper with a hinged door as seen below or the single-cast hoe-type dipper typical of the later hydraulic 'backhoe' excavators. The strut-braced forward 'A' frame was standard on the straight-boom Dragshovel whereas with the cambered boom a rope suspended 'A' frame was employed.

22-RB with cambered boom Dragshovel
equipment on an urban construction site.

The optional front-end equipments available to the original 22-RB included Skimmer and Straight-boom Dragshovel (seen opposite); their design was such that their boom and auxiliary forward 'A' frame could be retained when making the conversion from one to the other, thus reducing conversion time.

By the time the 22-RB was introduced, however, dragshovel performance had been greatly improved with the introduction of the 'cambered-boom' with its greater reach and digging depth and in 1957 the Cambered-boom Dragshovel was added as an optional alternative to the Straight-boom Dragshovel on the 22-RB. Also at this time, Skimmers were beginning to lose their popularity in the face of competition from tractor-based loading shovels. With the decline of the Skimmer the main justification for the straight-boom Dragshovel was removed so that by 1970, cambered-booms became the standard form of drag-shovel equipment. These trends were reflected in the fact that after 1970 Skimmers and Straight-boom Dragshovels were completely phased out of production at the Excavator Works and deleted from the RB Sales catalogue.

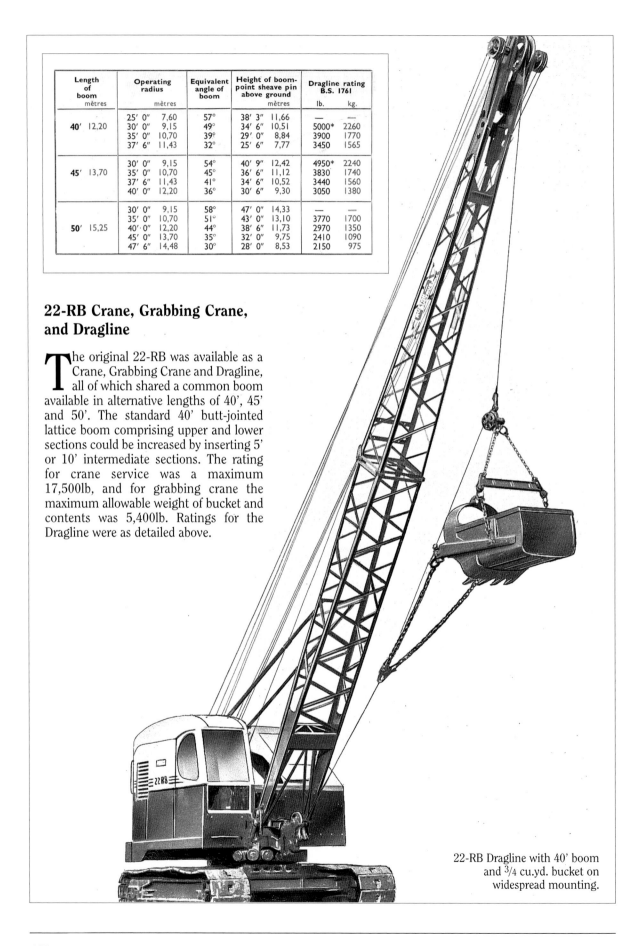

Length of boom		Operating radius		Equivalent angle of boom	Height of boom-point sheave pin above ground		Dragline rating B.S. 1761	
mètres		mètres			mètres		lb.	kg.
40'	12,20	25' 0"	7,60	57°	38' 3"	11,66	—	—
		30' 0"	9,15	49°	34' 6"	10,51	5000*	2260
		35' 0"	10,70	39°	29' 0"	8,84	3900	1770
		37' 6"	11,43	32°	25' 6"	7,77	3450	1565
45'	13,70	30' 0"	9,15	54°	40' 9"	12,42	4950*	2240
		35' 0"	10,70	45°	36' 6"	11,12	3830	1740
		37' 6"	11,43	41°	34' 6"	10,52	3440	1560
		40' 0"	12,20	36°	30' 6"	9,30	3050	1380
50'	15,25	30' 0"	9,15	58°	47' 0"	14,33	—	—
		35' 0"	10,70	51°	43' 0"	13,10	3770	1700
		40' 0"	12,20	44°	38' 6"	11,73	2970	1350
		45' 0"	13,70	35°	32' 0"	9,75	2410	1090
		47' 6"	14,48	30°	28' 0"	8,53	2150	975

22-RB Crane, Grabbing Crane, and Dragline

The original 22-RB was available as a Crane, Grabbing Crane and Dragline, all of which shared a common boom available in alternative lengths of 40', 45' and 50'. The standard 40' butt-jointed lattice boom comprising upper and lower sections could be increased by inserting 5' or 10' intermediate sections. The rating for crane service was a maximum 17,500lb, and for grabbing crane the maximum allowable weight of bucket and contents was 5,400lb. Ratings for the Dragline were as detailed above.

22-RB Dragline with 40' boom and 3/4 cu.yd. bucket on widespread mounting.

Development of the 22-RB Lifting Crane

The rapidly expanding U.K. construction industry led the Lincoln company to realise the potential for specialist crawler mounted lifting cranes and certain of their models were singled out for development by the Ruston-Bucyrus Engineering Department along these lines.

There were two aspects to this development, the need to achieve the maximum crane rating from a particular model, and to improve crane performance by the incorporation of specialized equipment such as power load lowering, etc.

The first step in this development came in 1957 when a Heavy Duty Crane/Dragline version of the 22-RB with increased crane rating of 12 tons was created by increasing its counterweight and providing a newly designed B.S.S. (British Standard Specification) lattice boom. This new version was followed two years later by the 22-RB Widespread, which had a wide mounting with proportions that permitted full convertibility to excavator equipments.

The 22-RB Widespread was followed by the 22-RB I.C.D. (Improved Crane Dragline); although available for excavator conversion, this was the first in a line of RB models leading to the Supercrane range of increasing capacity high performance lifting cranes. (This is described in the Lifting Crane chapter of Lincoln's Excavators Vol. IV.)

22-RB I.C.D. Magnet Crane operated by Shanks & McEwan Ltd. On scrap handling duties.

The 22-RB Two-in-One
'An Absorbing Entertainment'

It is said about a machine "if it doesn't look right, it is probably not a good design", and never was this more true than to the 22-RB Two-in-One Excavator. Originating in America from a basic Bucyrus-Erie design where it was given the name 'The Scooper', this ungainly attempt at a dual-purpose Dragshovel/loading shovel was selected by Ruston-Bucyrus in 1960 for further development with a view to adding it into their range of products. A prototype machine was built in the Lincoln factory on an experimental basis which was then put to rigorous and protracted testing.

Designed specifically for the 22-RB, power for the Two-in-One for main machinery and hydraulic pump was provided by a 66 h.p. Ruston 6YDAN air-cooled diesel engine. Its rope operation was provided by continuous 3-part hoist line and 3 to 1 drag pull line, with assist wrist-action for the dipper through twin hydraulic rams. Mounted between the forward A-frame and the foot of the boom is a non-powered hydraulic cylinder which reacts against the lifting of the boom. This 'hold-down' device is controlled through two micro-switches so that when digging the tendency for the boom to lift is resisted by oil pressure in the cylinder. The fabricated boom comprised twin box-section side members with box-section cross members and pin-connected to a spreader at the lower end of the handle is the dual-purpose dipper. The dipper is braced on either side to the handle members through a pin-connected linkage and hydraulic cylinder, enabling it to pivot about the handle for setting the digging angle or discharging the load.

Tests on the prototype at the Excavator works were not encouraging; the structural design of the whole front end equipment with its 6 foot wide lightweight dipper proved to be inherently too weak to withstand loads imposed upon it by hard digging conditions. The project was dropped and no further 22-RB Two-in-One excavators were built.

Surprisingly, the test machine was painted up and displayed with other models on the Ruston-Bucyrus stand at the first International Construction Equipment Exhibition, Crystal Palace, London, held in 1961. Ironically, it was selected as an unusual feature in the B.B.C. television broadcast from the Exhibition, in which it was seen operating and referred to as "RB's contribution to this absorbing entertainment was this experimental unit which combined Dragshovel and shovel loader into a single front end."

The experimental Ruston-Bucyrus 22-RB 'Two-in-One' combined Dragshovel/Shovel on display at the International Construction Equipment Exhibition at the Crystal Palace, London in June 1961.

Two more photographs of the experimental 22-RB 'Two-in-One' on test. With light-duty 1½ cu.yd. dipper it had; a maximum digging radius 27' 9" (shovel), 27' 0" (Dragshovel); maximum dumping height 12' 4" (shovel), 12' 4" (Dragshovel); and maximum digging depth for Dragshovel of 15' 6" over end or side of mounting.

22-RB WRIST-ACTION DRAGSHOVEL

In 1961 Ruston-Bucyrus began the development of a hydraulic excavator based on the 10-RB lower works. For this purpose John Wilcock had been recruited into the Engineering Department to head a team with the specific responsibility for this project and by the end of 1962 a prototype had been built.

This development towards a hydraulic machine also provided the opportunity and motivation for the Lincoln company to consider how other models in their production range could benefit from the incorporation of a hydraulic component in their design and an obvious candidate for their attention was the dragshovel front end equipments supplied with their range of Universal Excavators.

This was not a new idea, other manufacturers including Bucyrus-Erie had added hydraulic rams on their machines, but it established a policy at Ruston-Bucyrus for the further improvement of their existing range of dragshovel equipments following on from the introduction of cambered booms.

The 22-RB cambered boom, wrist-action dragshovel with hoe-type dipper was first introduced to the public at the Construction Equipment Exhibition held at Crystal Palace, London, in 1963, by which time they were in the Lincoln production line as an option to the 22-RB standard straight boom or cambered boom dragshovel equipments.

22-RB Wrist-action cambered-boom dragshovel on the test ground.

Two photographs of the 22-RB Wrist-action cambered boom dragshovel on the test ground; above with the digging rams fully retracted and below with the ram fully extended. The same basic boom, handle and hoe-type dipper are used as for the standard cambered-boom dragshovel equipment, except for minor modifications connected with the application of the hydraulic equipment.

The availability of hydraulic-actuated pivot action for the cambered-boom dragshovel gave additional versatility and effectiveness to this front-end equipment. The practical advantages of this feature can be summarized as follows;

(1) Availability of extra effort at the dipper teeth for greater digging force.

(2) Instantly adjustable dipper rake for matching dipper position to varying conditions during digging stroke.

(3) Dipper maneuverability for avoiding or overcoming obstructions and better trimming of excavation walls.

(4) Faster working cycle, because dipper can be adjusted to suitable angle for lifting and carrying as soon as full.

(5) Better carrying of heaped loads; less spilling and speedier dumping for increased output.

(6) Positive and controlled dumping.

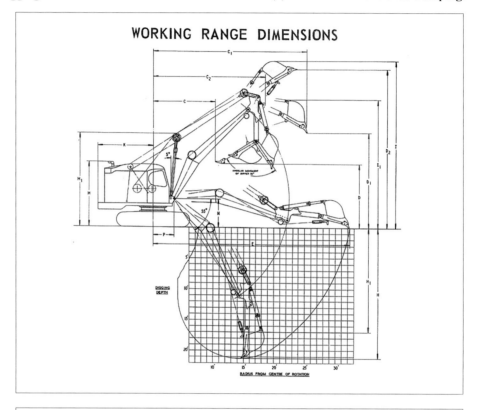

WORKING RANGE DIMENSIONS

Capacity of dipper		3/4 cu. yd.	600 ltr.
Width over side cutters*		36"	920mm.
C	Radius at beginning of dump	10' 3"	3.12m.
C_1	Radius at end of dump	25' 3"	7.69m.
C_2	Clearance radius, minimum	18' 6"	5.64m.
D	Clearance under dipper, beginning of dump	10' 3"	3.12m.
D_1	Clearance under dipper, end of dump	15' 3"	4.64m.
D_2	Clearance under teeth, maximum	25' 3"	7.69m.
E	Cutting radius, maximum	32' 3"	9.83m.
H	Digging depth over front or side of mounting	21' 3"	6.48m.
H_1	Digging depth over corner of mounting	17' 0"	5.18m.
I	Clearance height over dipper, maximum	27' 0"	8.23m.
1_1	Clearance height at end of dump	20' 9"	6.32m.
K	Clearance radius of revolving frame over counterweight	9' 0"	2.74m.
L	Clearance under revolving frame to ground level	2' 9"	838mm
M	Clearance height, auxiliary A-frame lowered	10' 6"	3.20m.
M_1	Clearance height, auxiliary A-frame raised	14' 9"	3.50m.
N	Height of boom-foot pin above ground level	4' 6 1/4"	1.38m.
P	Distance from boom-foot pin to centre of rotation	3' 5 1/4"	1.05m.

The Improved 22-RB
Wrist-action dragshovel

Ruston-Bucyrus had been working on the further development of the 22-RB Wrist-action dragshovel and in December 1966 it was announced that a new 'Improved' version was ready to replace the former version on the production line, of which almost 200 units had been sold since its introduction in 1963.

As a result of this development the scope of the machine has been increased by re-designing the boom and handle so that it could be used with a new 24" wide dipper, of 8 cu.ft. capacity, in addition to the 36" wide dipper of ¾ cu.yd. At the same time other improvements were made to the hydraulic system.

The improved 22-RB Wrist-action dragshovel incorporated the following changes;

1) The hydraulic-oil tank was increased in capacity from 12 gals. to 25 gals. in order to improve cooling.

2) To further improve cooling, the hydraulic-oil tank was positioned at revolving frame level in front of engine. In this position spillage of oil on to brake and clutch bands is eliminated.

3) The hydraulic piping was revised to give shorter runs and re-positioned on top of the boom for better protection.

4) The arrangement of the piping between boom head and hydraulic ram was re-designed to prevent damage to the piping, particularly when trenching.

5) The hydraulic ram was re-arranged with the cylinder down, (i.e. inverted in relation to the original arrangement), and the ram rod was guarded by a sleeve. Both these changes were designed to give better protection in service.

6) The dipper handle end was widened to improve the support for the dipper.

The working ranges with the new equipment remained the same and the 'Improved' version replaced the original model in production at Lincoln; some degree of adaptation would be necessary if the improved front-end equipment was required to be used with an earlier type wrist-action base machine.

Improved 22-RB Wrist-action Dragshovel on the test ground at the Excavator Works.

Wrist-action on the M18 Motorway

The 22-RB Wrist-action dragshovel could not have found more arduous work and greater test of its digging capabilities than that which faced the two new machines purchased by RB regular customer W & C French Ltd., and put to work on the first section of a new motorway, the M18, which would eventually link the two existing M1 and M6 motorways. French was awarded in October 1965 the contract for the construction of the first 8½ mile stretch of the new M18 from its interchange with the M1 at Thurcroft to its interchange with the A1(M) Doncaster By-pass at Wadworth. Several bridges were necessary and a further interchange was required where the new road crossed the A631 Gainsborough to Rotherham trunk road.

The ground was coal measures throughout and the whole motorway had therefore to be designed to cater for possible subsidence from earlier mining activity. Most of the bridges were cast in situ and this, together with the design for subsidence meant that they were slow to construct and required reinforcement. Drainage for the M18 was difficult, involving excavating sixty miles of drain trench up to 4ft. 6in. wide and 10ft. deep in solid rock.

The two 22-RB Wrist-action dragshovels involved in the M18 motorway construction were machine numbers 31036 and 31037 and they were delivered to W & C French Ltd., on the 18th and 20th March, 1966. Their task was two-fold, to excavate the rock for drainage trenching and for the footings of the many bridges required to span this first section of the new motorway. The final cost of the contract work carried out by W & C French was £5.2 million, the opening ceremony of the completed section of the M18 being performed by Mr. Stephen Swingler, Minister of State, in November 1967.

One of the French company 22-RB Wrist-action dragshovels put to a severe test excavating a trench through rock for the large diameter drainage pipes required on the M18 motorway construction.

The two 22-RB Wrist-action dragshovels, clearly identified by their black and white stripes as W & C French machines, at work on the construction of the first section of the M18 motorway. In the above photograph the machine is trenching in rock for the drainage pipes, whilst below one of the machines is excavating the footings in rock for one of the several bridges required on this section of the new motorway.

22-RB Wrist-action Dragshovel operated by Martin & Co, Ltd. in March 1968 digging footings at Marston Green, Birmingham. The project exemplifies the often precarious nature of a dragshovel's application on deep excavation where conditions require the machine to work at the extreme limits of its reach and capacity. In this particular case confidence is undermined by the fact that at some point in the work the machine has been allowed to exceed its hoist limit resulting in bent boom backstops rendering them useless from that point on. Fatalities are not uncommon when this has been allowed to happen and the over-riding front-end has crushed the driver.

22-RB WITH AIR CONTROLS

In 1965, Ruston-Bucyrus Technical Director, J.H. Page, decided that the 22-RB could be improved to some extent by the incorporation of air-controls. Unlike the air-controlled 30-RB of a few years earlier whose air-system was part of the machine's basic design, Page was faced with an existing manually controlled machine. His plan, therefore, was to develop an air system for the 22-RB which involved the minimum of change to the machine's existing main machinery and this task was given to RB Manufacturing Engineer Phil Bird. With the need to provide air-control on a low-cost basis and the minimum of change to the machinery, there was no question of designing new clutches with integral rotating air cylinders as fitted to the 30-RB. Phil's design had to be much simpler and he worked on the principle of retaining the mechanical linkage to the clutches and inserting air-control cylinders for their operation to replace the system of rods and levers.

Thus, a system was produced for the 22-RB which could better be described as 'air-assisted' controls and it became available as an alternative option on all versions of the 22-RB excavator, whether fitted with 6YDAN or 4YEN engines, on the 5th September, 1966. (Subsequently an air-controlled version of the 22-RB electric machine was developed.)

It was anticipated that the offer of both manual and air-assisted 22-RBs would boost sales, but there was no company recommendation for conversion from manual to air-assisted for existing machines in the field. Nor was the air-control system suitable for field conversion on existing wrist-action dragshovels, since the air compressor for the air-controls is directly driven off the free end of the engine which on wrist-action machines is utilized for the hydraulic pump drive.

Ted Ash, Ruston-Bucyrus Test Driver, at the controls of a 22-RB I.C.D. with air controls.

It was argued by the company that the 22-RBs partial air-control system still produced a degree of 'feel' which drivers of manual controlled machines were used to, nevertheless there were a few customers who preferred the physical contact with the machinery that manual control provided rather than the remote control of an air valve, so the option of manual control continued until well into the 1980s.

The first air-controlled 22-RB off the production line was a standard machine with 6YDAN engine, No. 31647P delivered to Ekstroms, RB's Distributor in Helsinki, in October 1966, while the first air-controlled 22-RB with 4YEN engine was sold to John Miller and delivered in February 1967. The price increase over the mechanically controlled machine with 6YDAN engine was £494, and with 4YEN engine £524.

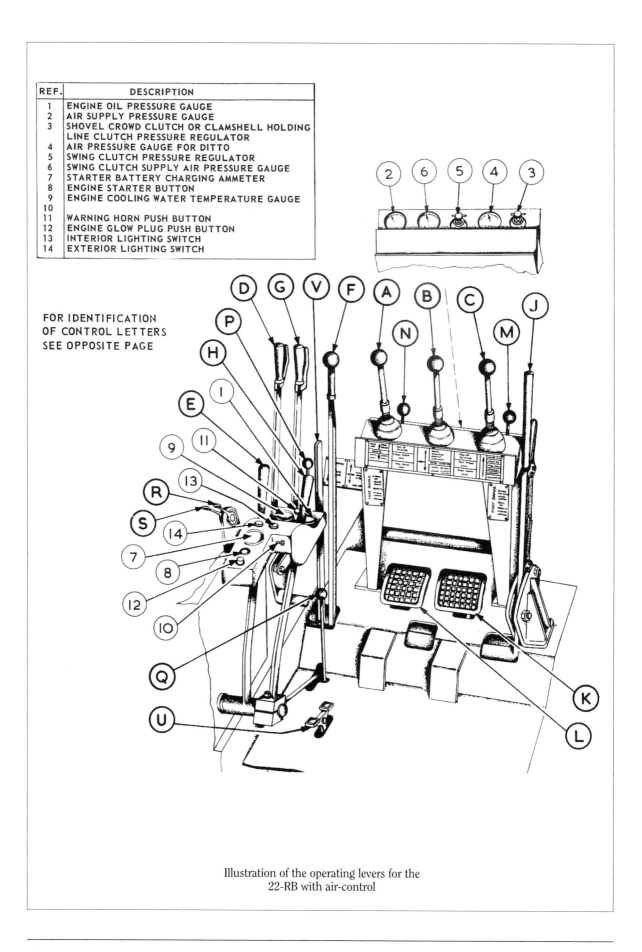

REF.	DESCRIPTION
1	ENGINE OIL PRESSURE GAUGE
2	AIR SUPPLY PRESSURE GAUGE
3	SHOVEL CROWD CLUTCH OR CLAMSHELL HOLDING LINE CLUTCH PRESSURE REGULATOR
4	AIR PRESSURE GAUGE FOR DITTO
5	SWING CLUTCH PRESSURE REGULATOR
6	SWING CLUTCH SUPPLY AIR PRESSURE GAUGE
7	STARTER BATTERY CHARGING AMMETER
8	ENGINE STARTER BUTTON
9	ENGINE COOLING WATER TEMPERATURE GAUGE
10	
11	WARNING HORN PUSH BUTTON
12	ENGINE GLOW PLUG PUSH BUTTON
13	INTERIOR LIGHTING SWITCH
14	EXTERIOR LIGHTING SWITCH

FOR IDENTIFICATION
OF CONTROL LETTERS
SEE OPPOSITE PAGE

Illustration of the operating levers for the
22-RB with air-control

LEVERS CONTROLLING MAIN OPERATING FUNCTIONS

		LEVER CONTROL	PUSH FORWARD	MID POSITION	PULL BACK
COMMON TO ALL FRONT END EQUIPMENTS	A	SWING AND PROPEL REVERSING CLUTCHES	TO SWING LEFT OR PROPEL FORWARD FROM DRIVE CHAIN	FOR NEUTRAL	TO SWING RIGHT OR PROPEL BACKWARDS TOWARDS DRIVE CHAIN
	K	DRUM BRAKE (RIGHT FOOT PEDAL)	TO BRAKE HOIST DRUM		SPRING RELEASED UNLESS LOCKED (LEVER 'M')
	L	DRUM BRAKE (LEFT FOOT PEDAL)	TO BRAKE SECOND DRUM		SPRING RELEASED UNLESS LOCKED (LEVER 'N')
	M	REAR DRUM BRAKE LOCK	PUSH DOWN TO LOCK BRAKE HARD ON		PULL UP TO RELEASE (NORMAL POSITION)
	N	FRONT DRUM BRAKE LOCK	PUSH DOWN TO LOCK BRAKE HARD ON		PULL UP TO RELEASE (NORMAL POSITION)
SHOVEL	B	CROWD (FRONT DRUM) AND/OR DIPPER TRIP	TO CROWD OUT DIPPER	FOR NEUTRAL	TO RETRACT DIPPER
			PUSH LEFT TO TRIP DIPPER DOOR LATCH, IN ANY LEVER FORE AND AFT POSITION.		
	C	HOIST (REAR DRUM)	TO HOIST DIPPER	TO RELEASE TO LOWER	NOT USED
DRAGLINE	B	DRAG (FRONT DRUM)	TO DRAG BUCKET IN TOWARDS THE MACHINE	TO RELEASE TO SWING BUCKET OUT UNDER THE BOOM POINT	NOT USED
	C	HOIST (REAR DRUM)	TO HOIST BUCKET	TO RELEASE TO LOWER	NOT USED
CLAMSHELL	B	HOLDING – LOWERING (REAR DRUM)	TO HOIST EMPTY BUCKET HOLD WITH FOOT BRAKE TO DUMP	TO RELEASE TO LOWER OPEN BUCKET	NOT USED
	C	HOIST – CLOSING (FRONT DRUM)	TO CLOSE AND HOIST LOADED BUCKET	TO RELEASE TO DUMP	NOT USED
CRANE	B	MAIN HOIST (FRONT DRUM)	TO HOIST	TO RELEASE TO LOWER	NOT USED
	C	AUXILIARY HOIST (REAR DRUM)	TO HOIST	TO RELEASE TO LOWER	NOT USED
DRAGSHOVEL	B	DRAG (FRONT DRUM)	TO DRAG	TO RELEASE TO RUN DIPPER OUT	NOT USED
	C	HOIST (REAR DRUM)	TO HOIST	TO RELEASE TO LOWER	NOT USED
SKIMMER	B	DRAG (FRONT DRUM)	TO DRAG (OR DIG)	TO RELEASE TO ALLOW BUCKET TO RUN BACK TO BOTTOM OF BOOM	NOT USED
	C	HOIST (REAR DRUM)	TO HOIST	TO RELEASE TO LOWER	NOT USED
PILE DRIVER	B	HOIST – HAMMER (FRONT DRUM)	TO HOIST	TO RELEASE TO DROP	NOT USED
	C	PILE HANDLING (REAR DRUM)	TO HOIST PILE	TO RELEASE TO LOWER PILE	NOT USED

LEVERS CONTROLLING AUXILIARY FUNCTIONS

		LEVER CONTROL	PUSH FORWARD	MID POSITION	PULL BACK
COMMON TO ALL FRONT END EQUIPMENTS	D	BOOM HOIST CLUTCH AND BRAKE	TO LOWER BOOM SAFETY PAWL RELEASED	TO HOLD BOOM	TO RAISE BOOM
	E	DIGGING LOCK	TO LOCK AGAINST MOVEMENT EITHER WAY	TO LOCK AGAINST BACKWARD MOTION ONLY	TO DISENGAGE PAWLS FOR MOVEMENT EITHER WAY
	F	STEERING JAW CLUTCHES	ALL THE WAY TO TURN SHARP RIGHT, CHAIN TO REAR / PART WAY TO TURN RIGHT GRADUALLY	TO STEER STRAIGHT AHEAD	PART WAY TO TURN LEFT GRADUALLY / ALL THE WAY TO TURN SHARP LEFT, CHAIN TO REAR
	G	SWING BRAKE (OPTIONAL EQUIPMENT)	TO APPLY BRAKE		TO RELEASE BRAKE
	H	SWING AND PROPEL JAW CLUTCHES	FOR PROPEL POSITION	NEUTRAL BOTH CLUTCHES OUT	FOR SWING POSITION
	J	MAIN ENGINE CLUTCH	TO ENGAGE		TO RELEASE
	P	BOOM HOIST SAFETY PAWL	PUSH DOWN TO LOCK		PULL UP TO RELEASE
	Q	SAFETY DEVICE AGAINST ACCIDENTAL ENGAGEMENT OF HIGH SPEED TREADLE 'U'	TO RELEASE BEFORE MOVING TREADLE 'U' TO 'HI' SPEED POSITION		TO ENGAGE SAFETY LOCK
	R	GOVERNOR CONTROL	FOR IDLING SPEED	TO SELECT INTERMEDIATE SPEED	FOR FULL GOVERNED ENGINE SPEED
	S	ENGINE STOPPING LEVER	LIFT AND HOLD UNTIL ENGINE HAS STOPPED		RELEASE FOR RUNNING POSITION
	U	HIGH SPEED TRAVEL TREADLE	PUSH DOWN REAR END TO ENGAGE		PUSH DOWN FRONT END TO DISENGAGE
	V	SWING LOCK	TO RELEASE		TO LOCK

The 22-RB Air-Assist Control System

Compressor; Twin-cylinder reciprocating type compressor driven from the engine supplying air for the air-operated motions.

Operating Controls; These consist of three graduated-type valves controlling the main excavator functions which, for the shovel are as follows - (1) Hoist, (2) Swing and Propel, (3) Crowd and Retract. On a shovel, the dipper trip is actuated by an 'on-off' type valve incorporated in the crowd/retract lever. The auxiliary functions of the machine, i.e. boom hoist, crawler steering, engine clutch and pedal operated drum brakes are operated by the normal direct mechanical linkages.

Clutches; Two types of clutch operation are used. The swing/propel clutches are each actuated by a single-acting cylinder mounted integrally with the clutch and operating the clutch band through a bell crank. During swing operation the clutches operate at reduced pressure and the regulator is automatically by-passed to give full air pressure when the swing to propel changeover hand lever is operated. The hoist clutch is actuated by a single-acting cylinder under the right hand deck plate, operating the clutch linkage through reach rods and shifter yoke as with the manual system. The shovel crowd and retract clutches are actuated by a double-acting cylinder mounted under the right hand deck plate and operating a cam as with the manual system.

1981 - The 10,000th 22-RB

Described as "the most famous Universal Excavator known to the construction industry", the 22-RB in its various versions was the most popular and the biggest selling of the Ruston-Bucyrus machines. In 1981, after thirty years of continuous production, the company celebrated the 10,000th new 22-RB to come off the Lincoln factory's production line and these well known machines were still being built when Ruston-Bucyrus closed down in 1985.

The 10,000th, described in the publicity as the 'Milestone Machine' was machine serial number 39204, a dragline version with long and wide crawler mounting which was sold through RB's Dublin Depot in April 1981 to customer the Office of Public Works, Dublin.

The Bucyrus-Erie 22-B excavator never enjoyed quite the same success in America and its declining sales led B.E. to cease its production in 1975. However, two years later customer demand in the U.S.A. for the Ruston-Bucyrus 22-RB Crane/Draglines, (which by this time were meeting O.S.H.A. standards, the American equivalent of B.S.S.), was such as to persuade the American company to introduce the Lincoln machines into their own domestic sales programme where they found a ready market.

A 22-RB with air controls in April 1966 re-handling
furnace slag for the Tarmac Road Stone Company.

LINCOLN'S EXCAVATORS

THE '100 SERIES'
110-RB / 150-RB

110-RB Full Electric Mining Shovel - Ketton

110-RB / 150-RB MINING SHOVELS AND DRAGLINES

By the 1930s the increased scale of open-cast mining had led to the development of heavy-duty shovel-type excavators specifically designed to meet the rigorous conditions of quarry or mine and with digging capacity to meet the scale of operation. There was the added bonus of their convertibility to dragline operation when a medium size dragline for general excavator duties was required. Such a machine was the Ruston-Bucyrus 3½ cu.yd. 100-RB which was introduced in 1933. In 1948 the larger 120-RB was introduced built to the same basic design but with 5 cu.yd. dipper.

At this time, it was generally considered necessary to have a fairly heavy boom on a mining shovel in order to hold the dipper into the working face and assist the crowd force to fill the dipper. However, a heavy boom meant limiting the size of dipper in order to maintain the necessary ratio of bucket capacity to machine weight, so consequently the output of such a machine was limited.

Early in 1950, Ruston-Bucyrus produced a lightweight two-part mining shovel front end to a design derived from the large stripping shovels where the lower part of a two-piece boom was integrated with the base machine structure which resisted the main digging forces. The upper section was light in weight as it acted only as a support for the hoist

function and this combination of strength with lightness meant that the dipper capacity could be increased for a given size of machine. To this was added the bonus of twin-rope boom hoist and twin-rope shovel crowd, also derived from the stripping shovels. The 110-B/RB, 150-B/RB and 190-B produced to this design were referred to collectively as the '100 Series'.

The machines produced at Lincoln to this design were the 110-RB of 4½ cu.yds. capacity and the 150-RB of 6 cu.yds., which replaced the 100-RB and 120-RB respectively. Both the 110-RB and 150-RB were electric machines using the Ward-Leonard system first fitted on the Ruston-Bucyrus 52-RB and which by this time had become the preferred method for medium to large electrically driven excavators. It is a measure of the success of their design, that both models were still on the Ruston-Bucyrus production list when the company ceased in 1985.

Although the 110/150-RBs were designed primarily as a heavy duty mining shovel, the 110-RB in particular found a market when equipped as a dragline, and it was as a dragline that in March 1955 the first 110-RB (Mc.No.18899) left the Lincoln factory for customers Marston Valley Brick Co., Bedfordshire.

The first 110-RB, Mc.No.18899, a W/L Electric Dragline, excavating clay at the Marston Valley Brick Works and loading it into a hopper. The non-standard high vision cab was a feature not uncommon on draglines supplied for deep excavation work in such locations as clay pits where it provided the operator with a better view of the bucket when digging.

Above: 110-RB 3½ cu.yd. capacity Electric Shovel, Machine No. 21922, is seen here loading iron-ore into standard gauge rail wagons at the Yarborough North Mine, Scunthorpe. The Redbourn Works can be seen in the background. The machine was delivered to operators United Steel Co. in April 1957 and is one of four 110-RB Excavators that eventually went to work in the Frodingham Ironstone Mines at Scunthorpe, replacing the well worn 100-RBs. Two, including the one above, were supplied to United Steel and two more to operator Richard Thomas & Baldwin. When iron-ore mining at Scunthorpe ceased in the 1980s, there was no sadder sight than that of a 110-RB Shovel left to rust away in the bottom of a disused mine, the last in a long line of Lincoln-built excavators that worked in the Frodingham field going back to the Dunbar-Ruston Steam Navvies at the turn of the century.

	Dipper capacity..........................	4¼ cu. yd.	
	Length of boom..........................	36 ft 0 in	
	Effective length of dipper handle..............	21 ft 6 in	
	Overall length of dipper handle...............	25 ft 10 in	
	Angle of boom..........................	45 deg	
A	Dumping height—maximum.................	23 ft 3 in	
A1	Dumping height at maximum radius..........	15 ft 9 in	
B	Dumping radius at maximum height A........	38 ft 6 in	
B1	Dumping radius—maximum.................	40 ft 3 in	
B2	Dumping radius at 12 ft 0 in elevation........	40 ft 0 in	
D	Cutting height—maximum..................	34 ft 9 in	
E	Cutting radius—maximum..................	46 ft 3 in	
F	Cutting radius at 8 ft 0 in elevation...........	44 ft 0 in	
G	Radius of level floor......................	31 ft 3 in	

H	Digging depth below ground level—maximum ..	9 ft 3 in
I	Clearance height of boom-point sheaves	36 ft 0 in
J	Clearance radius of boom-point sheaves........	34 ft 9 in
K	Clearance radius of revolving frame	18 ft 3 in
L	Clearance under frame to ground level........	5 ft 3 in
M	Clearance height with boom and A-frame lowered	16 ft 9 in
M1	Height of A-frame	24 ft 0 in
N	Height of boom foot above ground level	8 ft 5 in
P	Distance from boom foot to centre of rotation..	7 ft 4 in
U	Clearance under propelling gear case to ground level..................................	1 ft 3½ in
V	Width of superstructure with platform removed..	17 ft 9 in
W	Overall width of superstructure	19 ft 0 in

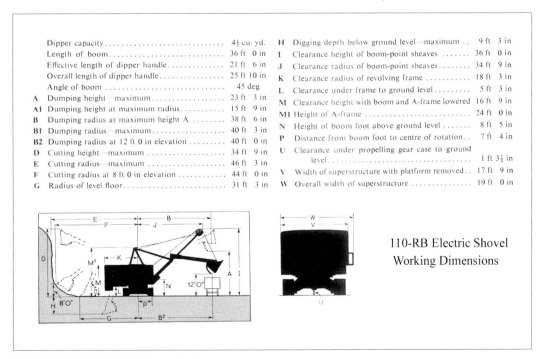

110-RB Electric Shovel
Working Dimensions

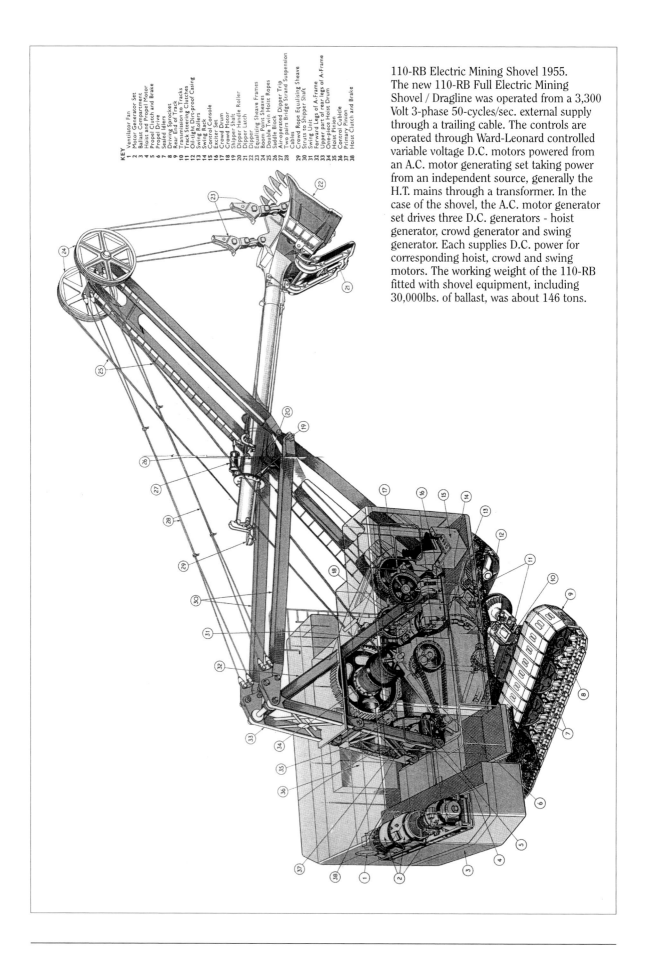

KEY
1 Ventilator Fan
2 Motor Generator Set
3 Ballast Compartment
4 Hoist and Propel Motor
5 Propel Clutch and Brake
6 Propel Drive
7 Sealed Idlers
8 Driving Sprocket
9 Rear End of Track
10 Transmission to Tracks
11 Track Steering Clutches
12 Oil-tight Dirt-proof Casing
13 Swing Rollers
14 Swing Rack
15 Control Console
16 Exciter Set
17 Crowd Drum
18 Crowd Motor
19 Shipper Shaft
20 Dipper Handle Roller
21 Dipper Latch
22 Dipper
23 Air-operated Dipper Trip
24 Equalising Sheave Frames
25 Boom Point Sheaves
26 Double Twin Hoist Ropes
27 Saddle Block
28 Two pairs Bridge Strand Suspension Cables
29 Crowd Rope Equalising Sheave
30 Struts to Shipper Shaft
31 Swing Unit
32 Forward Legs of A-Frame
33 Upper part of rear legs of A-Frame
34 One-piece Hoist Drum
35 Hoist Pinion
36 Control Cubicle
37 Primary Pinion
38 Hoist Clutch and Brake

110-RB Electric Mining Shovel 1955.
The new 110-RB Full Electric Mining
Shovel / Dragline was operated from a 3,300
Volt 3-phase 50-cycles/sec. external supply
through a trailing cable. The controls are
operated through Ward-Leonard controlled
variable voltage D.C. motors powered from
an A.C. motor generating set taking power
from an independent source, generally the
H.T. mains through a transformer. In the
case of the shovel, the A.C. motor generator
set drives three D.C. generators - hoist
generator, crowd generator and swing
generator. Each supplies D.C. power for
corresponding hoist, crowd and swing
motors. The working weight of the 110-RB
fitted with shovel equipment, including
30,000lbs. of ballast, was about 146 tons.

110-RB Crawler Mounting

The standard crawler mounting common to the 110-RB Shovel and Dragline is seen in the picture below. In each set of crawler tracks there are three large central idler rollers which support the machine and flanking these, on the left, is the driving tumbler connected to the propel machinery. On the right is the take-up tumbler similar to the idler rollers but with a provision for lateral adjustment so as to take up slack in the tracks. The overall width of the 110-RB mounting with standard 3ft. wide track links is 16ft. 3in., an extra 'long and wide' mounting was an available option in which the three large idler rollers are replaced by an assembly of five lesser size lower rollers and two small upper rollers.

Left: The transverse shaft on the driving tumbler end of the truck frame is made up of three sections. On the centre section is a bevel gear which meshes with a bevel pinion on the longitudinal propelling shaft. The two end sections of the transverse shaft are connected to the centre section by multiple jaw clutches used for steering and propelling. These clutches are air cylinder actuated and electrically controlled. By these clutches both tracks may be driven simultaneously or either track may be driven with the other disconnected to produce gradual turns. For sharp turns, provision is made for the clutches to be locked individually by hand from the ground.

Right: At the take-up tumbler end of the truck frame is mounted a safety propel brake. This is connected to the longitudinal propelling shaft by a spur gear reduction. The brake is spring set and air-released. The brake is automatically in the 'release' position when propelling, and sets immediately in the event of power failure while propelling. On the truck frame adjacent to the propel brake can be seen the junction box for the trailing electric power cable.

The '100' Series Shovel
Front End Equipment

The tubular dipper handle introduced on the '100 Series' Mining Shovels which replaced the twin-arm type fitted to previous shovel excavators allows the dipper handle to slide easily through the saddle block when digging and its freedom to rotate in the block relieves the torsional stresses.

There were other innovations; the 'A' Frame for example is designed with the apex high and well back so as to minimise boom suspension loads and compression in the boom. The forward legs and the upper portion of the rear legs are welded to form a strong rigid structure that can be pivoted forward when necessary to provide overhead clearance when travelling yet when in operation forms a rigid support for the struts to the shipper shaft tying the lower section of the boom into one complete fixed assembly. The upper boom section is the only non-rigid part of the front end equipment other than the dipper handle, ropes, sheaves etc.

There are several important advantages with this design - because the upper section is relieved of all loads other than those required for lifting the dipper the upper boom can be made considerably lighter, thus reducing the overall weight at the front end with all the loads from the boom being taken on the main revolving frame casting.

Further reduction in weight of the shovel front end is achieved by spreading the twin duel boom hoist to the outer edges of the dipper, providing direct pull where it is needed and eliminating the traditional heavy dipper bale and centre hitch.

On the original 110-RB and 150-RB, the crowd rope which moved the dipper handle outward ran over sheaves integral with the dipper handle roller within the saddle block, but by the early 1960s both models had re-designed shovel front-end equipments with large crowd sheaves mounted on the outside of the saddle block, incorporating spring-loaded crowd equipment on the dipper handle.

The original air actuated dipper trip mechanism mounted on the dipper handle which released the dipper door was replaced on the standard machines by a reel-type dipper trip operated by a variable torque motor and drum mounted at the foot of the boom.

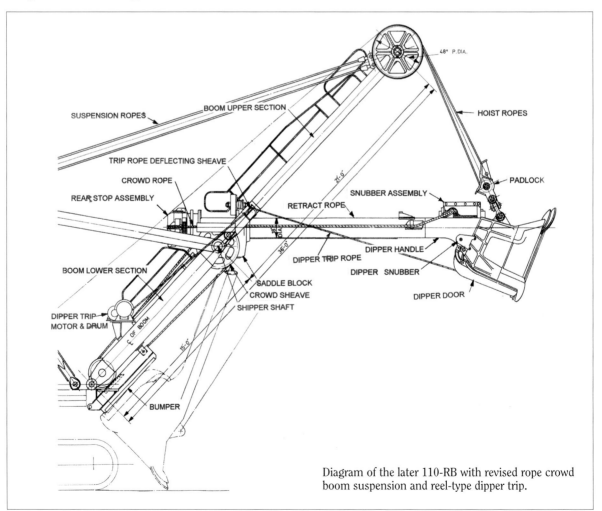

Diagram of the later 110-RB with revised rope crowd boom suspension and reel-type dipper trip.

Working dimensions

	Dipper capacity	4 cu. yds.	
	Length of boom	41′	9″
	Effective length of dipper handle	24′	1″
	Overall length of dipper handle	27′	2″
	Angle of boom	45°	
A	Dumping height—maximum	26′	6″
A1	Dumping height at maximum radius	18′	6″
B	Dumping radius at maximum height A	43′	0″
B1	Dumping radius—maximum	44′	9″
B2	Dumping radius at 12′ 0″ 3,66 m. elevation	43′	9″
D	Cutting height—maximum	38′	0″
E	Cutting radius—maximum	50′	3″
F	Cutting radius at 8′ 0″ 2,44 m. elevation	47′	0″
G	Radius of level floor	34′	3″
H	Digging depth below ground level—maximum	8′	9″
I	Clearance height of boom-point sheaves	40′	6″
J	Clearance radius of boom-point sheaves	39′	0″
N	Height of boom foot above ground level	8′	5″
P	Distance from boom foot to centre of rotation	7′	4″

Inset diagram key

110-RB Long Range Mining Shovel

Traditionally, the larger size Ruston-Bucyrus mining excavators had been offered with a longer and wider crawler as an alternative to the standard mounting when the machine was used as a dragline. This enabled a longer lattice boom to be fitted when required and the greater bearing pressure offered an advantage when operating in soft ground conditions.

This long and wide mounting was rarely used on the shovel version of the machine because of the restrictions it imposed on shovel operation. However, there was often a demand for a mining shovel with a longer reach than standard, so for the 110-RB, a long-range shovel equipment was developed that enabled long and wide mounting to be used whilst maintaining full freedom of action for the shovel operation. The 110-RB Long-Range shovel provided the working advantage of greater reach, height and stability when these were of primary importance.

110-RB Excavators at Barrington Quarry

Of the many sites where the 110-RB can be found working, Barrington Quarry south-west of Cambridge is unique for being the only surviving example in Britain of the traditional method of excavators loading directly into trains on the quarry floor, using both steam and diesel locomotives. Both the quarry and the adjacent Barrington cement works are owned and operated by Rugby Cement Ltd. The quarry exploits high-carbonate grey chalk and low-carbonate 'lower' chalk marl which is separated by a band of hard Totternhoe stone; the works uses the chalk from the quarry for the production of cement, and the stone, known locally as 'clunch' is used for building.

The extraction of chalk at Barrington and the establishment of a rail link to the main line dates back to 1913 and the Dreadnought Portland Cement Co. which was taken over in 1923 by Eastwoods Cement. In the early days the material was dug and loaded into trucks by hand, but mechanical excavators replaced manual labour and a variety of machines have found work at the Barrington quarry over the years. By the 1950s excavation at Barrington was carried out by three machines - a 37-RB Dragline working the lower chalk marl and two 38-RB Shovels working in conjunction to excavate the Totternhoe stone and upper grey chalk layer.

The take-over of Eastwoods by Rugby Cement Ltd. in 1962 was accompanied by the introduction of a 110-RB Dragline to replace the 37-RB and a 110-RB Shovel for working the upper layers of stone and grey chalk assisted by the two 38-RB Shovels. However, despite the increased size of excavators extracting and loading the material, the use of a rail system to transport the chalk out of the quarry continued.

(At the time of the author's visit to the Barrington quarry in 1996, the only remaining 38-RB had been replaced by a Komatsu hydraulic backhoe and a Liebherr crawler loader had been brought in to assist the 110-RB Shovel).

The 110-RB Ward-Leonard Electric Dragline, Machine No. 28075, was delivered to Barrington Quarry for customer Eastwoods Cement Ltd. (Rugby Cement Ltd.) on the 9th August 1963; it was equipped with a 3 cu.yd. bucket mounted on a 100ft. boom, and was fitted with a non-standard High Vision Cab. Its task was to excavate the low-carbonate chalk marl and load it directly into trains of wagons for transportation along a track on the Quarry floor to the processing plant adjacent to the quarry.

The photographs on the opposite page showing Mc.No.28075 at work were taken by the author on his visit to the quarry in 1996; the dragline, by now equipped with 120ft. boom and operating from a shallow bench, is excavating the chalk marl and loading it into a train of eight trucks hauled by a Ruston & Hornsby diesel electric locomotive. The driver shunts the train forward from the rear until the first truck is positioned accurately to receive the first load; as each truck is filled, the train is moved forward exactly the right amount to receive the next load from the dragline.

One bucket load filled a truck and the filling of all eight trucks took about twenty minutes, a cycle time which could have been reduced had the driver of the train not had to uncouple the engine from the line of trucks and back it clear before each received its load.

The dragline operator shrugged when the author questioned the necessity for this precaution and answered that "rules are rules but in all the years I have been working this system I have never yet deposited my load on top of the engine."

Above and below: Photographs taken in 1996 of the 110-RB Electric Dragline excavating low-carbonate chalk marl in Barrington Quarry and loading it into railway trucks running on one of two sets of tracks laid on the quarry main floor. The other set of tracks took the train that transported material from the 150-RB Shovel working further along the quarry. The operator and the new Dragline, No. 28075, had started work in the quarry at the same time in 1963 and had been together all their working lives - "We've grown old together and it looks as though we shall retire together," were his parting words to the author.

Opposite: View of the Rugby Cement Ltd. Barrington Quarry and Works, Cambridgeshire.

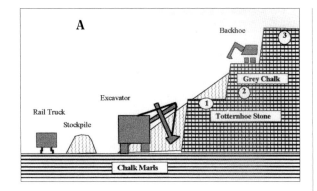

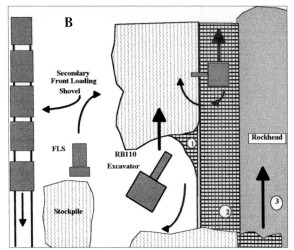

Left and left below: Diagrams showing the operation of the 110-RB Shovel at Barrington Quarry. Extraction of the high-carbonate grey chalk involves three distinct benches and is carried out by two excavators, the 110-RB Electric Shovel and a Komatsu 240 PCLC Hydraulic Backhoe;

(a) The Komatsu Backhoe operates on the upper two benches excavating chalk and discharging it to the lower bench and to the main quarry floor.

(b) The 110-RB Shovel operates on the main quarry floor, winning the lower bench and blending this 'face' chalk with chalk dug by the Komatsu, prior to primarily loading the material into the rail trucks or stock piling it for secondary loading into the trucks by a Liebherr 631 crawler front loader.

Photographs below and opposite:
These photographs taken in 1996 show the 110-RB Ward-Leonard Electric Shovel, Mc.No.28074, working in Barrington Quarry. The machine, supplied with 'Long Range' shovel equipment, long & wide crawler mounting, and 4 cu.yd. dipper, was delivered to the quarry in August 1963.

The 110-RB Shovel at Barrington Quarry excavating the lower face of
high-carbonate grey chalk and, together with similar material deposited from the
upper two benches, stock-piling it ready for loading into rail trucks for
transportation to the nearby works.

110-RB Diesel-Electric Shovel / Dragline

The Diesel-Electric powered version of the 110-RB Shovel and Dragline was developed at Lincoln in response to requests from RB's existing customers for an excavator of 110-RB size which could operate in mine or quarry independent of an external power source and therefore not restricted in movement on site by a trailing cable.

The result was a basic 110-RB powered by a self-contained power unit consisting of a diesel (compression ignition) engine driving a generator set supplying electric power for direct current motors and having variable voltage Ward-Leonard controls.

An alternative to the standard all-electric machine, this version of the 110-RB was available with either shovel or dragline equipment and offered a machine with the capacity and characteristics of the 110-RB that could be used on smaller scale operations, in difficult terrain, or in undeveloped locations where a suitable external electric supply was not available.

The power unit is a twelve-cylinder, four-stroke, normally-aspirated diesel engine with electric starting, and this drives a generator set comprising separate Hoist, Crowd and Swing generators and incorporating an alternator which supplies power for the A.C. auxiliary motors.

The Hoist, Swing, and Crowd D.C. motors operate the main functions with the Hoist motor also driving the propelling machinery through an electrically controlled air-actuated clutch.

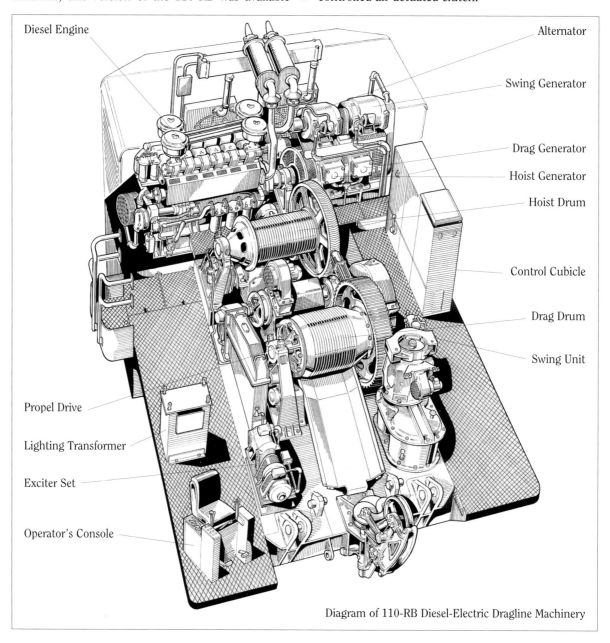

Diesel Engine

Alternator

Swing Generator

Drag Generator

Hoist Generator

Hoist Drum

Control Cubicle

Drag Drum

Swing Unit

Propel Drive

Lighting Transformer

Exciter Set

Operator's Console

Diagram of 110-RB Diesel-Electric Dragline Machinery

Pressurized Cabs

The Ruston-Bucyrus 110-RB, 150-RB and 195-B were all available with cab filtration and pressurisation equipment and the ugly box-like housing on the rear roof is indicative of those machines fitted with this equipment.

For early models of these mining shovels, the Farr 'Dynavane' filtration and pressurisation equipment was offered as an optional equipment and the cab of the standard machine was fitted with removable panels in the roof to accommodate it if and when it was required to be fitted. The benefits of cab filtration and pressurisation was sufficiently recognised for it to be eventually included in the standard equipment for the RB range of mining shovels.

The Farr 'Dynavane' filtration and pressurisation equipment comprised two fan units with dry-type, inertial self-cleaning filters mounted on the rear of the cab roof. Cooling air is forced through the main machinery compartment maintaining a pressure differential above the surrounding air to counter the tendency of dust, etc. to infiltrate into the cab. The dust automatically extracted from the main incoming air flow through the filters is carried, in a bleed air flow, through ducts to discharge at the rear of the machine.

110-RB Mining Shovel operated by Concrete Industries Ltd. fitted with Farr 'Dynavane' cab filtration and pressurisation system, loading rock in New South Wales.

The cab filtration and pressurisation equipment was an essential requirement for machines operating in the hot, dry, desert conditions such as experienced in the Middle East and southern Australia, and well worth the extra cost to an already expensive machine.

For example; by 1983 prices, the total cost of a basic standard 150-RB Ward-Leonard Electric Shovel without dipper but with Farr 'Dynavane' air filtration system was £758,990 - a 7½ cu.yd. dipper was an extra £42,710 and should the cab filtration / pressurisation system not be required and roof panels fitted in its place, the sum of £7,510 was deducted from the basic price.

Despite attempts at recovery this 110-RB Mining Shovel was declared a total write-off.
Fortunately this expensive accident, (machine value around of around £700,000, to say nothing
of the loss in working time), was not a common occurrence. It is to be hoped that the driver
survived the experience with less damage to his person than to his machine.

'Operation Century'
The One Hundredth 110-RB

By the end of 1964, Ruston-Bucyrus had good cause to celebrate; that year, in terms of turnover, tonnage and profits, had been a record one in the Company's thirty-four year history. The company's standard range of excavators were selling well, the outstanding orders for the 110-RB and 150-RB alone amounted to the value of well over a million pounds. To the standard range of cable excavators had been added in 1963 new lines which included RB's development of their first hydraulic excavators and tower cranes, and on top of all this Ruston-Bucyrus had received an order for two 480-W Walking Draglines, the largest excavators to be built by the Lincoln company since it was formed in 1930. So it was in a climate of great optimism that early in 1965 the Excavator Works had cause to celebrate a particular occasion.

Tuesday, 23 February 1965, was a special day at the Excavator Works; 110-RB owners from eighteen countries were invited to the Lincoln firm to celebrate the production of the one hundredth 110-RB Excavator and the inauguration of the '110 Club'. With flags of all the nations flying over the Administration Offices, the guests were received and their visit round the Excavator Works ended in No.22 Bay where the one hundredth 110-RB bedecked with flags was on display. (Though not part of the ceremonies, interest was also shown in the first 480-W Walking Dragline and two other 110-RBs that were under construction in 22 Bay at that time.)

J.H. Page, RB's Technical Director, made a speech of welcome to the assembled guests, and declared the '110-Club' truly launched whereupon, as reported later in the company's magazine -

"the engine of the one hundredth 110-RB roared into life, the bottle of champagne descended in a graceful curve, striking the 4½ cu.yd. bucket and pouring out the liquid in a sparkling stream and splash of white foam. Amid the applause of the spectators, the super-structure of the great machine swung in majestic fashion to face the 45-foot high doors which opened to allow the excavator to move out of the Bay. The ceremony was complete."

There followed a buffet lunch for the visitors at the Centurion Hotel, a sight seeing tour of Lincoln and the day ended with a celebratory dinner at Lincoln's White Hart Hotel where the host was E.S. Everitt, RB's Managing Director.

Above: Representatives from eighteen countries, now members of the 110 Club, assembled in front of the thousandth 110-RB.

Left: A group of Ruston-Bucyrus staff members witness the occasion.

150-RB Ward-Leonard Electric Shovel / Dragline

In little more than two years after the launching of the 110-RB, its big brother, the 6 cu.yd. 150-RB, was ready to go into full production at the Excavator Works. Sharing the same basic design as the 110-RB, any major differences of size and changes in machinery, such as the use of two swing units where the 110-RB only required one, were demanded by the machine's greater digging capacity. Like the 110-RB, the 150-RB was available as a dragline and though the first models were not offered with alternative long & wide crawler mounting designed for dragline application, one was soon developed and offered as an option to the standard mounting.

The first 150-RB was Machine No. 22348, which was delivered to I.C.I. in January 1958, it is a measure of its success that both this machine and the first 110-RB were working to maximum capacity when production of these models at the Excavator Works ceased. The last 110-RB left the Lincoln production line in May 1978 and the last 150-RB in March 1981, by which time a total of 155 110-RBs and 126 150-RBs had been produced.

150-RB Ward-Leonard Electric shovel operating in hard quarry conditions for which this heavy-duty excavator was ideally suited.

The 150-RB on Show

For the Lincoln company it was not a propitious time to introduce a new large and expensive model into their range of machines; in 1957/58 the country's economic difficulties had seriously affected the domestic market and the Excavator Works was suffering redundancies and short-time working. (Things were even more difficult for the Bucyrus-Erie company in America, where the manufacturing industry was in even greater recession.)

Yet early interest shown in the new 150-RB from potential customers and the advance orders gave hope for its success, so Ruston-Bucyrus were happy to show off their largest excavator on the test ground

to groups of visitors to the Excavator Works; (Upper photo - visit by 60 members of the Lincoln Engineering Society, August 1956; Lower photo - visit by 140 members of the East Midland District Municipal Engineers - September 1956).

The best opportunity came when it was decided to hold the company's Export Distributors Conference at the Excavator Works in October 1957, only the second such conference to be held since the first one a quarter of a century before. Flags were flying over the Ruston-Bucyrus administrative offices to welcome delegates and guests from Europe, Asia, Africa, Australia and America, they representing thirty-five countries in all. A highlight of the four-day conference was a display on the test ground of the new Ruston-Bucyrus 150-RB Shovel.

150-RB Demonstration at Amberswood

On the 25th September 1958, at the suggestion of Mr. J.R. Caseley, Director of Production, Open-Cast Executive, N.C.B., Ruston-Bucyrus organised the first public demonstration of a 150-RB Electric Dragline equipped with the newly developed option for this machine of long and wide crawler mounting.

The site chosen, by kind permission of contractors Sir Alfred McAlpine & Son Ltd., was the Amberswood open-cast coal site near Wigan and the large number of invited guests and visitors included other officials of the N.C.B. and many operators and contractors from all parts of the U.K.

In his welcoming address, Mr. Everitt, Managing Director of RB, drew attention to the fact that,

"though they may by now be familiar with the 150-RB Dragline, what they would see would be appreciably different from the standard machine since its new long and wide mounting was specially developed to provide the extra reach required on open-cast coal sites and, with its low ground pressure, to cope more ably with soft ground conditions."

Mr. Everitt also announced the fact that in two years he hoped to have available a Diesel/Electric version of the 150-RB and before closing his speech he took the opportunity to provide his audience with some measure of the success of Ruston-Bucyrus Ltd. at that time with the following facts;

"The company currently employs 2,700 people, precisely double what it was immediately before the war. In the two years preceding the war the company was producing excavators at the rate of 500 per annum; by 1955 and 1956, production had gone up to 1300 excavators per year. Expressed another way, the output in tons for this period went up from about 10,000 per annum to 35,000. The company's capital expenditure since the war has been in excess of three million pounds, resulting in a factory that is probably the finest of its kind in the world."

For the demonstration, the 150-RB Dragline's long and wide mounting made possible the fitting of a 100ft. boom with a 7 cu.yd. bucket, and thus equipped it is seen in the above photograph excavating the 28ft. of grey shale overburden that overlay one of the lower seams of coal at the Amberswood site and side casting the material to the spoil heap.

Its performance was measured and showed that with an operating cycle time of between 21 and 31 seconds, an output exceeding 500 cu.yds. per hour was obtained. Elsewhere on the site that day could also be seen a 110-RB Ward-Leonard Electric Shovel equipped with 4½ cu.yd. dipper stripping another coal seam and loading the sandy shale overburden into Euclid and Foden dump trucks, and a 54-RB Electric Dragline equipped with a 3 cu.yd. bucket on a 60ft. boom assisting with the stripping and loading the overburden into high capacity dump trucks.

At Amberswood, the coal was found in six separate inclined seams, all out-cropping and, at the time of the visit it was anticipated that 485,000 tons of coal would be extracted from the site, involving the removal of 8½ million cubic yards of overburden.

Above: 110-RB Electric Shovel at work at Amberswood open-cast coal site on the day of the demonstration of the 150-RB Dragline.

Below: This group of sightseers at the Amberswood demonstration of the 150-RB Dragline included, (left to right); Mr. Mathew McGregor, a Director of Robert McGregor & Sons Ltd.; E. S. Everitt, Managing Director of Ruston-Bucyrus Ltd.; Mr. Peter Bell, a Director of Sir Alfred McAlpine & Son Ltd. and J.H. Page, Ruston-Bucyrus Technical Director.

150-RB Electric Shovel in Opencast Coal operations

In view of the disastrous state of the British opencast coal industry at the time it is surprising to find that the greatest interest shown in the new 150-RB, as evidenced by instant firm orders which came from opencast coal operators. There had been a few Bucyrus-Erie 150-B shovels working in British opencast coal, but now they had an excavator of similar design but improved and developed to suit the particular needs of the U.K. industry - out of the nineteen machines sold in its first two years of production, fifteen were purchased by the N.C.B. or its contractors for opencast coal operation in the U.K.

Despite the growing competition from hydraulic shovels, a total of 155 110-RBs and 126 150-RBs were produced by the time the last 150-RB Shovel, Mc. No. 38488, left the Excavator Works for customer Rand Mining in October 1981. By this time the scale of opencast mining had increased and the Ruston-Bucyrus 12-16 cu.yd. 195-B Electric Mining Shovel had largely replaced the 150-RB as a primary loading excavator.

Above and on opposite page: 150-RB Ward-Leonard Electric mining shovel with 6 cu.yd. dipper at work on a U.K. opencast coal site, February 1962.

150-RB Shovel - Further Improvements

From its introduction in 1957/58, the 150-RB Ward-Leonard Electric Shovel, like the 110-RB, was subject to gradual improvement which led in 1962 to a revised shovel front end incorporating a number of new features. These changes involved new crowd rope anchorage and adjustment on the end of the dipper handle, addition of a dipper handle stabilising device, retract rope return anchor at the dipper end of the handle and replacement of the existing internal crowd sheaves with large diameter crowd sheaves mounted on the outside of the saddle block. All these changes are featured on the 150-RB shovel in the photograph below undergoing tests at the Excavator Works in 1963.

150-RB Shovel with revised front end equipment photographed on the test ground in March 1963.

150-RB Shovel with Live Boom Suspension

The 150-RB Shovel pictured on the opposite page on the Excavator Works test ground equipped with pressurised cab and 7 cu.yd. dipper has the non-standard feature of power boom hoist and 'live' boom suspension. Instead of the usual shovel fixed pendant suspension from 'A' frame to boom point, it is equipped with a special 'live' boom hoist unit on top of the cab with continuous suspension from 'A' frame to a floating bridle which is connected to the boom point by a shorter set of fixed pendants.

This boom hoist unit like that fitted as standard on the dragline version of the 110-RB / 150-RB is not powerful enough to perform any other function than to raise the boom into position for securing it at its fixed working angle.

The 150-RB Shovel with pressurized cab and non-standard 'live' boom suspension on the test ground.

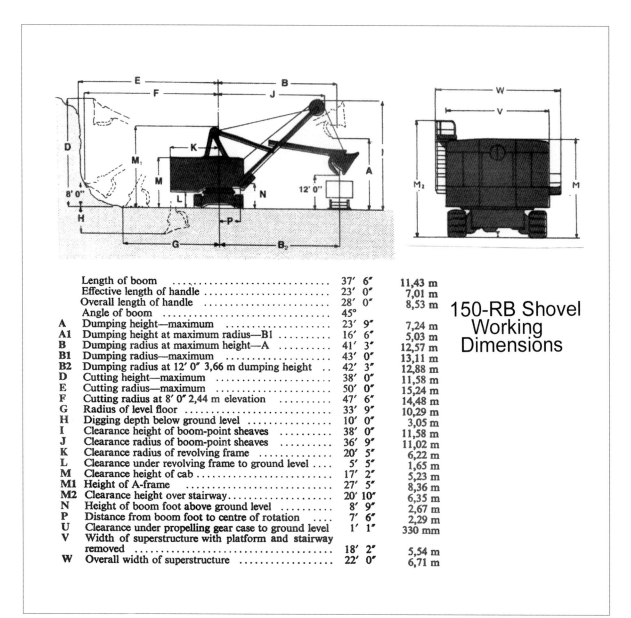

	Length of boom	37'	6"	11,43 m
	Effective length of handle	23'	0"	7,01 m
	Overall length of handle	28'	0"	8,53 m
	Angle of boom	45°		
A	Dumping height—maximum	23'	9"	7,24 m
A1	Dumping height at maximum radius—B1	16'	6"	5,03 m
B	Dumping radius at maximum height—A	41'	3"	12,57 m
B1	Dumping radius—maximum	43'	0"	13,11 m
B2	Dumping radius at 12' 0" 3,66 m dumping height ..	42'	3"	12,88 m
D	Cutting height—maximum	38'	0"	11,58 m
E	Cutting radius—maximum	50'	0"	15,24 m
F	Cutting radius at 8' 0" 2,44 m elevation	47'	6"	14,48 m
G	Radius of level floor	33'	9"	10,29 m
H	Digging depth below ground level	10'	0"	3,05 m
I	Clearance height of boom-point sheaves	38'	0"	11,58 m
J	Clearance radius of boom-point sheaves	36'	9"	11,02 m
K	Clearance radius of revolving frame	20'	5"	6,22 m
L	Clearance under revolving frame to ground level	5'	5"	1,65 m
M	Clearance height of cab	17'	2"	5,23 m
M1	Height of A-frame	27'	5"	8,36 m
M2	Clearance height over stairway	20'	10"	6,35 m
N	Height of boom foot above ground level	8'	9"	2,67 m
P	Distance from boom foot to centre of rotation	7'	6"	2,29 m
U	Clearance under propelling gear case to ground level	1'	1"	330 mm
V	Width of superstructure with platform and stairway removed	18'	2"	5,54 m
W	Overall width of superstructure	22'	0"	6,71 m

150-RB Shovel Working Dimensions

Towards a 110-RB / 150-RB Lifting Crane

Both the 110-RB and 150-RB were only designed for Shovel or Dragline operation and in 1960 Peter Wyatt, Development Engineer working directly under RB's Chief Engineer, Phillip Durand, was given the task of looking into the possibility of adapting both models for lifting crane operation. To this end, Peter produced design specifications and initial drawings for longer lattice booms on both models, (110-RB max. 130ft., 150-RB max. 140ft.), together with designs for new Standard 'A' frame, High 'A' frame, and Forward Mast.

The boom hoist on the existing 110-RB and 150-RB draglines was suitable for dragline use only, it was capable of raising the dragline boom, but only used infrequently when it was necessary to change the boom angle which was then locked in the new position. Any development of the 110-RB or 150-RB as a crane would require a boom hoist unit capable of luffing the boom with a load under full lifting crane ratings.

Peter came up with a design for a new boom hoist that would do this and which could be installed in place of the existing dragline boom hoist units. This had a special high-reduction gearbox that gave high torque, low-speed output, driven by 20-hp. motor for the 110-RB and 25-hp. for the 150-RB.

It is not clear why the idea of crane development for the 110/150-RB was never pursued by Ruston-Bucyrus beyond Peter Wyatt's preliminary investigation, but the development of a complete range of high performance specialist cranes would soon be occupying the full attention of the Lincoln design office.

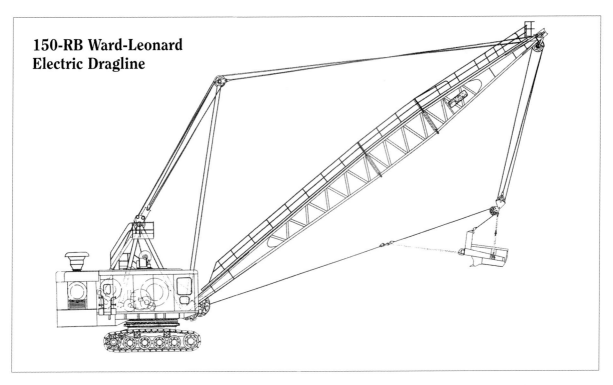

150-RB Ward-Leonard Electric Dragline

Above: The dragline version of the 150-RB Ward-Leonard Electric machine could operate with optional boom lengths from 90ft. to 130ft. with corresponding bucket sizes from 3 cu.yd. to 7 cu.yd. The forward mast was necessary for boom lengths over 90ft.

Below: A Ruston-Bucyrus 150-RB Dragline fitted with 100ft. boom is seen stripping overburden for a copper mine - Chambishi, Northern Rhodesia.

Static Control

In the 1950s the electrical industry began developing a number of control components, the operation of which did not depend upon the relative movement of component parts, but rather on the physical structure of the materials from which they were made. A control system built up from a number of these components and having no moving parts is generally referred to as 'Static Control'.

Static Control was first introduced on a Ward-Leonard electric excavator by the Bucyrus-Erie Co. in 1959 and by the mid 1960s, Ruston-Bucyrus - in conjunction with Associated Electrical Industries Ltd. Control and Machines Group, Rugby - had developed a static control system for both the 110-RB

and the 150-RB Ward-Leonard electric excavators as an option to the standard rotating controls.

Static Control provided a more direct control of the speeds, giving a fast response and smoother action to any of the excavator's operations, thus the impact loading when excavating a bank of hard material can be reduced as the operator has full control of the approach speed.

A machine's performance results from the co-ordination of excavator motions by the operator - with Static Control this is greatly increased while at the same time operator fatigue is reduced. Speed of response and smoother operation with Static Control reduces the shock loads on the excavator's machinery and equipment, thereby increasing life and reducing maintenance requirements.

The first 110-RB Ward-Leonard excavator with static control being unloaded at Maastricht, Holland.

The first 110-RB Ward-Leonard machine to leave the factory fitted with the newly developed A.E.I. Static Control system was machine number 31991 which was shipped to ENCI, Maastricht in November 1967.

ENCI, the largest cement manufacturers in Holland, could claim over 90% of that country's output. Extensive plans for the expansion of the processing plant were currently in progress to meet the increasing demands for high-grade cement and the new 110-RB valued at over £82,000 was to be used to extract a maximum of one million tons of limestone each year.

The photograph shows the base machine of the 110-RB being unloaded at Maastricht after a 100-mile barge journey up the river Meuse from Rotterdam.

Above: 150-RB Shovel with static control under construction in the
Excavator Works' new 22 Bay.

Below left: Factory photo of Static Control 150-RB operator's console.

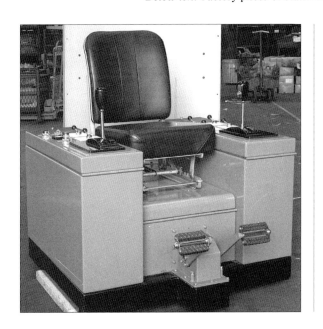

Initially, for the 110-RB, six complete Ward-Leonard Static Control drive systems were ordered from A.E.I. at a total cost of £77,000, which included motor generator sets, DC motors, high tension control gear and electronics.

Very soon, a similar system was available for the 150-RB. Though resulting in a more expensive machine, full Ward-Leonard Static Controls gave a marked improvement in the operator's command of the excavator and thus in overall performance; master controllers at the operator's position control the output of static excitation panels which supply the field current of the main generators. The output voltage of the generators is thus controlled, thereby governing the speed and direction of rotation for the hoist, crowd and swing functions. Since the control panels embody solid state static components and there is an absence of moving parts such as clutches and linkages, static control provides fast, smooth response with flexible machine operation.

Up-rating for the 150-RB

Customer demand for greater digging capacity from the current Ruston-Bucyrus 150-RB mining shovel led to further development at Lincoln resulting in 1970 to its up-rating from a 6 cu.yd. to 7 cu.yd. dipper capacity. This making it the largest European excavator in regular production.

The main changes were a new boom with alloy-steel upper section; a new dipper with cast alloy steel front and welded side members and one-piece teeth replacing the more usual H & L two-part teeth; revised dipper handle with spring cushion crowd equaliser and reel-type dipper trip to replace the original dipper trip. Revised rope sheaves and drums throughout and the provision of a centralised lubrication system gave increased working life. Removable cab-roof panels were added as a standard feature to allow for the possible fitment of cab pressurisation and air filtration equipment when required. With the new shovel front end, the cutting height and radius of the 7 cu.yd. 150-RB shovel was increased to 38ft. and 50ft. compared with the 36ft. and 48ft. for the previous 6 cu.yd. version. The working weight was increased from 201 tons to 211 tons.

Main photo shows the 150-RB shovel boom lower section in the factory;
inset photo shows a worker fitting teeth to the cutting edge of the
7 cu.yd. dipper where normally H & L two-part teeth would be used.

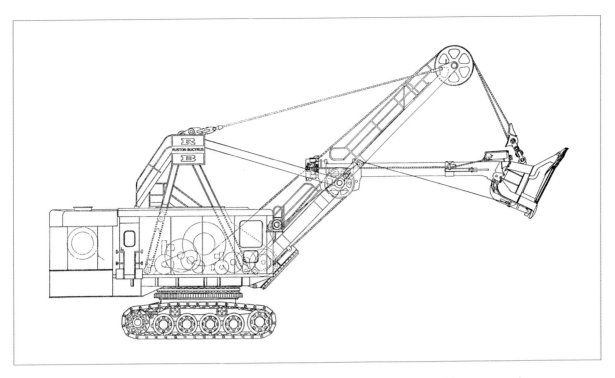

Drawing of the later 150-RB Shovel uprated to 7$\frac{1}{2}$ cu.yd. dipper, with revised boom suspension, revised dipper handle with spring-cushioned crowd eqaliser, and reel-type dipper trip equipment mounted on the lower boom.

Works photographs of 150-RB Shovel developments;

A. Revised boom suspension, introduced on Machine No. 34649 supplied to Messrs George Wimpey on 29th Sept. 1970. Each pair of pendant ropes are anchored at the boom point on each side of the sheaves.

B. Spring-cushioned crowd equaliser unit mounted on the dipper handle.

C. Reel-type dipper trip assembly in the factory; operated by an electric motor, this assembly replaced the original air-operated dipper-trip and is mounted on the boom lower section and operated by a push-button on the crowd master controller.

150-RB Shovels in Spain

Towards the end of 1968, the mining group of the giant Rio Tinto corporation purchased four Ruston-Bucyrus mining shovels for service in their opencast mines near Huelva, Spain. Three of these were 150-RB 6 cu.yd. Ward-Leonard electric shovels valued at £400,000 ordered by Rio Tinto Patino S.A. for development and future production at the Cerro Colorado copper mine north of Huelva.

The first of these three 150-RBs, Mc.No.32662, was dispatched from the works in October 1968 and by the following spring was commissioned and digging weathered gossan/leached overburden at the rate of 14,000 / 16,000 tons per day in two shifts. The gossan overburden had a small gold and silver content.

The overburden covered a large deposit of porphyry copper ore which would also be excavated by the three new 150-RB shovels for processing at the new concentrator currently being built at Rio Tinto. The second and third 150-RB shovels, Mc.Nos.33187 and 33189, were dispatched to join the first one at Cerro Colorado mine in March and November, 1969.

The fourth new Ruston-Bucyrus machine in the Rio Tinto 1968 purchase referred to above was a 110-RB 4.5 cu.yd. Ward-Leonard electric excavator valued at £110,000 ordered by Cia Espanola de Minas de Rio Tinto S.A. for service in the Corta Atalaya copper mine. One of the world's oldest known workings, this mine was first operated by the Phoenician settlers around 1000 BC. Here, the new machine would dig porphyry and slate overburden as part of an expansion programme in which it was expected that 50 million tons of material would be excavated in the following ten years.

Machine No. 32662, the first of the three 150-RB Ward-Leonard Electric mining shovels ordered by Rio Tinto Patino S.A., is seen removing overburden in the Cerro Colorado copper mine, north of Huelva, Spain.

LINCOLN'S EXCAVATORS

A NEW LOOK

A NEW LOOK FOR LINCOLN'S EXCAVATORS

In 1956, Lincoln's Excavators received a new look; the traditional 'box like 'shape of the cab on the smaller Ruston-Bucyrus excavators such as the 10-RB and 19-RB was replaced by a more modern looking rounded style of cab similar (though not identical) to that which had already been introduced on Bucyrus-Erie excavators. Even the cabs of the larger excavators in the range which maintained their basically rectangular form were given the 'modernising' treatment of rounded corners to soften the 'boxy' look.

Gone too was the familiar standard paint work of Lincoln Green sides and white roofs to be replaced by the two-tone livery of cream and maroon adopted by the American company. It is possible that the first Ruston-Bucyrus excavator to receive this new look was Mc.No.19485, a 19-RB which was supplied to South African distributors Hubert Davies towards the end of 1955, but the changes were introduced gradually by RB for different models over a short period of time.

By the summer of 1956 all machines not specified to carry an individual customer's livery went out from Lincoln in the new standard maroon and cream cabs.

Though the new livery made the machines more visible on a working site, it would be easy to see these stylistic changes as merely cosmetic and of more importance to the marketing of a machine than to its performance. However, the change of livery gave the Lincoln company the opportunity to evaluate their paint processes and the impetus for its improvement and re-equipment.

The durability of an excavator depends upon a careful and lengthy paint finishing process involving the hot-blasting of components, followed by several applications of anti-rust chemicals, oven drying, stove-painting with coats of red oxide and finally hot spraying with finishing coats of gloss enamel and further stoving. The size of some of the parts demanded a specialised paint plant in a section of the works and the limitations of RB's existing paint plant were soon realised. In 1963 the company acquired a complete new specialised Cab Finishing Plant which was installed in 18 Bay of the Excavator Works by United & General Engineering Co. of London. The new plant provided an increase in production of 35 to 40% over the old facilities.

The new Cab Finishing Plant at the Excavator Works with its first batch of cabs in
August 1963.

A New Livery

The new standard livery for Ruston-Bucyrus Excavators was a cream and maroon operator's cab with additional horizontal striping comprising three red and black bands along each side of the machine. Also applied to the sides of the cab was the traditional black and white Ruston-Bucyrus logo, (this logo was later replaced by a modern red and white logo). The counterweight, revolving frame, lower works, and front end equipment were painted dark green.

Despite the existence of a standard paint specification the new colour of the excavators as they left the factory, like the old colour of 'Lincoln Green' before them was not consistently the same shade. This was largely due to the company's alternate use of two paint suppliers - Dockers and I.C.I. When RB installed their stoving plant it was found that Docker's maroon paint went brownish under the process whereas the I.C.I. maroon was unaffected. In order to combat this and achieve a common shade it became the practice to air-dry the Docker paintwork and stove the I.C.I.

With I.C.I. paints, the cab parts - after the prepar-

ation process - were first sprayed with I.C.I. Stoving Red Oxide Primer-Surfacer F703-1048. After 15 minute stoving and a 16 minute cooling period, the parts were then hot sprayed with Stoving Ruston Cream F641-393. When cooled the cabs were assembled on a mobile jig, the upper half masked off and the lower half hot sprayed in Ruston Maroon F640-440.

The net result of the above was that the colour of one batch of say 22-RBs could not be guaranteed to have the exact shade of the next batch off the production line. But, in any case, the painting of the machines as they left the Lincoln factory was not as formalised as one might expect; certainly in the early days, it was often a question of what paint was available that came nearest to the required colour. Keith Bradshaw, RB's Quality Controller recounts that when the standard livery of RB's Excavators changed yet again from cream and maroon to red and white there was no formal specification and it was left to himself, Colin McCrae (Sales Dept.) and Norman Draper (Laboratories), to make an arbitrary choice from the British Standard colour chart and it became a 'toss-up' between Post Office Red and Signal Red - they chose Signal Red and any nearest equivalent.

The new RB two-tone livery introduced in 1955 to replace the traditional 'Lincoln Green'.
(Author's Note: Accuracy of colour of the machines, though of little importance to the general reader
is of interest to the model maker or renovator of old machines and as a model-maker myself I am
frequently asked "what is the proper colour" followed by a request for samples.)

Customized Liveries

While the Ruston-Bucyrus standard livery could make use of transfers, the personalized liveries often requested by customers depended upon the skill of company sign-writers. The complexity varied, but among the most difficult were the machines for Egypt which often required considerable sign writing in Arabic, often with only a torn off letter heading to copy from. Fraught with possible political embarrassment if it went wrong, Keith Bradshaw, RB's Quality Controller, on such occasions would have any text checked by an African Arabic speaker before the machine was dispatched.

Left: RB sign writers Dave Daley (right) and John Freeman busy with the familiar name of regular RB customer, Sir Alfred McAlpine. (Photo Lincs. Echo 1966).

Below: Customer's liveries on RB excavators.

Bottom: RB 35-XC Hydrocrane customized for Alwataary Trading & Agricultural Development Co. in the Yemen; a severe test for the RB sign-writing team.

Excavator Engines

In the formation of Ruston-Bucyrus Ltd. in 1929, certain policies were agreed between the new company and the two parent companies which would become binding on Ruston-Bucyrus, one of these related to the engines installed in the Lincoln company's excavators.

It was agreed that Ruston-Bucyrus would use only Ruston engines in their diesel powered excavators except when "they were not satisfied either in respect of price, specification or service", in which case they could obtain engines from other makers, (this 'get out' clause was rarely used). By the same token, it was agreed that Ruston & Hornsby Ltd. would not supply engines for new excavators built by any other manufacturer.

The following table prepared in November 1953 lists the R & H diesel engines used in the range of Ruston-Bucyrus excavators current at that time. (The only non-Ruston engine in the table is a Fordson Major petrol-paraffin tractor engine which was fitted to the 10-RB as a rare war-time expedient when the R&H engine was unavailable.)

DIESEL ENGINES

Model	No. of Cyl. & Type of Engine	Brake h.p.	r.p.m.	Approx. Fuel Consumption Gallons per hour
10-RB	3 VRHN	33	1000	0.8 to 1.1
19-RB	4 VROHN	54	1300	1.4 to 1.8
22-RB	4 YEN	66	1200	1.7 to 2.2
24-RB	4 VPHN	77	875	2.2 to 2.5
33-RB	5 VPHN	110	1000	2.8 to 3.2
38-RB	6 VPHN	132	1000	3.3 to 4.5
43-RB	6 VPHN	132	1000	3.6 to 4.8
54-RB	5 VCBN	202	650	5.2 to 6.5
3-W	6 VCBN	224	600	5.5 to 6.8
5-W	5 VEBN	290	440	7.2 to 8.5
22-RW	2 VSH	20	1200	0.6 to 0.8
60-RL	4 YC	45	1300	1.0 to 1.2
27-RT	3 VSH	30	1200	0.8 to 1.0
42-RT	4 VPHN	110	1250	2.6 to 2.9

PETROL PARAFFIN ENGINE

10-RB	4 Fordson 'Major'	30.75	1200	1.25

SINGLE-MOTOR ELECTRIC MACHINES POWER CONSUMPTION

Model	Motor h.p. Speed 1000 r.p.m.	Approx. 15-min demand kW	Momentary Peak approx. kW	Consumption per cu.yd. (solid) approx. kWh	Transformer Capacity kVA
10-RB	25	20	40	3 to 7	30
19-RB	35	25	65	3 to 7	38
22-RB	40	32	80	3 to 7	40
24-RB	45	40	90	3 to 7	55
33-RB	65	55	120	3 to 8	65
38-RB	75	60	150	3 to 8	75
43-RB	100	80	200	3 to 8	100
54-RB	125	100	250	3 to 8	125

WARD-LEONARD ELECTRIC MACHINES

54-RB Shovel		75	200	25 to 4	125
110-RB Shovel		110	350	4 to 6	250
150-RB Shovel		160	525	4 to 6	350
5-W		120	370	4 to 6	250

Excavator Engines - Freedom to Choose

In the early years the arrangement made between the two companies regarding RB excavator engines made good commercial sense and was of benefit to both Ruston-Bucyrus and Ruston & Hornsby, so despite the apparent 'conditional' clause, Ruston-Bucyrus were happy to accept their Lincoln parent company as sole supplier of engines for their excavators. However, as the markets for the excavators and the engines which drove them grew and became more competitive the agreement to use only Ruston engines on RB machines became a constraint for both parties rather than an advantage. For Ruston-Bucyrus the Ruston engines were generally more expensive than their competitors and this was reflected in the total cost of their machines.

There was also a desire in the late 1940s on the part of Ruston & Hornsby to be free to offer their engines to other excavator manufacturers, for the situation by this time was utterly restrictive on Ruston & Hornsby who had no permitted 'get out' clause in the agreement.

The situation was resolved when the 'Restrictive Trades Practices Act of 1958' was introduced and the agreement over RB's sole use of Ruston engines was formally cancelled; either company was now free to do what it wanted. However, Mr. Everitt, RB's Managing Director, believed wholeheartedly in Ruston engines and was reluctant to use other alternatives, which may explain why it took several more years before other makes of engine appeared to any extent in Ruston-Bucyrus excavators.

The first Ruston-Bucyrus excavator to be offered with a non-Ruston engine as a standard alternative option was the new 71-RB and the first one of this model to have a Cummins diesel engine instead of the Ruston 6RPHN was Machine No. 31613 which was supplied to A. McAlpine on the 15th March 1967. Later a further engine option was offered on the 71-RB in the G.M. (Detroit Diesel).

From this time it became the practice to offer a choice of alternative engines on the diesel versions of the Ruston-Bucyrus range of products; the 38-RB, for example, was the first to offer a Dorman engine (Mc. No.35008) and during its long production at the Lincoln factory enjoyed a number of engine changes, from the Ruston 4RPH to the 6YEX, to the Dorman 6-LET, then to the General Motors 6-71N or the Cummins NH-55.

71-RB under construction in the factory with Cummins NT-855 diesel engine.

A New Bay for the Mining Shovels

Increasingly over the years, the two high Erecting Bays Nos. 2 and 3 of the original Navvy Works had been equipped with machine tools to the point where space available was inadequate for the assembly of the larger RB Excavators. As a result, the decision was taken in 1959 to construct a new large workshop, Bay 22, which would be used for fabrications and the erection of the 110-RB, 150-RB, and 5-W Walking Draglines.

Built specifically with large mining shovels in mind, the height of the proposed building was such that the complete upper works of an assembled 150-RB (and later the 195-RB) could be lifted off its crawler base as a complete unit for transportation. At this time also there was speculation among the Ruston-Bucyrus management concerning the possible manufacture of a larger walking dragline at the Lincoln works and the 770-W was hinted at as a possible candidate, but there was no thought that three years later an unexpected order for two 480-Ws

would result in these machines being built in 22 Bay alongside the 5-Ws and shovel excavators. Following the usual practice, 22 Bay was built at the end of the line of existing workshops along Beevor Street, with the Test Ground moved further along to make room for it.

By the Spring of 1961, the new Bay was completed and the leading dimensions were; length 340ft., width between crane centres 90ft., height to crane rail 50ft. The building was equipped with two 40-ton capacity overhead cranes; part of the floor was laid with sleepers to protect it from the crawlers of travelled excavators. A further part was laid with cast iron rails to enable large fabrications to be accurately aligned, though in 1974, Bill Winter the Managing Director would commission designs for an even bigger workshop Bay with 50% more ground area than 22 Bay and designated 28 Bay. This never materialised and 22 Bay would prove to be the last of the Excavator Work's series of workshops along Beevor Street that began with the creation of 1 Bay at the time of World War I.

Above: Final stages of construction of the new 22 Bay at the Excavator Works.

Right: The completed 22 Bay ready for work.

Ruston-Bucyrus - A 'Family Firm'

The photograph on opposite page taken in the early 1960s shows a critical stage in the assembly of a 150-RB Excavator when the complete upper works assembly is lowered on to the crawler mounting, a procedure requiring great precision made more difficult by the heavy weight involved. The scene of activity is the new 22-Bay at the Excavator Works to where the assembly of the big excavators had just been moved from the over-crowded No.3 Bay and it is likely that this was the first 150-RB to be built in the Bay.

The photograph is also significant for a different reason; traditionally the products of Lincoln's great engineering companies were not only 'made in Lincoln' but 'made by Lincoln people', often whole families were involved, with sons (and daughters) following fathers into the same firm, even sometimes into the same job. Generations of the same family have been associated with a particular company and it was not uncommon to find several members of the same family working together. Such a tradition gave rise to loyalty and dedication to the company often spanning an individual's whole working life, but more than this it invoked a genuine concern for the work and a pride in the product.

Through the years of the Excavator Works a number of 'RB Families' could be found, typical of which was the group in this photograph involved on the assembly of the 150-RB in 22-Bay.

Those involved when the picture was taken are;

Dad, Arthur Fatchett joined the company in 1937 as a member of the Fitting Dept., became Ganger fitter in 3-Bay, working with his sons David and Arthur junior on the big shovels before the operation was transferred to the new 22 Bay. He retired from RB in 1965.

Son, Arthur Fatchett, started at RB as an apprentice in 1943, working in 3-Bay, eventually became Foreman fitter in 22 Bay working on the assembly of 61-RB, 71-RB, 480-W and 1260-W excavators. He retired from RB Lincoln in 1991.

Son, David Fatchett, started as an apprentice fitter with RB in the late 1940s and was appointed Foreman in the fitting shop in 1964 taking over from his dad. David left RB for a while (see below) but returned to his old firm in 1980.

Uncle, Frank Fatchett, joined RB before the War as a fitter, and during it worked on installing tank engines. He continued as Ganger in the fitting department where he worked with his brother Arthur (Senior).

Stan Gibbons, who is also featured in the picture, worked as a Slinger at RB, first in 3 Bay then 22 Bay. His family again had strong ties with the firm as Joe Gibbons (Stan's brother) worked at RB as a fitter assembling 38-RBs in 3 Bay, eventually becoming Foreman fitter. Arthur Gibbons (the third brother) was a long-time member of the RB Field Department and among his jobs was the erection of the 1150-B and 1260-RB walking draglines.

Right: David Fatchett.

In 1970, after twenty-four years with Ruston-Bucyrus David, the more adventurous member of the Fatchett family, left the 'family firm' to take up the job of Senior supervisor of mechanical equipment with the Sierra Leone Development Corporation. In that capacity he was dealing largely with RB machines so his links with Lincoln excavators were maintained. After a spell in Africa, David returned to take a job with Tarmac followed by a spell with the Staffs. Public Works in Stoke. In 1980 the wanderer returned to Ruston-Bucyrus to work in Parts Sales Department with responsibility for H&L Teeth.

Left: Arthur Fatchett Junior fitting 54-RB gears in 22 Bay of the Excavator Works in 1961.

Assembly of 150-RB Shovel in the new No.22 Bay. Stan Gibbons at the right stands behind Arthur Fatchett
Senior whilst Frank 'Ginger' Fatchett (Arthur Senior's brother) stands at the left. David Fatchett (Arthur's son) is
also involved in the procedure but out of sight. So precise was the lowering procedure that it is possible David,
in keeping with the usual practice, was on the suspended load checking with a spirit level.
Arthur Fatchett Junior (David's brother) is behind the camera taking the photograph.

A Welding Challenge

Continuing the RB 'family' theme at the Excavator Works is welder Carl Halliwell, whose uncle, aunt and father worked for the company. One of the more challenging welding operations at the Lincoln factory occurred on the large mining shovels with the attachment of the large end casting to the tubular dipper handle and it was Carl's job to carry out this lengthy and difficult operation.

The casting to which the dipper is connected is at the business end of the excavator and its size and mass is such as to withstand the considerable loads imposed during digging operations. Understandably, the welding which secured the casting to the handle had to be equal to these demands and was very much a specialised operation.

The photographs opposite taken in 8 Bay of the Excavator Works show Carl Halliwell engaged upon this work; Carl was one of only two welders allowed to do this job, each of whom though experienced welders had to undergo a monthly welding test to prove their continued competence for the task.

In preparation for the welding, both components (casting and handle) were pre-heated by strapping around them ceramic heat pads. The first root weld in the bottom of the prepared groove was semi-automatic, but all subsequent welds were carried out by stick welding. After the root welding was completed the heat pads could be removed as the welding itself generated sufficient heat, but for the duration of the complete welding process each night after Carl's shift the assembly was wrapped in an insulating blanket to retain heat for the next morning's work.

Welding was awkward and strenuous as once the root weld had secured the two components the whole assembly could not be moved and the welder had to work round the job. After a week's work, a 3" weld had been built up and Carl's task was completed.

Above: Dipper Handle and Dipper assembly for a 150-RB Shovel Excavator awaiting dispatch from the Excavator Works; the Shovel Dipper and Handle for the 150-RB and 110-RB was usually shipped to the customer as a complete assembly and the 33ft. long load with standard size Dipper had a gross weight of around 12 tons.

A footnote to Carl Halliwell endeavours detailed above. Carl's aunt was Miss Queenie Cowlam who retired (right) from Ruston-Bucyrus in 1979 after fifty years service. Since 1932 Queenie had been employed in the company's Publicity & Sales Technical Department, most of this time as secretary to the manager. It was Queenie who in 1949, unofficially and out of kindness, supplied this author, a raw young RB apprentice draughtsman, with regular press cuttings and items on excavators for his private scrap book. (Seeds of an obsession?)

Two photographs of Ruston-Bucyrus welder Carl Halliwell in 8-Bay welding the large end casting to the dipper handle of a 150-RB Mining Shovel. Carl's other large scale welding work was on the mining shovel dippers, one of which can be seen in the lower picture.

Photograph taken in 1963 of 22-Bay showing the assembly of mining shovel (left of picture) and 5-W Walking Draglines.

LINCOLN'S EXCAVATORS

THE 30-RB

30-RB UNIVERSAL EXCAVATOR

By the early 1950s there was clear evidence for the Ruston-Bucyrus management that their current production range of construction size cable excavators did not match the requirements of the company's European markets.

Central to this was an evident need to retire the elderly 7/8th. cu.yd. 24-RB and 1¼ cu.yd. 33-RB and replace them with a new 1 cu.yd. Universal Excavator. The RB Engineering Department had drawn up a specification for such a machine that would become the 30-RB but, as in the case of the 10-RB, it was necessary to persuade a reluctant parent company in America of its necessity. Referring to this in a letter to Eugene Berg, President of Bucyrus Erie Co. in September 1964, Mr. Everitt, RB's Managing Director wrote;

"There would have been no 30-RB had Savage (RB's Chief Engineer) and I not fought very hard for this at a time when we were producing a 7/8 cu.yd. machine and a 1¼ cu.yd. machine, both of ancient vintage, and were determined to have one modern machine designed around the size and range we specified to replace these two. Due to lack of interest in this size by the Bucyrus-Erie domestic sales organisation we achieved no result until eventually I persuaded Mr. Coleman to issue appropriate instructions."

The 30-RB prototype was first exhibited at the Public Works Exhibition at Earls Court in November 1956; this was a diesel powered version which, following the Exhibition, was given machine no. 21406 and later supplied to fulfil an order by customer G. Wimpey. Full production at the Lincoln factory quickly followed, the new 30-RB replacing the old type 33-RB on the assembly line at the Excavator Works.

The 30-RB was the first Ruston-Bucyrus machine to have full air control and in its design and use of modern refinements it could be claimed that it marked the company's entry into the 'new age' of excavator design and development.

Initially the sales for this new model were slow and production outstripped the orders resulting in surplus machines lined up outside the workshops suggesting that the Lincoln management's optimism might have been misplaced. Gradually, however, sales improved and the fact that over two thousand 30-RBs in its various forms were built throughout the life of the company demonstrates its eventual success and popularity with RB customers.

Above: 30-RB on display at the Public Works Exhibition at Earl's Court, November 1956. On its introduction, a big selling point for the new 1 cu.yd. 30-RB Excavator was the full air control resulting in increased output due to ease of operation and more efficient handling. With regard to the machine's durability in the field, attention was drawn to the unique hardening processes of major components which was adopted as standard in its production.

Above: 30-RB Main Machinery as equipped for shovel operation; power was supplied on the early models by a Ruston 5YFN 5-cyl. four stroke oil engine rated for excavator service, 96.80 hp. at 1200 r.p.m.

The new 30-RB as introduced in November 1956 was available with two alternative crawler mountings - the standard crawler frame with 30" wide track links giving a bearing area of 56.8 sq.ft., and a long/wide crawler frame with 30" or 36" track links giving a bearing area of 65 sq.ft. and 78 sq.ft. respectively. Conical hook rollers were a standard feature with two equalised pairs at the front and two single rollers at the rear of the cast steel revolving frame. Power was supplied by a Ruston 5 cyl. oil engine mounted on the rear of the revolving frame and transmitting power to the main machinery via multi-strand roller chain.

The truck frame is a single steel casting incorporating internal swing gear, double-flange roller path for the conical swing rollers and bearings for vertical and horizontal propelling shafts. Air-operated clutches on each end of the main drum shafts give two-directional propelling via a direct drive through gears and single horizontal propel shaft beneath the truck frame. The final drive for propelling is via chains to the left and right hand crawler tumblers. Spring set, air-released jaw clutches connecting centre and outer sections of the horizontal propelling shaft. Steering is obtained by disengaging one or the other of these jaw clutches.

Left: 30-RB underside of truck frame and propelling machinery.

30-RB Standard Shovel with cab removed photographed in September 1966 outside the workshops at the Excavator Works. Assembly of the 30-RB took place at the north end of No.3 Bay alongside the 38-RB where Charlie Dixon was the ganger and where traditionally the 24-RB, 33-RB and 43-RB had been built before them.

In 1961 the 30-RB received its first change of engine, the original Ruston 5YFN was replaced by the 5YEN 5-cyl. water cooled four stroke oil engine seen in the above photograph, rated for excavator service, 98hp. at 1500 r.p.m. At the same time a single motor electric version of the 30-RB was produced as an alternative to the diesel machine, which had not been available on the original model. (Eventually the standard 30-RB would be equipped with a 125hp. Dorman 6LE diesel engine, with G.M. (Detroit Diesel) offered as an alternative.)

The shovel boom with its box-section lower and divided upper section, combined strength with lightness, and the powerful chain-driven crowd drum located at the foot of the boom drove the positive twin-rope crowd / single-rope retract system which by this time had replaced the hoist-assisted rope crowd that had been fitted to the first 30-RB machines.

The increase in engine power and accompanying strengthening up of the lower works raised the 30-RB shovel's nominal capacity to 1¼ cu.yd.; with 20ft. boom, 17ft. dipper handle, and 1¼ cu.yd. dipper. The 30-RB shovels working weight was around 40 tons.

Above: 30-RB Shovel with 1 cu.yd. rock dipper photographed in December 1963 working at Holcombe Quarries, Shepton Mallet.

Below: 30-RB Shovel on display at the Bauma Exhibition, Munich, in March 1965.

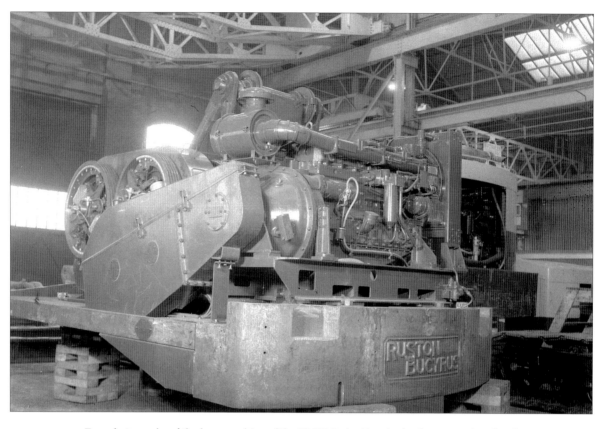

Two photographs of the base machine of the 30-RB Series Four in the factory equipped with a 125hp. Dorman 6LE diesel engine. This engine became standard on this model with a G.M. (Detroit Diesel) as an alternative option.

Above: 30-RB Series One Dragshovel with hydraulic wrist-action hoe-type dipper on the test ground.

The traditional straight boom type of dragshovel equipment was gradually being replaced by cambered booms and from the outset it was with the latter type that the 30-RB, as seen in these photographs, was equipped as standard when operating as a dragshovel. The standard 30-RB dragshovel with 1 cu.yd. dipper had a maximum digging radius of 40'-0" and a digging depth over the corner of the crawler mounting of 23'-0". When the 30-RB was developed into the up-rated Series Four model the dragshovel, with the same boom, was equipped with a 1¼ cu.yd. dipper.

Following the example of the 22-RB, a hydraulically operated pivot-action dipper was developed for the 30-RB Dragshovel (above picture). The pivoting of the dipper is achieved by replacing the standard dipper with a front pivoting hoe-type and installing a hydraulic ram in place of fixed stays. This innovation offered as an optional extra on the 30-RB for drag-shovel operation, gives additional versatility to this type of front end equipment.

Left: 30-RB Series four standard cambered boom Dragshovel with 1¼ cu.yd. dipper operated by E. Light and Sons Ltd. On the dipper handle can be seen the three alternative locating positions for the dipper braces to permit a limited adjustment of the digging angle.

30-RB Full Air Controls

An air-cooled 2-cyl. compressor driven from the main engine provided air for the operation of the five machinery clutches transmitting power to the rope drums and the reversing motions of swing and propel. The swing brake was spring set and air released, and an independent boom hoist gave power-controlled raising and lowering of the boom. Although described in the catalogues as a 'full-air' operated machine, this was not strictly true - operation of the five main clutches was by graduated air control valves at the operator's console and the shovel dipper trip, steering jaw clutches and brakes, and swing brake were controlled by poppet valves. However, direct mechanical controls were provided for the engine clutch, operating brakes and locks, boom control clutches and safety pawl, and swing-propel gear change.

The original operator's controls with three air valve levers in front of the operator (pictured below right) was later changed to provide four main graduated valves in front of the operator when the former manual levers operating the swing/propel jaw clutches, boom hoist clutch and engine clutch were replaced by air controls, though the mechanically operated foot pedal brakes remained (main photo).

Initially the 30-RB air control system was fitted with copper air piping but this was awkward to install and service so it was later replaced by flexible hose.

Operation

For the operator used to mechanical controls on a crane or excavator, the transition to full air-controls could be a problem. With manual controls comprising mechanical linkages and levers it was possible for the driver to ease the hand levers and feel the drive being taken up, but air-controls, though easier to apply and less tiring, did not provide this mechanical 'feel'. Air-assist brakes had a 'feel' but with full-air, where there was no mechanical connection between pedal and air cylinder, this 'feel' was absent. In time, of course, as full-air controls became a common feature, the problems experienced at the transition faded.

30-RB Air Controls.

Above: Operator's Controls on early 30-RB

A Swing Clutch

B Crowd / Retract Clutch

C Main Hoist Clutch

D Boom Hoist Clutch and Brake

E Propel Brakes

F Steering Clutches

G Swing to Propel Jaw Clutches

H Swing Brake

I Engine Clutch

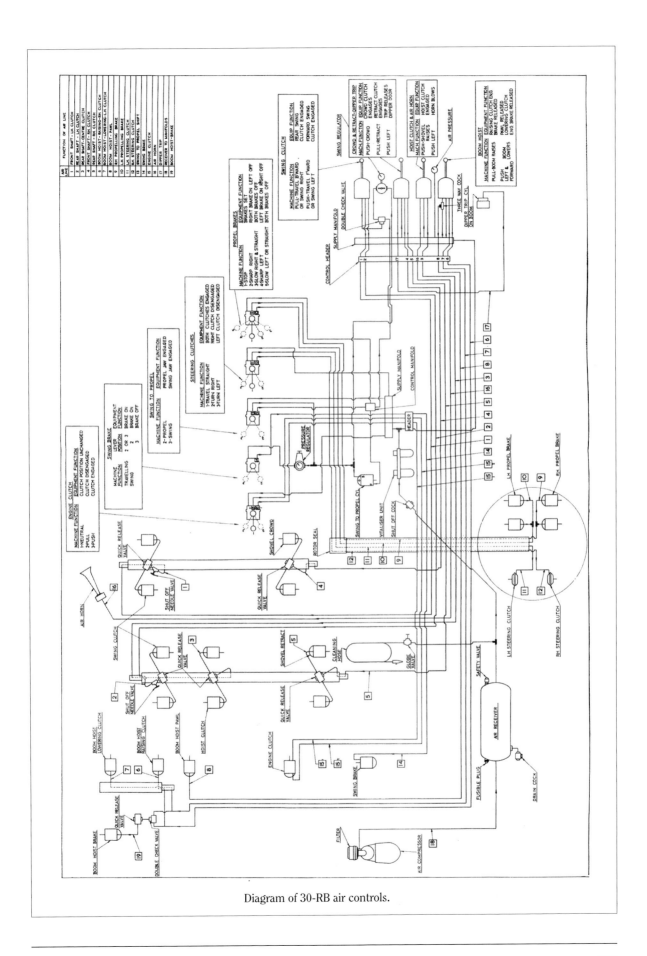

Diagram of 30-RB air controls.

Innovations - Involute Splines and Cut-Hardened Gears

The 30-RB was the first Ruston-Bucyrus excavator to incorporate involute splines on the machinery shafts in place of the traditional straight splines and cut hardened gears in place of the traditional cast and lightly dressed gears. These innovations meant much re-tooling in the factory and expenditure on new machinery. (Following the 30-RB, the square-sided splines of the 38-RB Series I were replaced by involute splines for the Series II; the new larger machines like the 61-RB and 71-RB were designed with involute splines.)

The 'cut-hardened' process led the Lincoln factory into increasing its hardening facilities and equipment became available to harden any component likely to need it in the Ruston-Bucyrus range of machines. In the case of the 30-RB this meant all the gears - which included the hoist and swing gear on the drum shafts and the hoist pinion - together with the cone roller path in the truck frame and the swing rack. (The 30-RB was the first to have a cut and hardened swing rack integral with the truck frame, the 38-RB and 54-RB had separate racks with cut teeth.)

The following sequence of photographs shows the cutting and hardening process of the 30-RB combined spur/bevel gear which is mounted on the vertical swing shaft.

Turning the blank.

Drilling for the lubrication nipples.

Cutting the spur gear.

Finishing cut of the bevel gear.

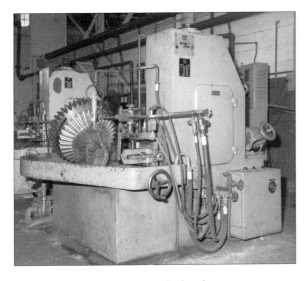

Flame hardening the bevel gear.

Flame hardening the spur gear.

Machining the ball race.

Turning the inside bore before cutting the splines.

Mating and testing the gears.

Cutting the internal splines.

175

'Christmas Island' and Problems with the Hardening Process

There were teething problems with the new hardening process on the 30-RB, with the most serious being the occasional field failure of the hardened lower roller path in which a portion of the hardened surface became separated under the loadings of the machine in operation. This was serious because on the 30-RB the roller path was part of the truck frame and any such failure could mean the replacement of the truck frame which usually led to a warranty claim from the customer whose machine had failed.

One such warranty claim involving the failure of a 30-RB truck frame came from the British Phosphate Commission on the Australian territory of Christmas Island in the Indian Ocean, where the 30-RB was one of several machines used to dig up, crush and bag the vast amounts of guano (seagull droppings) that covered the island.

In answer to the complaint D.A. 'Snowy' Clawson, RB Field Engineer, was dispatched to Christmas Island to assess the situation. Snowy's on-site inspection, to the embarrassment of the operators, revealed a catalogue of neglected maintenance, excessive cone-roller clearances, and badly set clutches and brakes, unrelated to the warranty claim.

However, such was the world-wide respect from customers for 'Snowy's' abilities as an engineer, that by the time he had corrected these deficiencies, with due admonishments to the customer for the obvious neglect, the question of a replacement truck frame under warranty was somehow overlooked. One is tempted to think that here is one case where a Field Engineer had got his company 'out of the guano'.

Below: 30-RB Heavy Duty crawler mounting with 36" wide track links.

Right: 'Snowy' Clawson

The above photograph shows the 30-RB lower works with the truck frame in the centre bolted on to the crawler cross members. The truck frame is a single steel casting incorporating internal swing gear with machine cut teeth, double-flange path for the conical swing rollers and bearings for vertical and horizontal propelling shafts. The swing gear and roller path were flame-hardened, as were the crawler roller paths in each set of track links.

It is easy to see how a truck frame roller path failure could involve the operator in an expensive lay off of the machine and entire truck frame replacement. Conscious of this possibility, the Lincoln production team kept spare truck frames in the factory for just such a contingency.

The Swing Brake and an alarmed Ship's Captain

The air-released spring-set swing brake mounted on top of the vertical swing shaft on the 30-RB served a dual purpose, to provide gradual braking for accurate load spotting and when fully applied to prevent the superstructure from revolving when the machine is travelling or stood down. In the former case, a manually set pressure valve was incorporated in the swing air circuit which enabled the operator to partially cancel out the effect of the spring during swing operation, thereby obtaining a pre-determined degree of 'drag' to assist in positioning the load.

In reality, in its function of fully braking the superstructure against swinging, the 30-RB swing brake proved ineffectual and the story is told of the 30-RB stowed on the foredeck of the M.V. Mary Rose, being shipped to a customer in Denmark. Though the excavator was lashed securely to the deck at its base, the swing brake was no match for the expected North Sea gale and the upper works of the machine began to swing wildly with the rolling of the ship directly in front of an alarmed captain's wheelhouse windows.

The 30-RB was later fitted with a graduated control valve for swing-brake application which allowed the actual swing brake pressure to be adjusted by the operator up to the pre-set maximum, allowing him to control the braking effect to suit changing conditions.

On the first 30-RB Supercranes a double-acting air cylinder was fitted into the swing brake system to achieve air-assisted setting of the swing brake whilst propelling, and in 1976 on the 30-RB Series Four Heavy Duty and Supercranes air-assist braking was incorporated for both propelling and swinging. However, as a consequence of the limited performance of the swing brake on the 30-RB, a mechanical dog-type swing lock was developed at the Lincoln factory which engaged with the swing gear to supplement the swing brake for transport purposes and it was offered as an optional extra.

Cargo ship Captains would be relieved when, from the 30-RB Series Four onward, the swing lock was standard equipment on all versions of this machine, bringing it in line with other models in the RB production line.

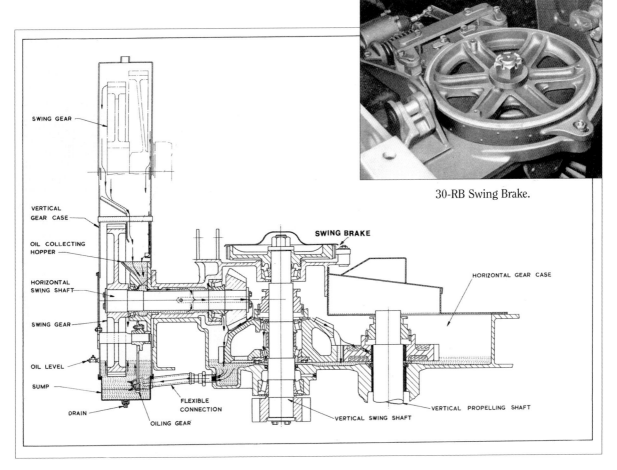

30-RB Swing Brake.

Sectional diagram drawing showing the drive through the vertical swing and propel shafts on the 30-RB; this gearing arrangement is typical of the 10-RB, 22-RB and 30-RB crawler excavators.

Logging Cranes for New Zealand

Over the years a large number of Ruston-Bucyrus machines were sold through agents Brown Douglas for logging work in New Zealand. Large areas of New Zealand are covered with forests of soft wood trees, pines, firs and spruces, and the production of timber for pulping for the paper and allied industries is a major source of revenue. The same timber is also greatly in demand for house construction, as most of the country's houses are made of wood.

After felling and trimming, the large trunks were dragged by crawler tractors equipped with logging arches to a loading point where specially equipped 19-RBs and 22-RBs loaded the timber onto 18 to 20 ton capacity vehicles for transit to the saw mills. A 19-RB handling 35ft long timber weighing 2½ to 3 tons each could load an 18-ton trailer in about two minutes.

As the scale of New Zealand's logging operations increased so did the need for larger logging cranes and the introduction of the 30-RB provided the ideal tool. The ease of operation provided by its air-controls, the high operating speed, and the greater lifting capacity, combined to make the 30-RB the first choice for New Zealand's logging industry.

30-RB Series II Logging Crane specially adapted for logging duty in New Zealand.
The boom, logging grab and tagline were supplied by agents Brown Douglas.
Note the tagline which restrains the grab against excessive swinging is of the old type running up the inside of the boom - all taglines supplied with 30-RB grabbing cranes from the factory were of the B&A automatic external drum type mounted on the lower boom section.

30-RB Series II being specially prepared in the Lincoln factory for logging
duties in New Zealand.

The popularity of the 30-RB for logging operations in New Zealand is evidenced by the fact that from the first one, Mc.no. 26858, a 30-RB Series II delivered to agents Brown Douglas in August 1962, the same agent ordered a further 36 machines between this example and Mc.No. 32758 delivered in July 1968. All were specially adapted for logging work with high vision cab and dual operator's controls and in every case Brown Douglas fitted their own booms and grab equipment.

30-RB Dragline with 40ft. boom owned and operated by the Amey
Group Ltd., Oxford, digging aggregates at Queenford gravel pits,
Oxfordshire.

30-RB Dragline / Crane / Grabbing Crane

The new 30-RB was introduced in 1956 as a 'Universal' machine with convertibility from shovel or dragshovel to lifting crane or grabbing crane equipments. As a lifting crane it was rated at max. load of 17 tons (40' boom with max. counterweight) and was available with boom lengths up to 90' (booms 70' to 90' requiring forward mast suspension). For dragline and grabbing crane service booms 40' to 60' were available and maximum permissible loads of bucket and contents were 7200 lbs (dragline) and 8300 lbs. (grabbing crane).

From the outset, the 30-RB was selected by the Lincoln company to join the group of machines being developed as specialist purpose-built high-performance lifting cranes, culminating in 'Supercrane' status. In keeping with this policy, the excavator and crane functions gradually became separated with the result that by the late 1960s with the Series Two Heavy Duty the 30-RB was represented by two distinct production models - the 30-RB Shovel / Dragshovel and the 30-RB Crane / Dragline.

Development as a purpose-built lifting crane resulted in different phases of constantly increasing performance and capacity culminating in the Ruston-Bucyrus 550SC Supercrane with the remarkable rating for this size of machine of 55 tons. (This machine will feature in Lincoln's Excavators Volume IV).

LINCOLN'S EXCAVATORS

PILING & SPECIAL APPLICATIONS

RB Cranes pile-driving on the construction of Drax Power Station

PILING AND SPECIAL APPLICATIONS

From the earliest days, Lincoln's Excavators had been supplied for piling and other special applications associated with the building and construction industry; usually this meant a machine from their range of universal excavators with lattice - boom crane front-end adapted as necessary to operate with various types of piling or boring equipment.

Though Ruston-Bucyrus on occasions supplied a machine complete with piling rig, more often than not the Lincoln company supplied the adapted basic machine for the customer to provide the additional piling rig or boring equipment. As the scale of construction in building and civil engineering increased, so piling methods had to develop to support the massive and heavy structures.

Not the least of the factors contributing to the increased scale of piling and boring equipment was the availability of ever larger capacity rope-operated cranes with improving features and the necessary heavy counterweight such as were being developed by Ruston-Bucyrus with their range of Heavy-Duty Cranes and Supercranes.

Drop Hammer Pile Driving

Wooden piling had been used since ancient times, but it was the introduction of steel piling in the early 1900s which revolutionised the use of piles in construction work. The increasing use of concrete in construction projects of the 1920s inevitably led to this material also being used for piling, either pre-cast or in-situ, which in turn led to large diameter piling and curtain walling.

Traditionally, drop hammer pile-driving was offered as an option with small to medium Universal Excavators, utilising the crane boom to support the piling leader which acted as a guide to the heavy cast-iron drop hammer. The leader, usually of lattice construction for lightness, was either suspended from the boom or permanently attached to the machine and could be angled forward, backward or sideways to accommodate angled piling. The use of longer steel piles meant longer leaders extended beyond the boom point and often heavier hammers, and this pushed the piling operation beyond the capacity of a standard crane,

creating the need for heavy duty machines offering greater stability and lifting capacity. Further developments to the basic crane for piling use included an additional rope drum to winch in the piles for setting in the frames, and eventually to separate lines in addition to the existing crane hoist for drop hammer hoist, pile hoist and pile handling. Any modifications necessary to the basic machine to accommodate these additional features were usually carried out and the equipment tested at the Lincoln factory.

Power Hammer Application

The simple reliance on gravity, with a hammer weighing approximately the weight of the pile being released to strike the pile head, is a method now almost entirely reserved for light work and has largely been replaced by the use of independent diesel hammers. Used either with a fixed leader or simply suspended on a single line from the crane boom, the self-contained hammer employs a ram which is raised by explosion at the base of a cylinder. In the case of double-acting diesel hammers, a vacuum is created in a separate annular chamber as the ram moves upward and assists the return of the ram, almost doubling the output of the hammer over the single-acting type.

Left: Although Ruston-Bucyrus supplied a number of customers with base machines adapted for piling, their best and most loyal customer was Wests Piling and Construction Ltd. and this long association proved a successful and enduring partnership. In this photograph, taken in 1967, Mr. R. Bradley, executive director of Wests Piling and Construction Company Ltd. (right) is inspecting a specially equipped 38-RB Series II at the Excavator Works. With him is Peter Meanwell, RB Field Dept. Manager (centre) and Mr. F. Finley, Senior Field Plant Engineer for Wests. The machine has been fitted with a swan-neck boom for use with piling rigs and it was the thirty-ninth Ruston-Bucyrus crane to be supplied to Wests for piling work.

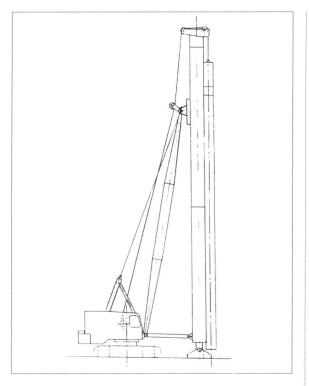

Above: Boom suspended piling rig.

Right above: Direct mounted piling rig.

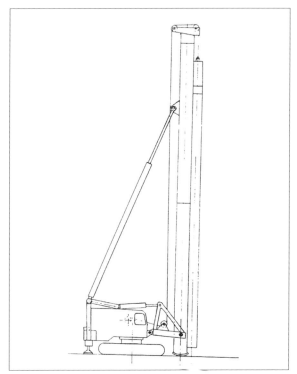

The simpler boom suspended rigs usually only required modification at the boom point where the leader attaches to the crane boom and anchor points welded to the revolving frame near the boom foot pins to take the adjustable tie-bar between machine and leader foot. As longer and heavier piles were developed stronger leaders were required and eventually it was realised that the leader could be made self-supporting by attaching the leader directly to the machine. Several ways were found to do this and create a more rigid and inherently stronger rig, though it made conversion to other equipments more difficult and reduced the machine's usefulness as a Universal Excavator.

Whether boom suspended or directly attached, piling rigs can be operated with leader set at an angle, either raked forward, backward, or to either side. (Usually sideways rake was used to maintain the piling operation vertical when operating on sloping ground.)

Left: Ruston-Bucyrus 38-RB Series II Heavy Duty crane with 50ft. boom operating as a piling rig driving raked piles using diesel powered hammer. The extended lattice type leader is supported at the foot by a fabricated hollow section steel frame. The site is the Nigg Bay North Sea Oil Project in the north of Scotland.

This 38-RB Series II Heavy Duty crane working on the Nigg Bay North Sea
Oil Project fitted with 50ft. boom and suspended piling rig, is driving forward
raking steel piles for the foundations. The extended piling leader is attached
to the machine at its foot by twin hydraulic rams by which the angle of piling
can be adjusted as required. Accompanying the 38-RB is a 22-RB I.C.D.
handling and setting the piles.

At Nigg Bay in the Cromarty Firth, Scotland, the biggest dry dock in Europe was constructed for the fabrication of drilling platforms used in the exploitation of the British Petroleum concession oil and gas fields in the Forties area of the North Sea.

A number of Ruston-Bucyrus machines were employed on various duties on this massive project, these included; two 61-RB Cranes (one Standard, one Heavy Duty), two 38-RB Heavy Duty cranes, four 22-RB I.C.Ds, and a 25-T Transit Crane. In the foundation work piling duties were carried out by the 38-RBs and 61-RBs equipped with British Steel piling rigs and 22 Delmag hammers, with the 22-RBs handling piles for the larger machines.

One of the many machines supplied to West's Piling and Construction Co. for piling duty was this 38-RB seen here in 1964 equipped with 6-ton hammer preparing to drive the first 17½" dia. pile for the foundations of a block of flats in Trionfale, Rome. Senor Caccio, the head of the company for whom the flats were being built, was able to observe the operations from his office in the adjacent block of flats also built by his company.

Above: 38-RB Series Two Lifting Crane with boom suspended piling rig working on the construction of Drax Power Station in 1974. Drax Power Station near Selby, North Yorkshire was originally built, owned and operated by the Central Generating Board. The first stage of its construction was in 1974, with a second stage in 1986.

Photos on opposite page: A 38-RB Series Two Lifting Crane engaged on piling duties in the first stage of construction of Drax Power Station with a second 38-RB Series Two crane assisting on pile-handling duties.

22-RB I.C.D. with special Dowsett pile driving equipment.

Direct mounted piling rigs may need considerable structural modifications to the basic machine, as in the case of this Dowsett rig, and further changes to the standard machine may be required to accommodate additional equipment such as;

Special rope drums for pile hammers.
Third drums for winching piles or extra hoist line.
Special drum drives for extraction ropes.
Rear end mountings for auxiliary power packs.

Suspension anchor points for rotary auger drives.
Low power hydraulic circuits for adjustment cylinders.
High power hydraulic circuits to replace external power packs.
Ratchet and pawl on hoist drum to hold hammers.

Most of these modifications can be seen in the photographs on the opposite page of the Dowsett machine, including auxiliary hoists, third drum at jib foot and extra large main hoist drums, etc.

Above: This shows the Wests Piling 43-RB at work with piling equipment supplied by British Steel Piling, Ipswich. The air compressor with large air receiver mounted on a special rear platform illustrates how much additional equipment is required for some piling duties.

Sand Drain Piling

Ground preparation on construction sites is important and piling rigs can be used to install vertical sand drains in order to effect rapid consolidation of sub-soils to allowing easier drainage. A tube is driven to the required depth through clay or silty soil and the driving plug expelled. The tube is then filled with compacted sand then withdrawn; the spacing of the sand drains and the depth to which they are installed is decided according to soil conditions. The two photographs show a Wests 43-RB excavator with vertical sand drain equipment working in the construction of the Thelwall Viaduct section of the new M62 Motorway in December 1959.

The contract was by Wests Raymond Piling (joint venture with an American company). Wests were responsible for much of the piling work, but since this was a high viaduct spanning both the River Mersey and the Manchester Ship Canal, some extra long piling was required and this was undertaken by the Raymond Company from the States.

Left: The 43-RB with boom suspended piling rig is seen here at work on the viaduct embankment; the drop hammer is driving a tube into the ground, after which the sand-filled skip mounted on the leader pours its contents down the tube. Compressed air is injected into the tube to consolidate the sand and the tube is withdrawn.

Bored (none-displacement) Piling

Apart from pile driving, many Ruston-Bucyrus excavators have been supplied for boring duties associated with non-displacement piling. The use of cast-in-place concrete as a piling material and the need for larger diameter piling capable of sustaining greater loads gave the impetus for bored piling, generally referred to as non-displacement piling to differentiate it from driven piling in which the soil is displaced radially as the pile shaft enters the ground. Ruston-Bucyrus Heavy Duty and Super-cranes have provided the basic machine for a variety of rotary auger and drilling units required for this type of piling operation in which holes are bored as a preliminary to casting a concrete pile.

Bore holes for concrete piling in cohesive soils need not be lined with permanent or removable steel casing, but should cohesion-less soil be experienced it may be necessary to line the bore hole with steel tubing to prevent the inflow of surrounding soils when pouring concrete. Such casing can be positioned in a pre-drilled hole or driven into the ground and the soil drilled and removed from inside the tubing afterwards. (Where casing is driven directly into the ground beforehand, electrically powered or hydraulic vibratory hammers can be used to do this; the amplitude of the vibration is sufficient to break down the skin friction of the casing.)

Frankipile Ltd., world experts in piling techniques have, among their many innovations, developed a system for casing a bore hole using short sections of tubing that can be connected together as they are driven deeper into the ground.

The photographs on this page illustrate an example of Franki large diameter bored piling in which long lengths of removable casing were used. To increase output, this particular project involved two teams comprised of one lifting crane and one vibrator, with a boring rig serving both teams. The method of piling was as follows;

A hole was drilled to a depth of 4-5ft. (until ground water was reached) to receive the end of the first section of casing which was 30ft. long. The hollow casing was driven to its full depth with the vibrator and was then drilled out by the boring rig, which then continued its boring through the silty clay until water was again reached at a depth of approximately 50ft.

A second 90ft. long casing was placed through the 30ft. tube and the vibrator was used to drive it on to the bed rock at between 85ft. - 90ft. below ground level. The borer then drilled out this second casing and a further 4ft. into the rock. Readymix trucks were placed in position at the head of the casing to deposit the concrete and the 90ft. casing was completely filled before it was extracted using the combined efforts of crane and vibrator. It was necessary to add further concrete as the tube was withdrawn to allow for the larger diameter of the 30ft. section of hole as well as the consolidation of the concrete.

Above: 90ft. long casing being lifted into position. Working together the two teams averaged 15 piles per week throughout the contract.

Right: Rotary drill auger.

Above and opposite page: RB 25-SC Supercrane operated by A. Barker of Scunthorpe
with boring rig attached, is drilling 24" dia. holes for piling to 40ft. depth. The crane is equipped
with a 75ft. boom which at the close working radius seen here gives a maximum lift of 10.25 tons.
Mounted on long and wide crawlers, Mr. Barker's machine carries at the rear the optional
hydraulic equipment supplied for the removal of the Supercrane's heavy counterweights.

A 22-RB Heavy Duty crane with foundation borer attached; the crane is equipped with a 55ft. main boom utilised for drilling with a continuous flight auger (CFA), and 10ft. offset jib over which an auxiliary hoist line is being used for placing concrete reinforcing rods.

Continuous Flight Auger (CFA)

Usually in non-displacement piling the bore hole is made, either with or without casing, and the infill of concrete is poured afterwards; by using a continuous flight auger the two processes of drilling and infilling are combined. The auger has a hollow tube centre which is capped at the end during the hole drilling operation. On reaching the required depth, highly workable concrete is pumped through the hollow stem of the auger and, under the pressure of the concrete, the protective cap is detached. While withdrawing the auger, it is rotated in the same direction as during the boring stage and during this process the spoil is expelled and the pile is formed by filling with concrete.

In this process it is important that the rotation of the auger and the flow of concrete is matched to avoid gaps in the flow resulting in voids and gaps in the concrete where the side of the hole has collapsed.

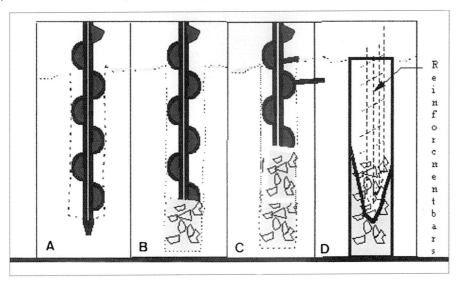

A Drilling   **B** Pumping concrete   **C** Auger withdrawal while concreting   **D** Finished pile

38-RB Heavy Duty lifting crane with Watson caisson drill attachment
drilling for cast in-situ concrete piles. A second crane in the
foreground supports the casing whilst concrete pouring takes place.

Types of Piling

A. Cohesion Piles

In ground where piles transmit most of their load to the soil through skin friction they are described as cohesion piles. The process of driving such piles in close groups has the effect of reducing the porosity and compressibility of the surrounding soil and increases the piles' effectiveness.

B. Friction Piles

Also depends upon skin friction, this term refers to those conditions where the piles do not compact the soil appreciably, giving rise to the name 'floating pile foundations'.

C. End Bearing Piles

This refers to piles which transmit their load onto a firm stratum at the base of the pile, thus behaving as a normal column with most of its carrying capacity derived from the penetration resistance of the material at the toe of the pile.

D. Under-Reamed Piles

This is a variation of cast-in-situ end-bearing piling to increase its effectiveness by enlarging the end-bearing area with the use of a special under-reaming tool.

Method of Under-reaming

For under-reaming, the soil has to be capable of standing open unsupported, and stiff clay is ideal. The pile shaft is bored down to the hard bearing strata and the under-reaming tool in its closed position is inserted down the shaft. At the bottom of the shaft the under-reamer is expanded and boring is resumed to create a conical cavity at the level of the bearing strata (right). It is recorded that it is normal, after installation and before the concrete is poured, for a man-carrying cage to be lowered and the under-reaming inspected.

Above: Ruston-Bucyrus crane fitted with special under-reamer with 36 hardened H&L teeth. (Under-reamer in a partially open position).

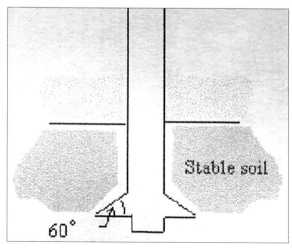

196

Two 30-RB Series II Heavy Duty lifting cranes fitted with 40ft. booms and 'Trencha' grabs excavating deep narrow trenches for diaphragm wall construction. The spoil excavated is temporarily replaced by a Bentonite suspension which stabilises the walls of the trench and prevents caving in. After the full trench depth is reached, the Bentonite is replaced by reinforced concrete as required to form a cast-in-situ separating or diaphragm wall. The third machine is placing the reinforcement.

Diaphragm Walling

Ruston-Bucyrus crawler mounted cranes were used for aspects of foundation work in civil engineering projects other than piling., among them the excavation of deep trenches for curtain or diaphragm walling. Firstly, a narrow trench of the required size is excavated and panels are formed in the trench using pre-cast or cast-in-situ techniques to form a diaphragm wall or barrette.

Generally, trenching work is best suited to excavation by dragshovels, but at the depths required for the construction of retaining walls and foundations for buildings, quay walls, coffer dams, etc., a specialised trenching equipment has been developed for use with a heavy duty crawler mounted lifting crane base machine.

One such equipment is the hydraulically powered 'Trencha' grab; suspended from the crane boom, the 'Trencha' is equipped with telescoping kelly bars to suit the depth of excavation required, which can be up to 120ft. Power for operating the clamshell type grab is supplied by a hydraulic pump mounted at the rear of the base machine which has to be adapted to this purpose.

Four sizes of 'Trencha' rig are available requiring matching base machine boom lengths of 40ft., 60ft., 70ft., and 90ft. accordingly. The lifting capacity required of the base machine depends on size of grab and nature of the soil but would vary from 19,900lb to 54,000lb. at 75% tipping load.

SALES PROMOTION

RUSTON-BUCYRUS

Special letter 72.1.
31st July 1972

SPECIAL APPLICATIONS

        Recent analyses of R-B sales trends in respect of lattice-
boom equipped crawler-mounted excavators and cranes indicates that
a significant proportion of orders received are for machines for
use on duties not wholly anticipated in our standard technical
specifications and price pages. R-B recognise that this is a
development which has to be fully accepted, and in fact encouraged,
as showing how versatile the rope-operated crawler-mounted type
of machine continues to be: this despite the onset of competition
from hydraulic excavators and cranes and notably from wheel-
mounted machines.

        It is our intention therefore, to try to focus more
publicity attention on those applications where the adaptation of
purchased equipment of a specialised type to an R-B basic machine
has proven successful in accomplishing some particular aspect of
contract work such as power pile driving or drilling holes for piles,
etc. with rotary auger attachments.

                                        T.W.Broughton
                            Manager, Sales Promotion

30-RB with Akerman piling rig.

The RB Sales Promotion letter featured above reflects the extent to which pile-driving, regarded for many years as the least important of a Universal Excavator's optional equipments, could now be marketed in its own right. This was at a time when the development of Ruston-Bucyrus Heavy Duty and Supercranes was gathering momentum, offering a range of highly suitable base machines for piling duties, both in their greater capacities and in their advanced special crane features.

A testament to the success of Ruston-Bucyrus for piling duties - and to the loyalty of one RB customer - came at the end of 1967 when project engineer Peter Wyatt was handed the task of modifying a 30-RB crane to accept the front end piling equipment of an Akerman crawler mounted self-contained piling rig.

This unusual one-off request came from Ruston-Bucyrus customer Wests Piling who wanted the 'business end' of the Ackerman machine but wanted it removed from its purpose-built base machine and mounted on a Ruston-Bucyrus base machine. The excercise was carried out successfully on a 30-RB Heavy Duty crane and the machine was delivered in March 1968.

LINCOLN'S EXCAVATORS

THE CARRIERS - PART TWO

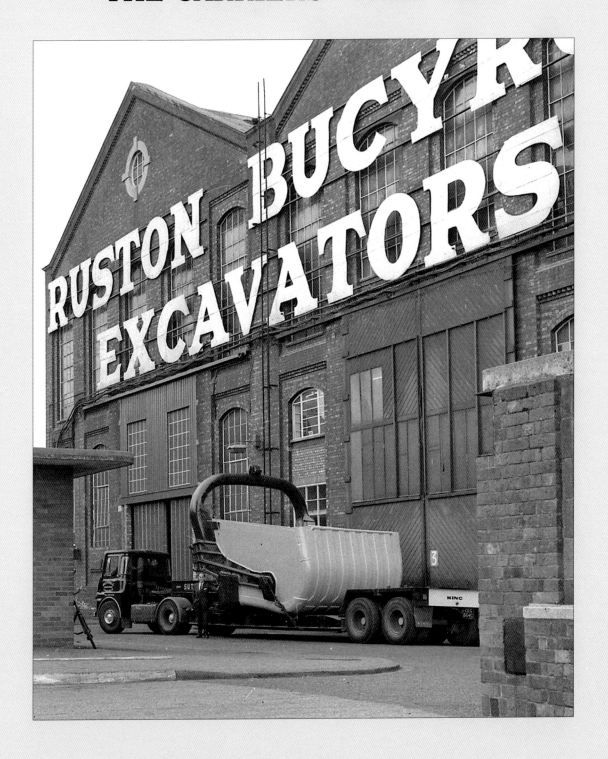

27 cu.yd. walking dragline bucket leaving the Excavator Works on Suthrell transport

THE CARRIERS - PART TWO

The original Ruston & Hornsby Navvy Works built in 1918 and later to become the Excavator Works was conveniently located next to the main line railway and a series of spur lines connected the assembly shops to the main railway. In the early days the excavators and almost all their components were transported by rail, but improvements to Britain's road system and matching developments in heavy transport led to a decline in the use of rail in favour of road such that by the 1960s most of the products of the Excavator Works were carried by road.

This Section continues the theme of the carriers who delivered new Ruston-Bucyrus machines and spare parts from the works to the customer at home and abroad. With the larger loads it was often necessary for RB to call on the services of the major heavy haulage companies specialising in dealing with abnormal loads and their vehicles became a familiar sight to the people of Lincoln; some of these are included in this chapter.

Railway wagon at the Excavator Works in 1960 loaded up with a 150-RB revolving frame casting; as the traditional rail transportation declined this heavy excavator component was regularly carried by road transport. On the left of the photograph is Mr. Walter Gray, British Rail Supervisory Foreman and on the right is Walter 'Wally' Ashcroft, loader in the RB Yard Dept., later the Packing Dept., who retired from the company in 1964 after twenty years service.

An 'Island' Works

During the time of Ruston-Bucyrus Ltd. the transportation by road from works to customer of even the smallest excavator was not without its difficulties. This was a legacy of the Ruston steam navvy days when in 1918 the choice of site for Ruston's new Navvy Works (Excavator Works) was Spike Island, an area of land cut off on all but one side by canals and railways and to which there was limited road access. Since the method of transporting the products then was by rail and the works was directly connected to the main line the location of the factory did not present a problem, for the narrow streets could easily accommodate the bicycles of thousands of factory workers. However, from the time Ruston-Bucyrus took over the Navvy Works, the transporting of goods by road gradually increased and eventually became common practice.

With narrow winding streets of worker's houses adjacent to the Excavator Works on its only open side, the only practical route away from the works for vehicles carrying loads was via the narrow but busy 'Rope Walk' at the top of which was a narrow hump-backed bridge, a notorious hazard for low-slung vehicles. Having negotiated this the driver was left with two choices, neither of which was very promising - a left turn along the narrow east side of Lincoln's Brayford Pool to an impossibly tight iron swing bridge over the River Witham, or straight on for a few more yards to St. Marks where the Rope Walk spills out into Lincoln's bustling High Street.

Above: This 54-RB photographed in November 1948, leaving the Excavator Works on Wynns low-loader, was at the time the largest RB machine to be transported by road. It is about to start its journey along Lincoln's Rope Walk ahead of a patient group of other road users. The building to the left of the picture is James Dawson's Leather Works.

Below: In 1950, this 38-RB was being transported from the Works along the Rope Walk (today the multi-lane Tritton Road) on a Pickfords low-loader. It hadn't got very far along the narrow but busy road before its size began to cause problems. That the vast number of heavy machines and equipment produced at the Excavator Works arrived safely at their destinations around the world attests to the skill and patience of the drivers in 'escaping' from Lincoln's Spike Island.

Ruston-Bucyrus Conventions for Road Transportation

Over the years the Lincoln company had established conventions for the transportation of the different types and sizes of their machines which represented the safest option for a particular load and met the necessary safety regulations. The smaller machines could be carried complete with the front-end in place (F.I.P.), or in two loads with the front end separate (F.E.S.). Medium size machines could be transported this way or when necessary split into three separate loads of base machine, cab, and front-end (SPLIT). The largest Ruston-Bucyrus machine to be transported complete (less front-end) was the 71-RB. The largest machines like the walking draglines were dismantled after testing and the sub-assemblies were transported as individual loads, (PACKED). Perhaps the largest load in terms of weight and size to leave the Excavator Works on road transport was the 110-RB base machine complete with crawlers; this was not uncommon practice and it represented a challenge for driver and vehicle in negotiating the route out of Lincoln.

However, whether arranged by the customer, or by Ruston-Bucyrus on behalf of the customer, the safe transportation of a new machine once it had left the Excavator Works was the responsibility of its new owner, and not always did they follow the Lincoln company's recommendations. (Note; the smaller machines up to the 30-RB could be transported from the Excavator Works without prior notice to the police authorities.)

22-RB I.C.D. Crane on low-loader with complete 35' basic boom suspended from the machine's forward mast. Short additional boom intersections are stored in spare space on the carrier.

When it came to machines transported with their lattice-type crane or dragline booms attached there was developed at RB a recommended way in which a particular model's boom should be carried. This was either suspended over front or rear of the carrier, complete (as in the above photograph) or in separate sections, depending upon length and make-up of the boom. (When pin-jointed lattice booms began to replace the traditional bolted butt-jointed booms on RB cranes, arranging a boom for road transportation became easier.)

However, RB's recommended practice was sometimes ignored as in the case of the new 22-RB I.C.D. Crane seen in the lower photograph on opposite page about to leave the Excavator Works on transport provided by customer Seymore Plant. The machine was equipped with the standard butt-jointed 35' boom with sections to make a further 40' of length slung under the main boom for travelling. The Lincoln company made it very clear that this was not their recommended way for this machine to travel but despite warnings the vehicle left with its load anyway.

Opposite above: 22-RB I.C.D. Crane with boom lower section suspended from its forward mast loaded on transport ready for departure from the works. The remaining boom sections to be transported separately.

Opposite below: 22-RB I.C.D. Crane on Seymour transport in a "not-to-be recommended" state, with 75 feet of boom suspended.

Suthrell Haulage Contractors

The Suthrell haulage company of Lincoln, like the Bradshaw company described in Volume Two of Lincoln's Excavators, had its seeds almost literally in Lincolnshire agriculture, for it was Albert Suthrell's potato merchant brother who provided him with the opportunity to form his own haulage business. The brother, though with lorries for his potato business, was less interested in the

Bert Suthrell and his first vehicle in 1935.

transport side and holding a 'B' licence for which he had no need in his own business passed this on to Albert.

So it was that in December 1935, Bert, as he is more widely known, acquired his first lorry and, initially under his brother's name, began his haulage business from the potato merchant premises on Burton Road, Lincoln. The first vehicle used by Bert's haulage company was a Bedford lorry with a long tipper body; Bedfords were the only type of vehicle used in the early years by Suthrell of Lincoln until the fleet was gradually replaced by ERF. Throughout the war years, Bert carried on his haulage business and one of his tasks was to disperse the products of Lincoln's engineering factories around the county for safety against possible enemy bombs. After war, and with long-distance licence, Suthrell's main contract was with Smith Clayton Forge of Lincoln for whom, using a long-wheel-based vehicle, he carried castings for motor cars to Derby.

Always to some extent restricted for space at Burton Road, Bert Suthrell took the opportunity when it came to move to larger premises. In the war years the Albion Brick Works on Lincoln's Long Leys Road had been closed and in 1946 Bert, together with his potato merchant brother, purchased the factory and its adjoining lands which he transformed into workshops and accommodation for his vehicles. Attached to the Brick Works was Albion House, private residence of the former owner, and this became the Suthrell family home for Bert, his wife, and their two daughters, Jenny and Charlotte.

Bert Suthrell, on left, with his driver Henry Ford, is seen at the Albion works proudly standing in front of his first articulated low-loader, a Ford Thames. Just able to carry the 10 ton 10-RB, this was the vehicle with which Suthrells began a long association with Ruston-Bucyrus and Lincoln's excavators.

Photograph taken in the late 1950s of the yard of Suthrell's Albion Works haulage depot on Long Leys Road, Lincoln. Bert Suthrell is the second figure from the left seen leaning nonchalantly against one of his lorries, in the centre are Suthrell driver brothers Jack and Frank Briggs, and far right of the group is Mike Hoyes, Bert's Transport Manager. Of the three Suthrell vehicles in the picture, the far one, an ERF, was appointed specifically to the long-standing contract with Smith Clayton Forge of Lincoln.

With the larger premises Suthrell transport had the room to expand its operation and its first acquaintance with Ruston-Bucyrus came when Bert purchased his first articulated low-loader, this being a Ford Thames which was just capable of carrying a 10-RB excavator.

In the ensuing years, Suthrell vehicles were often seen at the Excavator Works collecting the small to medium machines while at the same time maintaining a diverse number of other haulage contracts, including Lincoln's first ready-mixed concrete operation and Lincoln's first skip business.

In 1971 Bert Suthrell sold the haulage business to Amalgamated Anthracite (A.A.H.), maintaining ownership of the Albion Works land, and went into semi-retirement as consultant for the new company which continued to operate the vehicles under the Suthrell name.

Many of Bert's loyal workforce, including his Transport Manager, Ken Lynn, a former Ruston-Bucyrus employee, continued to work for the new company. Gradually, over the next few years A.A.H. pared down their haulage operation in Lincoln and eventually the time came for them to 'rationalise' their many interests by centralising them at Grantham. The depot at the Albion Works was closed

Bert Suthrell at the wheel of one of his vehicles.

down and the haulage side, no longer under the Suthrell name, was transferred to Grantham.

Albert Suthrell lived in happy retirement until his death in October 2008; fondly remembered and greatly respected, he was a member of that small group recognised and celebrated in the volumes of Lincoln's Excavators whose business it was to carry with pride and dedication the products of Lincoln's famous engineering companies.

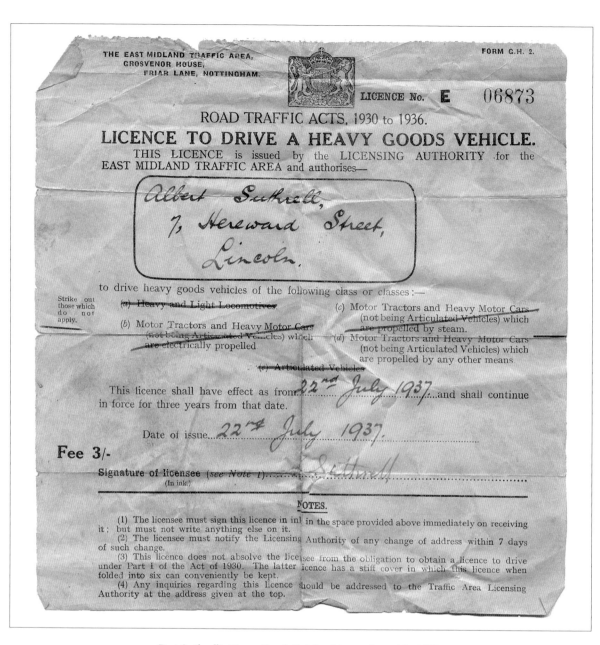

THE EAST MIDLAND TRAFFIC AREA,
GROSVENOR HOUSE,
FRIAR LANE, NOTTINGHAM.

FORM G.H. 2.

LICENCE No. **E** 06873

ROAD TRAFFIC ACTS, 1930 to 1936.

LICENCE TO DRIVE A HEAVY GOODS VEHICLE.

THIS LICENCE is issued by the LICENSING AUTHORITY for the
EAST MIDLAND TRAFFIC AREA and authorises—

Albert Suthrell,
7, Hereward Street,
Lincoln.

to drive heavy goods vehicles of the following class or classes:—

Strike out
those which
do not
apply.

(a) Heavy and Light Locomotives.

(b) Motor Tractors and Heavy Motor Cars
(not being Articulated Vehicles) which
are electrically propelled.

(c) Motor Tractors and Heavy Motor Cars
(not being Articulated Vehicles) which
are propelled by steam.

(d) Motor Tractors and Heavy Motor Cars
(not being Articulated Vehicles) which
are propelled by any other means.

(e) Articulated Vehicles.

This licence shall have effect as from 22nd July 1937 and shall continue
in force for three years from that date.

Date of issue 22nd July 1937.

Fee 3/-

Signature of licensee (see Note 1) ....
(In ink.)

NOTES.

(1) The licensee must sign this licence in ink in the space provided above immediately on receiving
it; but must not write anything else on it.
(2) The licensee must notify the Licensing Authority of any change of address within 7 days
of such change.
(3) This licence does not absolve the licensee from the obligation to obtain a licence to drive
under Part I of the Act of 1930. The latter licence has a stiff cover in which this licence when
folded into six can conveniently be kept.
(4) Any inquiries regarding this licence should be addressed to the Traffic Area Licensing
Authority at the address given at the top.

Bert Suthrell's Heavy Goods Driving Licence issued in 1937.

In the early 1930s the nation was deep in a world-wide depression and it was the Government's misguided policy to restrict the scope and development of road transport. To this end the Government introduced the Road Traffic Act of 1930 which established in thirteen areas Commissioners responsible for the licencing and control of road passenger service. Even more contentious was the introduction in 1933 of the Road and Rail Traffic Act under which all goods vehicles used on the roads had to be authorised by a carrier's licence.

An 'A' licence allowed the professional haulier to use his vehicle for hire and reward, and had a two years, later a five years currency. A 'B' licence, with a currency of two years, entitled its owner to carry goods in connection with his own business and, subject to certain conditions attached by the Licencing Authority, also for hire and reward. 'C' licences were granted to private traders for vehicles used solely for their particular business and never for hire or reward.

Despite the difficulties and obstacles imposed by the 1933 Act, and the even greater concerns for the future of road transport arising from the Railways 'Square Deal' campaign of 1938, the 1930s saw a considerable increase in the carrying of goods by road; in 1924, the railways were carrying nearly 75% of the agricultural produce of the country, but by 1938 some 60% of farmer's national produce was transported in road vehicles.

Above: Suthrell's Albion Works Haulage Depot.

Below: A Suthrell lorry parading with other local transport companies through the streets of Lincoln in protest at the Government's 1967 Transport Bill introduced by Barbara Castle, Labour's Minister of Transport (1965-68). The reference to Guy Fawkes suggests an unpleasant end to the Bill's author. Among its many proposals was the creation of a National Freight Corporation whose function it would be to "co-ordinate the movement of goods by sea, land or rail, on the basis of the most appropriate means of transportation." This involved controlling the increasing amount of road freight and ever larger vehicles by imposing a selective additional taxation. The British Road Foundation strenuously opposed the Bill, as did the nation's hauliers.

Above: Suthrell Scammell low-loader with 30-RB base machine loaded up at the Excavator Works.

Below: View of Suthrell's Albion Works haulage yard with 22-RB base machine mounted on a low-loader ready for delivery.

Above: Suthrell low-loader with 22-RB base machine at the Excavator Works.

Below: A busy day for the RB Dispatch Department as two transporters with their loads await clearance from the Excavator Works; a Suthrell vehicle with 30-RB base machine in the foreground and a Alexandria Transport Co. vehicle of Glasgow behind it loaded up with a 22-RB base machine.

On September 29th 1966, Suthrell Transport had the task of delivering a B.H. heavy duty 27 cu.yd. dragline bucket weighing 25 tons from the Excavator Works to the Coldrife opencast coal site in Northumberland owned by the Opencast Executive of the N.C.B. and operated by Derek Crouch (Contractors) Ltd.

This was the first of four similar buckets to be supplied by the Lincoln factory for use on Bucyrus-Erie 1150-B walking draglines which had been acquired second-hand from America after the war and used by the N.C.B. for stripping overburden in U.K. opencast coal sites.

The bucket parts were manufactured by Bucyrus-Erie in America and assembled at the Lincoln factory; their leading dimensions were - height 13ft. 6in., width 12ft. 6ins., length 17ft., and each of their six teeth weighed 1¾ cwt.

Above: Out of a total of four second-hand Bucyrus-Erie 1150-B walking draglines purchased for operation in U.K. opencast coal mines two were being operated by Crouch at Coldrife O.C.C.S. at the time of Suthrell's delivery of the first of the replacement buckets in 1966. These were machine numbers 41525 and 47125, one of which is seen in the above photo at work removing overburden.

Left: 27 cu.yd. dragline bucket in the Excavator Works ready to be loaded onto Suthrell transport for delivery to Coldrife opencast coal site, Northumberland in September 1966. (Photo; Lincs. Echo)

Opposite top: The Suthrell transport about to depart the factory with the first of the four 1150-B buckets ordered by customer N.C.B. for the 1150-B draglines.

Opposite bottom: The first tricky part of the bucket's journey north occurs soon after leaving the Excavator Works when the transport has to negotiate the junction at St. Marks where the narrow Rope Walk leading from the factory spills out into Lincoln's busy High Street.

Wynns

Robert Wynn, who started his business as a haulier in 1863, was a pioneer of road haulage; working with two horse-drawn vehicles he carried wheat, flour, cereals between Newport docks and various mills, cartage which was not invaded by the all-powerful railway companies.

At his death in 1878 the business passed to his young son Robert who at the age of 15 found himself head of a rapidly expanding business. At this time Newport was developing from a market town into one of the most important industrial centres in the west and Wynn's grew with it, playing its own part in Britain's industrial development carrying boilers, engines, cranes and a variety of heavy machinery.

In 1903, Wynn's acquired their first road steam locomotive, and in 1908 their first steam lorry, enabling heavier loads to be carried greater distances. When, in 1910, the company acquired the first of its motor fleet, Robert Wynn and Sons Ltd. was set on the path to becoming one of the leading heavy-haulage specialists in the country. It was a success built upon the principle of providing any class of vehicle for any type of load it may be called upon to move, and Wynn's were called upon frequently to transport heavy loads that came out of the Ruston-Bucyrus factory.

Above: The complete base unit for a 110-RB (Mc.No. 21657) is seen here in March 1957 on Wynn's low-loader hauled by one of the company's Pacific tractors about to leave the Excavator Works en route to customer Messrs. Lehane, Mackenzie and Shand Ltd; this constituted a wide heavy load, comprising as it did the revolving frame, truck frame and complete crawler mounting.

Opposite: This photograph taken in 1957 illustrates the problems with the location of the Ruston-Bucyrus Excavator Works; the Wynn transporter is in trouble even without its load as it tries to negotiate the narrow swing bridge over the River Witham at Brayford Pool on its way to collect an excavator from the works. Coming from the west the driver has chosen this route in preference or the complexity of ancient gateways and steep hills that fed traffic into Lincoln's one main High Street. It is a depressing thought that having solved this problem he has yet another difficult hump-backed bridge to clear before reaching the straight run of the Rope Walk to the works. What's the betting that he chooses the complicated and busy High Street for his heavily laden return journey?

Here are two photographs of a 71-RB Dragline base machine equipped with extra long mounting and wide 46" crawler links on Wynn's transport leaving the Excavator Works en route to the customer. The practice of carrying the complete 71-RB like this represented the largest load to be transported on a regular basis from the Excavator Works. From these pictures it is easy to see why transportation of the 71-RB was notoriously prone to 'grounding' on the narrow hump-backed bridge at the end of the Rope Walk leading from the works. The height of the load also caused problems and it was the practice when considered necessary to remove the raised roof portion of the operator's cab before transportation. On one occasion when this was not done, a new 71-RB on low-loader bound for the British Gypsum quarries at Newark became stuck under the railway bridge over Lincoln's High Street. Field Engineer Ken Spur was dispatched from the works and, once the machine had been backed up, he removed the operator's roof to clear the bridge.

In April 1968, two 30-RB diesel cranes (Machine Nos 32548 and 32549) fitted with high vision cabs and equipped with 6YDAXN engines were delivered to the Slag Reduction Company, London. One of them is seen in these two photographs loaded onto a Wynn's transporter ready for departure from the Excavator Works. The extra height of the fixed high-vision cab here does not pose a problem for transportation, but for RB cranes fitted with the even higher elevated cabs such as those supplied as dock cranes, the operator's cab is designed as a completely separate unit that can be pivoted down for transportation.

Pickfords

Pickfords is the firm with the longest unbroken connection with road haulage, going back to the pack horse days of the 17th Century. With the coming of the canals, Pickfords established a regular service of canal boats in addition to its road wagons and as the railways gained ascendancy, rather than seeing them as enemies, found ways of combining their own interests with those of the Railway companies. In the 1840s Pickfords developed the use of steam traction engines for road haulage and steam navvies were among the loads towed along the roads by this means.

Throughout the early part of the 20th Century the company expanded its operations and diversified into different areas of goods transportation, until in 1934 Pickfords was bought out by the four main railway companies as the major part of the Hayes Wharf Cartage Company.

By the mid 1940s Pickfords had grown into a vast organisation employing 7,800 staff in their 170 depots and 250 warehouses around the country. It was from one of these depots located on Lincoln's Rope Walk, a stone's throw from the Excavator Works, that the company provided a variety of heavy haulage vehicles for the transportation of Lincoln's Excavators. Initially, Pickfords had a small office on Lincoln's High Street with Mr. Crawford its Manager, but as the business with the Excavator Works and the Boiler Works increased the office was moved to the Rope Walk depot.

Like many other haulage companies, Pickfords was nationalised in 1947 and in 1953 became part of the publicly owned British Road Services, (B.R.S.), who had their own depot on Monks Road in Lincoln. The two sides of the business in Lincoln continued to operate individually from their respective depots, with the Pickfords branch now known as B.R.S. (Pickfords) Ltd.

The first of a batch of six 54-RBs en route to Ireland departs the Excavator Works on Pickfords transport.

Opposite and following page: In 1961, six 54-RB Draglines (Mc. Nos. 25324 to 25329) were ordered by the Office of Public Works of the Republic of Ireland for work on the main arterial drainage scheme on the River Inny, a tributary of the Shannon. Shipped as complete machines (less their 70' boom and 2½ cu.yd. bucket), these were the largest RB machines to be shipped to Ireland without major dismantling. The photographs on the following two pages show the first of this batch of six 54-RBs being loaded on to the ship bound for Ireland.

The first 54-RB arrives
at the dock.

Loading the 54-RB onto the ship.

The 110-RB was one of the larger Ruston-Bucyrus Mining Shovels and required three or four separate loads to deliver the complete machine - the complete base machine in one load, cab in another, and two more loads for the front end equipment of boom, dipper handle and dipper. In these two photographs the cab of a 110-RB is about to leave the Excavator Works on Pickfords transport. This relatively light but bulky load had a width over the cab (as here with stairways and platforms removed) of 18 feet and it is being transported on a Scammell tractor unit with knock out back axle. Fitted with 'motorcycle' type mudguards, this type of tractor with its own ballast box is referred to as a 'Locomotive' since there is no pay-load on the tractor. The B.R.S. 'Lion' logo on the vehicle indicates that this photograph was taken when Pickfords was a nationalised part of British Road Services.

Hallett Silbermann Ltd.

Hallett Silbermann are a company prepared for a wide range of transportation projects but it is with Heavy Haulage that the company was first formed and for which it is best known. It had the capability of moving loads up to 80 tons, either with its own fleet or with owner-drivers working on exclusive contract to the company with vehicles liveried in Hallett Silbermann colours.

The company had its roots in the clearing house business which John Silbermann formed in September 1946 under the trading name of Peterson Ltd. John had a background in heavy haulage, first during the Second World War as an apprentice straight from school with C.E.A.C. Howard in Bedfordshire who ran ERF 20-tonners, and from there to Coupar Transport of Acton whose business was mainly clearing house with the use of heavy haulage vehicles.

From this experience, John Silbermann decided to set up his own business, choosing for it the name Peterson for no reason other than he felt it would be more easily remembered by operators and customers than his own. The first office premises were in East Finchley and among the owner-drivers engaged by the Peterson company was Tom Hallett, a man who had been in haulage since finishing soldiering in the First World War.

By 1951 Peterson's business with the clearing house traffic was booming, prompting an office move to Cricklewood, and it was at this time that Tom Hallett, wishing to retire, offered to sell to John his sole vehicle, a bonneted Dodge low-loader together with its all-important open 'A' Carriers licence. To process the sale, a limited company of T. Hallett Ltd. was set up with the Dodge and its licence the sole assets and in 1953 Silbermann purchased the company.

By 1958, the combined fleets of T. Hallett Ltd. and John Silbermann Ltd. operating from their depot off the North Circular Road, London, had grown to around ten vehicles. Silbermann, in addition to his heavy haulage and clearing house business, moved into the plant hire business in the London area under the name Metroplant Ltd. and in the ensuing years continued to expand his heavy-haulage activities by the acquisition of other well-known companies.

In 1963 the two halves of the company were joined to form Hallett Silbermann Ltd. which has its main base at Hatfield, with depots in Rotherham, Birmingham, Leicester, and on the Continent.

Above and opposite page: A 38-RB Base machine on Hallett Silbermann transport photographed in May 1963 about to depart the Excavator Works. This is a standard Series Two machine and offers a maximum load width of 10' 4" (width of cab less run boards). The total weight of the 38-RB Series Two base machine was 41$^{1}/_{4}$ tons.

Excavators for Sweden

Over the years a large number of Ruston-Bucyrus excavators were shipped for export and Sweden was traditionally a valuable export market for the Lincoln firm. In December 1958 a large order for a batch of excavators worth £112,000 was received from RB's Swedish distributors Tornborg and Lundberg. The order comprised four 30-RB shovels, four 22-RB shovels, four 22-RB dragshovels and one 19-RB dragshovel.

Prompt delivery of the order was promised by the Lincoln firm, with a loading date of 1st and 2nd of January, 1959. The machines were to be transported to Hull Docks by road, with different carriers involved, and the thirteen excavators shipped as one load in the MS. Skagern; John Good and Sons Ltd. of Hull were the loading brokers.

Here was a case of careful planning and co-ord-ination required by all participants, made more complicated by the fact that on this occasion the loading procedure at the docks involved two stages with a secondary transfer of the shipment by pontoon in separate loads from the quayside to the ship.

The consignment of excavators was first divided into batches and each batch in turn was loaded from the quay onto a pontoon crane and towed by tug to the waiting MS. Skagern where it was loaded into the ship by the floating crane. Marshalling the individual loads into place at each stage of this loading procedure was a time consuming operation, but one which must have been familiar to those concerned, for delivery of the smaller RB excavators abroad was invariably made in batches of several machines at a time. In 1959 / 1960 alone, twenty 19-RBs, one hundred and twelve 22-RBs, and thirty-two 30-RBs were purchased and shipped to Sweden through RB distributor Tornborg and Lundberg.

Above: The different carriers with their excavator loads have arrived at Hull Docks ready for shipment to Sweden.

Opposite: In this photograph the first batch of six excavators to make the journey to the waiting ship has been assembled on the quayside ready for lifting onto the pontoon crane.

Above: Loading the pontoon for transfer to the waiting ship begins as more excavators arrive on the docks.

Opposite: The pontoon crane with its first load of excavators is towed to the MS. Skagern and loaded onto the ship.

George Wimpey

Some of the larger customers for Ruston-Bucyrus excavators had their own transport, and one of the largest of these was George Wimpey. Over the years many Ruston-Bucyrus machines had been supplied to the different divisions of the Wimpey company and their distinctive all-green livery was a familiar sight to the Lincoln public as they were driven away through the city roads on Wimpey's equally distinctive transport.

The two photographs detailed below show a new 22-RB I.C.D. Crane loaded onto Wimpey's low-loader hauled by a company Scammell Constructor ready to leave the Excavator Works and join that company's massive fleet of RB machines which included almost every model the Lincoln firm produced from 22-RBs to 195-RB mining shovels.

This Wimpey transporter with its load of a complete 110-RB base machine collected from the Excavator Works has just negotiated the sharp turn from St. Marks into Lincoln's High Street under the watchful eye of a policeman. The year is 1956, before this busy junction had traffic lights and the traffic was directed by a policeman in the centre.

'A Bridge Too Far'

The last possible hazard for vehicles travelling south with excavator loads out of Lincoln was the steel railway bridge spanning the southern section of the High Street. Now gone, together with the thunder of trains and the lines that carried them, this bridge during Ruston-Bucyrus days provided not only useful advertising space but a few brief moments of concern for any driver of a high vehicle who had not 'done his homework'.

Such was the case with the driver of a low-loader carrying a secondhand 52-RB through Lincoln some time in the 1960s; former owners, the Ore Mining Branch of British Steel at Scunthorpe, had just had the elderly machine overhauled but had decided after all that they didn't require it and it was sold to the British Gypsum company of Newark.

The day came for the machine to be delivered to its new home which in those days meant going through Lincoln and now the 52-RB on its transport was halted halfway through its journey at the railway bridge on Lincoln's High Street with a concerned driver and mate wondering whether they dare risk passing under it with their high load to continue their journey south to the Newark Gypsum Quarries. Putting caution before valour, the driver contacted Ruston-Bucyrus who dispatched a man to assess the situation, resulting in the drastic decision to dismantle the upper parts of the 52-RB to reduce the height as it stood on the transport, then re-assemble it once through the bridge.

A crane was ordered to carry out the lifting, the police were informed, and the busy southbound carriageway through the bridge was closed to traffic. With much disruption to the traffic the 52-RB was stripped of its roof, 'A' frame, and other major components, and several hours passed before it was declared safe for the load to pass under the bridge, and several more before the machine was re-assembled ready to continue its journey.

Just who had the idea to check the head room as the partly dismantled 52-RB went through the bridge and compare it with the height of the fully re-assembled load is not recorded, but it is unlikely he would have been thanked when it was pointed out to an embarrassed driver and exhausted work party the simple fact that the original 52-RB load would have passed under the bridge with several inches to spare.

The same High Street railway bridge as featured above, but this Eastern Roadways
International Volvo powered low-loader with its cargo of a Drum Assembly Unit for
a new Ruston-Bucyrus 380-W Walking Dragline does not appear to have any
problems as it passes through on its way to the customer in 1980.

LINCOLN'S EXCAVATORS

TWO NEW PRODUCTS

Ruston-Bucyrus stand at the International Building Exhibition, Olympia, London in November 1963

TWO NEW PRODUCTS

y 1960 and the creation of the European Common Market there was growing concern on the part of the Ruston-Bucyrus management that their range of excavators did not fully meet the needs of their domestic and european markets and it was felt that from a history of continuous growth and profitability, business was now standing still. Among the measures taken as a consequence of this concern was the Lincoln company's decision to enter the Tower Crane business, produce their own hydraulic excavator and enter the large machine market. This decision was made and the course embarked upon with the agreement and approval of Mr. Allen, Chairman of Ruston-Bucyrus and President of Bucyrus-Erie Co.

For some years tractor-mounted excavators and front-end loaders fitted with hydraulic digging attachments produced by companies abroad and in the U.K. had formed serious competition for the smaller Ruston-Bucyrus excavators. Since the Lincoln company had been producing tractor equipment for a number of years, the logical solution would seem to be the development of tractor based hydraulic front - end excavator equipments alongside their existing range of tractor equipments. However, customer research indicated that what was needed to meet the demands of their domestic and overseas markets was a crawler-mounted hydraulic excavator equivalent to the size of their 10-RB. To this end, a design team was set up in the Ruston-Bucyrus Engineering Department with instructions to design such a machine to the specifications laid down by the company's Products Planning Committee. The result was the prototype 2-RB which led in turn to the first Ruston-Bucyrus hydraulic excavator, the 3-RB.

The Lincoln company's decision to enter the Tower Crane market was founded upon the need for greater mechanisation of the construction industry, for at this time over eight per cent of Britain's total labour force was engaged on construction work. Building contractors at home and abroad sought to keep down operating costs by the greater use of specialised lifting equipment and Ruston-Bucyrus recognised a growing market for mobile, crawler-mounted independently powered Tower Cranes.

This expansion by Ruston-Bucyrus of their product range had been made possible by a carefully planned increase in their manufacturing resources at the Excavator Works over the preceding years; new machine tools of the latest design and type had been installed involving investment of considerable capital. In addition there had been a great deal of re-organisation in the works to facilitate more efficient production of all types and sizes of machines.

The new 3-RB Hydraulic Excavator and 12/60 Tower Crane are introduced to the public at
the International Building Exhibition, Olympia, in November 1963.

A New Chairman for Ruston-Bucyrus Ltd.

In December 1962, Robert Allen, Chairman of Ruston-Bucyrus Ltd. and President of Bucyrus Erie Co. retired from active business duties, his successor in both those offices was Eugene Berg who had joined the American company as Executive Vice President in 1960. Berg was elected to the Bucyrus Erie Co. Board of Directors in the year of his arrival, and to the B.E. Executive Committee in 1961.

For twenty-three years before joining B.E., Berg had been with Link-Belt excavator manufacturers as General Manager of their Chicago operations and such was his dynamism and force of personality that his presence was soon felt within the Bucyrus-Erie organisation. In September 1963 Berg was elected Chairman of Bucyrus-Erie in addition to his Chairmanship of Ruston-Bucyrus, while retaining his position as President and Chief Executive Officer of Bucyrus Erie Co. The fact that all these offices were held by one person meant in effect that his individual powers as titular head of the organisation extended through the Executive to a greater involvement in the direct management of the company.

Berg's appointment as Chairman of Ruston-Bucyrus was welcomed by the Lincoln management, but it soon became apparent that the new Chairman saw the relationship between Ruston-Bucyrus and Bucyrus-Erie, in different terms to that of his predecessor, W. Coleman.

Coleman, President of B.E. and founder Chairman of Ruston-Bucyrus Ltd. had been instrumental in the creation of the Lincoln company, supported its independent status, and recognised that its value to its two parent companies, Ruston & Hornsby Ltd. and Bucyrus Erie Co., lay in its own ability to meet the demands of its own markets, which were not necessarily the same as those of the American parent. However, Berg saw Ruston-Bucyrus less as an independent company in its own right and more in terms of a manufacturing branch of the Bucyrus Erie Co., and he was in a position of influence to make his views felt. Ruston-Bucyrus saw this as a constraint upon their own development and the repercussions of this conflict of views was a determining factor in the Lincoln company's future.

A Break with Tradition

On the 7th. July, 1964, for the first time in the history of Ruston-Bucyrus, the Excavator Works was chosen as a venue for an executive committee meeting of the Bucyrus Erie Company. A surprise to both Ruston-Bucyrus and their English parent company, Ruston & Hornsby Ltd., this action might be interpreted as a reflection of Eugene Berg's wish for a closer relationship between B.E. and RB.

Executive Committee of Bucyrus-Erie Co. on the occasion of their meeting at the Excavator Works, July 1964. Pictured in the boardroom left to right; S.M. Fleming (director), J.A. Thierry (vice-president, secretary & treasurer), E.P. Berg (chairman, president and chief executive officer), P. Ryan (director), L.S. Clemons (director), E.S. Everett (director). On the wall is a photograph of W. Coleman, founder chairman of Ruston-Bucyrus Ltd.

A New Chairman's Concerns

Letter - Mr. Berg to Mr. Everitt - 9th. Sept. 1964

Development of the Ruston-Bucyrus hydraulic excavator and crawler mounted Tower Crane were well under way when Eugene Berg, now settled in as President of Bucyrus-Erie and Chairman of Ruston-Bucyrus, wrote a letter in September 1964 to Mr. Everitt, RB's Managing Director, expressing his displeasure at the initiative taken by the Lincoln company in entering into the manufacture of hydraulic excavators and tower cranes, and with their plans to produce their own range of large excavators.

Letter - Mr. Everitt to Mr. Berg - 24th. Sept. 1964

In reply, Mr. Everitt wrote to Mr. Berg on 24th. Sept. 1964 explaining the basis of his company's moves; he describes his concern that a majority of RB's production range was based upon B.E. designs which were at best pre-war and in some cases older than that, and that he attributes this state of affairs to
> "a lack of design and development in recent years by Bucyrus-Erie in the range of products suitable to RB and its markets."

Everitt's letter draws attention to the fact that there would have been no 10-RB nor 30-RB but for RB's insistence and sustained campaign by Savage and himself to convince B.E. of their need and goes on to suggest that the root of this problem for the Lincoln company was its historic dependency upon B.E. for the bulk of its design and development.
> "This arrangement", says Everett, "worked well and to RB's advantage throughout the early years but the conditions are now different and in this more highly competitive world, identifying and meeting ones particular market requirements is essential."

In reference to hydraulic excavators, Everitt continues;
> "Despite the strongest representations, we made no progress with Bucyrus Erie in the development of hydraulic excavators the need for which was there for all to see and since proved by their production in numbers by competitors which must amount to thousands a year, and all the time biting increasingly into our small machine market." ......
> "We were faced with the prospect of being overtaken by competitors both in the hydraulic and conventional excavator field unless we did something for ourselves. Hence a start in hydraulics with the 3-RB, with Tower Cranes, and an urge to get into production with large machines." ......

> "It must be born in mind that as a result of the engineering policy between our two companies we really had neither the staff nor the experience in hydraulics so we had to recruit and feel our way. We have done this with what we consider to be the minimum expenditure and perhaps too much so by using existing components such as 10-RB tracks rather than developing a complete new machine."

In his letter Everitt also described his own feelings at what he felt was undue intervention on the part of the American parent company. The following extracts are an indication of the deteriorating relationship between the RB management and B.E. Co. at this time;
> "I know that it is the last thing that you would wish or intend, but your unbounded interest in Ruston-Bucyrus is having an unfortunate side effect. The morale of our Executive Directors at least is not what I would wish nor what it has always been until recently" ......
> "I am sure it is not your intention and that you will find it difficult to believe, but another result of your increasing interest in us is the impression that we are considered to be a branch, or division, of Bucyrus-Erie Co. with myself as General Manager and my colleagues as Departmental Heads instead of an associated Company with equal financial responsibility to Ruston & Hornsby Ltd." ......
> "A number of things contribute to this feeling, not least the fact that it is your intention that Bucyrus-Erie should take a substantial share in the equity of any joint venture manufacturing agreements in our territory, so far without reference to Ruston & Hornsby, despite the fact that they have a 50% interest in us and that by formal agreement you are barred from manufacturing in our territory."

Despite this lack of accord between Ruston-Bucyrus Ltd. and Bucyrus Erie Co. it was business as usual at the Lincoln Excavator Works with the main production lines of excavators, to which was now added the new line of Tower Cranes and the company's first all-hydraulic excavator. In his Christmas address, Everitt was able to say
> "1964 has been a record year in the company's thirty-four year history - in terms of turnover, tonnage, and monetary profitability."

LINCOLN'S EXCAVATORS

TOWER CRANES

Ruston-Bucyrus 12/60 Tower Crane

TOWER CRANES

The Lincoln company's decision to enter the Tower Crane market was founded upon the need for greater mechanisation of the construction industry, for at this time over eight per cent of Britain's total labour force was engaged on construction work. Building contractors at home and abroad sought to keep down operating costs by the greater use of specialised lifting equipment.

Ruston-Bucyrus recognised a growing market for mobile, crawler-mounted independently powered Tower Cranes but their first move towards production of Tower Cranes was an agreement with Abelson & Co. Ltd. of Birmingham in late 1959 to manufacture Buildmaster rail-mounted tower cranes under licence for Abelson who would be the sole sellers of these machines in the U.K. and British Commonwealth. However, these machines were not the basis upon which RB would develop their own crawler mounted tower cranes and between 1960 and 1964 only twelve of these Buildmaster 50Rs were built at the Excavator Works.

Following the decision to develop and build their own tower cranes, the Lincoln company's first move was to enter into an agreement in February 1963 with Star Cranes Ltd. involving certain manu-facturing and selling arrangements whereby the Lincoln company would buy in the Star model 12/60 Tower Crane and adapt it in their factory for mounting on a 10-RB crawler base. Before the year was out, however, it was officially announced by Ruston-Bucyrus that,

"as a logical development of the arrangements entered into in February 1963, we have now acquired financial control of Star Cranes Ltd."

Ruston-Bucyrus began building their own 12/60 Tower Cranes and a number of these models were produced before it was replaced on the Lincoln production line in March 1965 by the first Ruston-Bucyrus designed Tower Crane, the 12/52. In 1967, the larger Ruston-Bucyrus designed 34/80 Tower Crane was added to the production line and from that time on both the 12/52 and 34/80 Tower Cranes were available from the rapidly expanding range of company products.

A total of 68 Ruston-Bucyrus Tower Cranes were built, from the first 12/60 - Mc.No.27886 - supplied to the customer on 3rd. May 1963, until production ceased with the last 34/80 Tower Crane - Mc.No.32799 - delivered to Taylor Woodrow International in November 1972.

Ruston-Bucyrus 12/60 Tower Crane ready on site erected to its minimum working height.

Ruston-Bucyrus 12/60 Tower Crane with 40ft. basic tower at its maximum height on
test at the Excavator Works.

The 12/60 tower crane working heights were as follows;

Minimum working height (tower retracted)..29'-1½" (beneath hook)
Working height with tower extended (basic 40' inner extension)........................37'-10" (..   )
    (Note; erected crane could be moved on its crawlers with tower at minimum working height)
5' sections were available to increase the basic inner tower as follows;
Adding one 5' section...43'-9" (beneath hook)
Up to seven further sections could be added giving heights in 5' increments
    to a maximum..78'-9" (..   )

12/60 Tower Crane safe working loads;

Radius 33ft..........load 2688 lb.   Radius 36ft..........load 2352 lb.   Radius 41ft..........load 2016 lb.
Radius 48ft..........load 1680 lb.   Radius 58'-3"......load 1344 lb.

Above: 12/60 Tower Crane base frame less the crawlers in the factory.

12/60 T.C. control panel and wandering lead.

12/60 T.C. drive motor and chain driven steering controls.

Ruston-Bucyrus 12/60 Tower Crane in road travelling condition.
(This photograph shows an inherent weakness in the design
of 12/60 transporting arrangement from the fact that though
there was very little load at the point of attachment to the towing
vehicle, there was considerable loading on the rear
bogey structure.)

Road towing dimensions;

Width overall	9'-6"
Length, approx	45'-0"
Height, approx	15'-9"
Length of crane only	39'-0"

The Ruston-Bucyrus 12/60 Tower Crane was powered by a Ruston air-cooled 2YWA diesel engine driving a fully compensated, self-exciting, self-regulating type alternator rated to give an output of 15kVat 1500 r.p.m. All operations of the crane were controlled from a 30ft. remote 'Wanderlead' with push buttons. During operation the crane was protected by standard overload safety devices with additional visible and audible warning devices.

Articulated onto a suitable towing vehicle, the crane was travelled along the road on its own road wheels. The erection of the 12/60 required no alteration to the reeving from its road travelling condition and it was said that the crane could be operational within two hours of its arrival at the site.

On arrival at the site, the diesel engine is started and the hydraulic outriggers lowered to the ground, the road wheels are then removed and the towing frame released. Rotation of the electrically powered universal erection screw brings the tower to the vertical position and it is secured by bolting to the base frame. The counterweight jib, already fixed in position, was then raised by using the same universal screw gear and pulling rope and then secured at the head. The main jib can now be raised, first to 45° and then to the horizontal position and after it is secured at the head the crane is ready for operation.

Above and right: 12/60 Tower Crane in Coventry. Two photographs of a 12/60 Tower Crane owned by the Coventry Corporation working in Coventry in October 1963. The machine, Serial No. 27890, came off the Lincoln production line in July 1963 and is seen here on its first application. The 12/60 Tower Crane was specifically designed to meet the needs of builders, where mobility on site and between different sites was important. Movement and erection costs were virtually nil, making it possible for the crane to be used on a particular site for a few hours only and on two or three sites in as many days. Said the RB Sales material, "Standing time is eliminated and the crane will show appreciable savings in cost when used on semi-detached housing, 5-storey flats, schools, hospitals, etc."

Above & left: 12/60 Tower Crane in Taunton. The photographs on this page taken in September 1964 show a Ruston-Bucyrus 12/60 Tower Crane, Mc.No.28240, at work on a construction site in the Taunton area. The machine was delivered to contractors Hill & Lang in the summer of that year and this building project was the 12/60's first proper job. On a congested site like this, with restricted working space, the choice of an expensive crawler-mounted tower crane like the 12/60 over a cheaper lorry-mounted tower crane is justified, for the latter would have occupied a lot of ground while wasting its biggest single asset, mobility. The other alternative of a simple crawler-mounted lifting crane would have required the added cost and inconvenience of special road transport.

The 12/52 and 34/80 Tower Cranes

After the 12/60, Tower Crane manufacture at the Excavator Works settled into the parallel production of small batches at a time of the RB designed 12/52 and 34/80 models. Crawler mounted and self-propelled with the ability to travel on site fully erected, these Tower Cranes could operate on sites where lack of space and rough ground conditions made it impossible for truck-mounted mobile cranes to operate. Speed of erection and dismantling and the easy attachment of towing wheels provided mobility of movement for the fully folded machine between sites and on site the crawler mounting with the addition of outrigger jacks provided the stability for maximum crane performance.

Loads could be lifted with the jib horizontal or set at the inclined position when loads could be travelled up and down the inclined jib giving increased height of lift at increased radii when desired. Once the master settings are made at the machine's main control panel, both the erection of the machine and the crane functions can be operated by remote control using the push-button 'Wanderlead'.

Basic Design

The 12/52 and 34/80 Tower Cranes designed by Ruston-Bucyrus were similarly comprised of three main units;
1. Base Unit; this is the mobile base or foundation upon which the platform rotates and it comprises the crawler sub-assembly, side frames, road wheels and axles, and outriggers.
2. Platform and Platform Machinery; consisting of the slewing platform assembly, which carries the tower and much of the main machinery and the ballast-box counterweights.
3. Tower and Tower Machinery; comprising inner and outer tower, a pivoting and folding jib with its associated supporting 'A' frame, suspension tie bar, together with all ropes, pulleys and locking devices on the towers and jib. Also included with the tower machinery are assemblies attached to the jib including trolley, trolley motor and gear box. (The 12/60 and the larger 34/80 were built in their entirety at the Excavator Works, but contrary to RB's usual practice, fabrication of the 12/52's tower and jib structures was 'farmed out' to French tower crane manufacturer Pignon.)

The 12/52 Tower Crane was on display for the first time on the Ruston-Bucyrus stand at the I.C.E.E. Exhibition, Olympia, London, 17th November - 1st December 1965.

Above & below: These two photographs are of the 12/52 Tower Crane on final tests at the Excavator Works prior to its appearance at the I.C.E.E. Show at Olympia. The upper photo shows the machine in the process of erecting its tower and in the lower photo the crane tower is in its minimum erected operating position with the jib horizontal, giving a height under the hook of 36' and an operating radius of 52'-6".

Above & below: A Matador A.E.C. towing unit for the 12/52 Tower Crane is waiting at the Excavator Works; the Tower Crane was classed as Engineering Plant and came under the regulation governing the speed limit to 12 mph. Brakes were not required on the crane provided that the hauling vehicle carried scotches to place behind the crane wheels when at rest (though the 12/52 was fitted with brakes). The width of the 12/52 was such that the regulations required the towing vehicle to have one attendant in addition to the driver.

Above: Fitting road wheels to the 12/52 Tower Crane at the Excavator Works.

Below: Dimensions for the 12/52 Tower Crane in road towing condition.

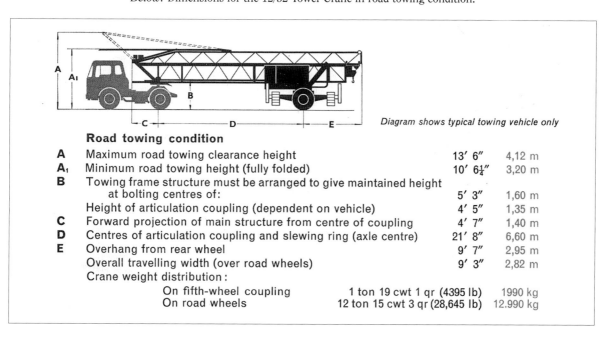

Diagram shows typical towing vehicle only

Road towing condition

A	Maximum road towing clearance height	13′ 6″	4,12 m
A₁	Minimum road towing height (fully folded)	10′ 6¼″	3,20 m
B	Towing frame structure must be arranged to give maintained height at bolting centres of:	5′ 3″	1,60 m
	Height of articulation coupling (dependent on vehicle)	4′ 5″	1,35 m
C	Forward projection of main structure from centre of coupling	4′ 7″	1,40 m
D	Centres of articulation coupling and slewing ring (axle centre)	21′ 8″	6,60 m
E	Overhang from rear wheel	9′ 7″	2,95 m
	Overall travelling width (over road wheels)	9′ 3″	2,82 m

Crane weight distribution:

On fifth-wheel coupling	1 ton 19 cwt 1 qr (4395 lb)	1990 kg
On road wheels	12 ton 15 cwt 3 qr (28,645 lb)	12.990 kg

This 12/52 Tower Crane is working on a building site in Sussex with its tower at its maximum height and jib inclined; this set up gives a maximum height under the hook of 77ft. and a maximum operating radius of 46ft. The advantage of the machine's remote control is apparent as the operator using the 'Wanderlead' has been able position himself close to the work.

Max. lifting capacity (Jib horizontal) 3360lb up to 22ft. radius; 2688lb up to 28ft. radius; 2240lb up to 33ft. radius; 1680lb up to 43ft. radius; 1344lb up to 52ft. radius. (Jib inclined) 1344lb at all radii to 46ft.

Above: 12/52 Tower Crane (Mc.No.29606) pouring concrete on a building site for Rowlinson Construction Ltd., Kings Lynn. The machine was delivered to this customer on 8th June 1965.

Below: 12/52 Tower Crane (Mc.No.29602) was the second 12/52 to come off the Lincoln production line and it was delivered to customer Gazeway Plant Hire Ltd. on 11th March 1965. It is seen here working on the site of a new University in Norwich.

12/52 Operating Machinery

Power for the 12/52 Tower Crane is supplied by a Ruston air-cooled 2YWA diesel engine driving an alternator giving an output of 12.5 KVA at 1500 r.p.m. This provides the electric supply for the separate motors which operate the different functions on the machine. These are;

1. Propel Motors and Gearboxes - There are two propel motors, each driving, through a reduction gearbox, the left hand and right hand crawler tracks. A drive sprocket on the end of the extension shaft from the gearbox of each motor is connected by chain drive to the drive tumblers in the right and left hand crawler assemblies.

2. Slew/Erection Motor and Gearbox - This has the dual function of slewing the platform and operating the 'raising' motion of the Tower. A three-position selector lever can be set to;

(a) 'Slew' - this engages a pinion with the swing gear for slewing the platform to right or left.

(b) 'Neutral' - the pinion is out of engagement with both the slewing gear and the erection gear.

(c) 'Erection' - the pinion engages with a gear on the erection rope drum below the platform.

3. Hoist Motor and Gearbox - This two-speed motor with a built in safety brake drives the hoist drum located at the foot of the tower through a train of gears. The crane's hoisting speed is controlled by varying the speed of the motor using the remote control 'Wanderlead'.

4. Trolley Motor and Gearbox - This totally enclosed motor and gearbox drives the trolley rope by which the trolley is propelled along channels on the Jib. This trolley rope is reeved to include a trolley rope spring-loaded tensioning device.

(Note; It will be seen that the erection of the crane and the crane operations are all rope-drum operated manoeuvres.)

Above: 12/52 Tower Crane (Mc. No.29605) here working on a building site was the first 12/52 to leave the Ruston-Bucyrus production line. It was delivered to customer W. Kendrick & Sons Ltd., Walsall on the 10th March 1965.

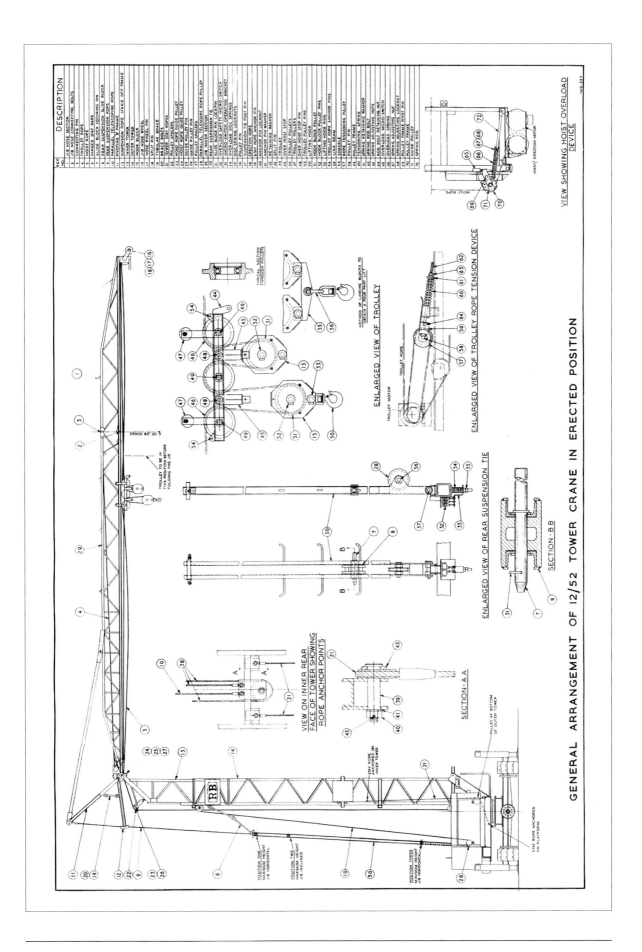

REF NO.	DESCRIPTION
1	JIB NOSE SECTION
2	JIB NOSE CONNECTING BOLTS
3	CONNECTING PIN
4	TROLLEY ROPE
5	HOIST ROPE
6	HINGED STAY BARS
7	SLIDE BLOCK SECURING PIN
8	REAR SUSPENSION SLIDE BLOCK
9	LIFTING SUSPENSION ROPE
10	PARALLEL TELESCOPING ROPE
11	PIVOTING X FRAME
12	SUSPENSION ROPE STAND OFF FRAME
13	INNER TOWER
14	OUTER TOWER
15	HOOK BLOCK
16	JIB NOSE WHEEL
17	HOSE WHEEL PIN
18	SPLIT PIN
19	TUBULAR BRACE
20	BRACE BOLTS
21	TOWER STAY ROPES
22	PULLEY SPACERS
23	HOIST ROPE GUIDE PULLEY
24	HOIST ROPE GUIDE PULLEY
25	GUIDE PULLEY PIN
26	GUIDE PULLEY PIN
27	PULLEY SPACERS
28	PARALLEL TELESCOPE ROPE PULLEY
29	JIB INNER SECTION
30	REAR SUSPENSION TIE
31	SLIDE BLOCK PIN LOCKPIN
32	OVERLOAD SAFETY MICRO-SWITCH
33	MICRO-SWITCH OPERATING BRACKET
34	OVERLOAD DISC SPRINGS
35	DISC SPRING LOCKNUTS
36	PULLEY PIN
37	SUSPENSION TIE FOOT PIN
38	ERECTION ROPE
39	STAY ROPE ANCHOR PIN
40	ANCHOR PIN LOCKNUT
41	ANCHOR PIN WASHER
42	RETAINING WASHER
43	SPLIT PIN
44	TROLLEY
45	OVER HOIST STOP
46	TROLLEY POLLEYS
47	TROLLEY POLLEYS
48	OVER HOIST STOP PIN
49	TROLLEY PULLEY PINS
50	HOOK BLOCK PULLEY
51	HOOK BLOCK PULLEY PINS
52	LIFTING HOOK PINS
53	LIFTING HOOK
54	TROLLEY ROPE ANCHOR PINS
55	LINK BEAM
56	SHACKLE
57	ROPE TENSIONING PULLEY
58	PULLEY PIN
59	PULLEY FRAME
60	TENSIONING SPRING
61	SPRING RETAINING WASHER
62	SPRING ROD BOLT
63	SPRING ADJUSTING NUTS
64	ROD BOLT RETAINING NUT
65	OVERLOAD MICRO-SWITCH
66	OVERLOAD SPRING
67	SPRING ADJUSTING NUT
68	SPRING ADJUSTING LOCKNUT
69	PULLEY FRAME PIVOT PIN
70	PULLEY FRAME
71	GUIDE PULLEY
72	SPRING ROD

DWD-557

VIEW SHOWING HOIST OVERLOAD DEVICE

HOIST/ERECTION MOTOR

TYPICAL SECTION THROUGH PULLEYS

METHOD OF LINKING BLOCKS TO OBTAIN A FOUR PART LIFT

ENLARGED VIEW OF TROLLEY

ENLARGED VIEW OF TROLLEY ROPE TENSION DEVICE

TROLLEY MOTOR

TROLLEY ROPE

ENLARGED VIEW OF REAR SUSPENSION TIE

SECTION-B.B

TROLLEY TO BE IN THIS POSITION BEFORE FOLDING THE JIB

€ OF JIB HINGE

VIEW ON INNER REAR FACE OF TOWER SHOWING ROPE ANCHOR POINTS

SECTION-A.A

PULLEY AT BOTTOM OF OUTER TOWER

STAY ROPE ANCHORED ON INNER TOWER

STAY ROPE ANCHORED ON PLATFORM

RB

POSITION ONE MAXIMUM HEIGHT JIB HORIZONTAL

POSITION TWO MAXIMUM HEIGHT JIB INCLINED

POSITION THREE MINIMUM HEIGHT JIB HORIZONTAL

GENERAL ARRANGEMENT OF 12/52 TOWER CRANE IN ERECTED POSITION

247

Ruston-Bucyrus 12/52 Tower Crane on demonstration at Exeter, April 1965.

34/80 Tower Crane

In 1966, Ruston-Bucyrus introduced the 34/80 Tower Crane; similar in basic design to the 12/52, it was a much bigger machine, in both physical terms and in its crane performance. Equipped with the more powerful Ruston 3YDA Mk.II air cooled engine driving an alternator and hydraulic pump, the following comparisons show the relative size of the two machines.

	12/52	34/80
Crawler track centres	8'- 6"	11' 4"
Overall width over jack feet	12'-3"	18'-4"
Stability outrigger base	11' x 11'	15'-8" x 12'-10"
Bearing area of tracks	18 sq.ft.	18 sq.ft.
Crawler link width	14"	26"
Total working weight	14¾ tons	42 tons

The basic machinery and operation of these two Tower Cranes were similar with the most significant difference being the incorporation on the 34/80 of a hydraulic operating system for tower erection (twin telescopic rams); load hoist and tower telescoping; crawler drive; and the stability jacks. The alternator provided power for the electric motors to operate slewing and trolley on the 34/80 and all the crane function controls, both hydraulic and electrical, were grouped on a portable operator's station linked by a 45ft. 'Wanderlead'.

Propel and steering hydraulic controls were grouped on the revolving superstructure and the hydraulic stability jacks were individually controlled from control valves located in the crawler frame.

Demonstration at the Excavator Works on the 16th December 1966, of the first Ruston-Bucyrus 34/80 Tower Crane. The group of spectators comprised works engineering staff and invited guests, including potential customers.
The designation of the titles 12/60, 12/52, 34/80 for the RB Tower Cranes derived from their respective crane ratings; 12/60....12 cwt. load at 60ft. radius; 12/52.....12 cwt. load at 52ft. radius; 34/80.....34 cwt. at 80ft. radius.

Above & below: The 34/80 Tower Crane ready for transportation utilising its detachable road wheels. The crane is complete in itself being permanently ballasted, self-propelled and requiring no ancillary equipment to erect or dismantle it; once at the construction site it can be erected and fully operational within an hour.

Above: Removing road wheels from the 34/80 Tower Crane at the Excavator Works.

Below: Dimensions for the 34/80 Tower Crane with 60ft. Jib in road towing condition.

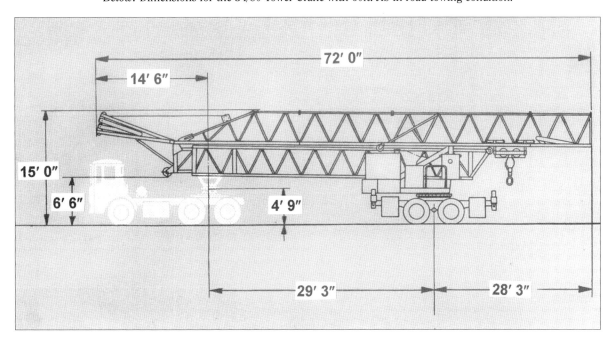

Above & below: 34/80 Tower Crane on the test ground
with jacks set and crane in its operating condition.

Above: Main Lucas pump and chain drive to the gearbox / motor unit.
Below: Hydraulic rotary distributor.

Above: Tower telescoping drum; also seen is the electric slewing motor and slewing gear.
Below: Crawler side frame and drive chain.

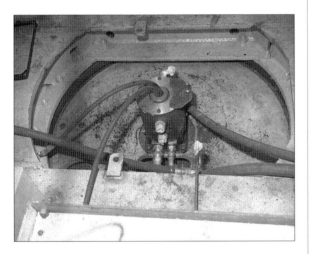

Hydraulic Rotary Distributor Crawler Side Frame and drive chain 34/80 Tower Crane Hydraulic System

The incorporation of a hydraulic system on the 34/80 Tower Crane for certain functions not only improved the operation of the machine it also provided a greater degree of safety. The engine drives the main and booster hydraulic pumps - the main pump is a Lucas variable stroke servo controlled pump and the booster pump is a Dowty hydraulic gear pump.

These supply the hydraulic power for the following operations;

(a) Tower Telescoping & Hoist Drum Machinery -
Located in a central position immediately to the rear of the tower are two winch drums (erection and hoist), which may be individually driven by the hydraulic hoist motor. The speed of the hydraulic motor is controlled by varying the stroke of the main hydraulic pump.

(b) Crawler Drive and Steering Mechanism -
Power for the crawler tracks is provided by a reversing hydraulic motor, driving through a reduction gearbox to the divided horizontal propel shaft and then by separate final chain drives to the crawler tracks. The propel shaft is divided by the right and left steering jaw clutches.

(c) Erection Rams -
A pair of hydraulic erection rams link the tower to the base structure which are supplied from the main pump via a control valve providing the 'Erection Up' or 'Erection Down' operation of the Tower.

(d) Hydraulic Jacks -
These have two functions, to jack the machine on to its crawlers for removal of the road wheels and vice versa, and to level and stabilise the crane during operation.

A 34/80 Tower Crane with 80ft. jib is seen here on final tests at the Excavator Works; the crane could be fitted with alternative jib lengths of 60ft. or 80ft. and the table below shows the ratings for the 34/80 at different operating radii.

RATINGS
Jib horizontal

Working load			Radius R₁ (60′ 0″ 18,30 m. jib)			Radius R₁ (80′ 0″ 24,38 m. jib)		
tons	cwt.	kg.	ft.	in.	m.	ft.	in.	m.
1	15	1750				80	0	24,38
2	0	2000				72	0	21,95
2	10	2500				59	9	18,21
3	0	3000	60	0	18,30	51	3	15,63
3	10	3500	52	6	16,00	45	0	13,72
4	0	4000	46	9	14,25	40	0	12,19
4	10	4500	42	3	12,88	36	3	11,05
5	0	5000	38	6	11,73	33	0	10,06
5	10	5500	35	6	10,82			
6	0	6000	33	0	10,06			

Jib inclined

Working load			Radius R₂ (60′ 0″ 18,30 m. jib)	Radius R₂ (80′ 0″ 24,38 m. jib)
tons	cwt.	kg.		
2	0	2000	to 51′ 0″ 15,54 m. radius	to 68′ 0″ 20,72 m. radius

The trolley travels along the inclined jib

HEIGHTS UNDER HOOK

			60′ 0″ 18,30 m. jib	80′ 0″ 24,38 m. jib
Jib horizontal	Tower at minimum height	H₁	39′ 0″ 11,89 m.	39′ 0″ 11,89 m.
	Tower at maximum height	H₂	70′ 0″ 21,33 m.	70′ 0″ 21,33 m.
Jib inclined	Tower at maximum height	H₃	100′ 0″ 30,48 m.	110′ 0″ 33,55 m.

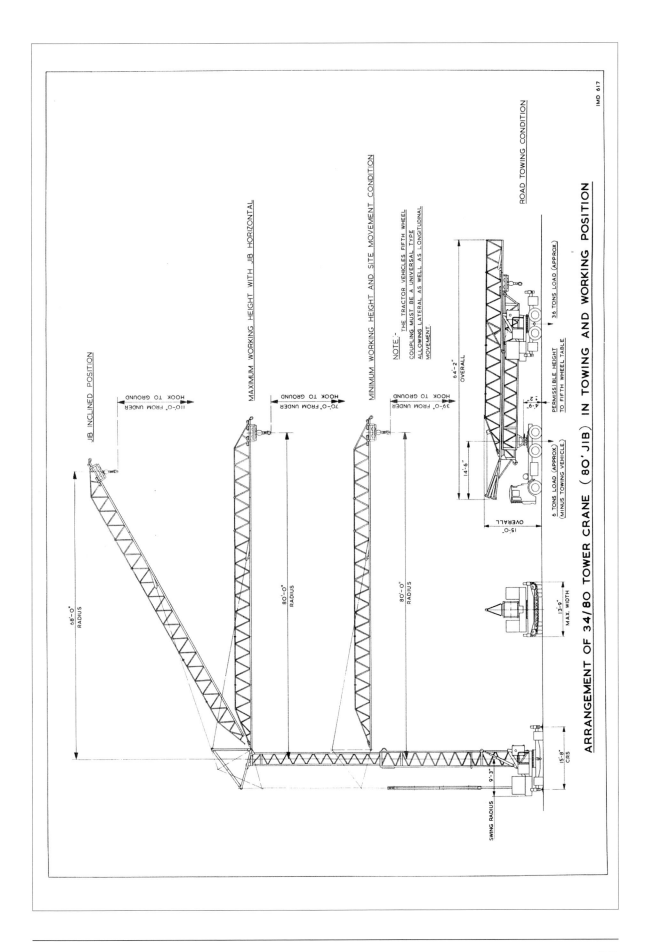

JIB INCLINED POSITION

68'-0" RADIUS

MAXIMUM WORKING HEIGHT WITH JIB HORIZONTAL

HOOK TO GROUND
110'-0" FROM UNDER

80'-0" RADIUS

MINIMUM WORKING HEIGHT AND SITE MOVEMENT CONDITION

HOOK TO GROUND
70'-0" FROM UNDER

80'-0" RADIUS

HOOK TO GROUND
39'-0" FROM UNDER

NOTE:- THE TRACTOR VEHICLES FIFTH WHEEL
COUPLING MUST BE A UNIVERSAL TYPE
ALLOWING LATERAL AS WELL AS LONGITUDINAL
MOVEMENT.

ROAD TOWING CONDITION

IMD 617

64'-2" OVERALL

14'-6"

PERMISSIBLE HEIGHT
TO FIFTH WHEEL TABLE

4'-9"
11'-2"

36 TONS LOAD (APPROX)

6 TONS LOAD (APPROX)
(MINUS TOWING VEHICLE)

15'-0" OVERALL

13'-9" MAX. WIDTH

9'-3"

15'-8" CRS

SWING RADIUS

ARRANGEMENT OF 34/80 TOWER CRANE (80' JIB) IN TOWING AND WORKING POSITION

255

Ruston-Bucyrus 15/50
Tower Crane Prototype

Towards the end of the RB involvement with Tower Cranes development began on an improved and up-rated version of the 12/52 Tower Crane incorporating hydraulic operation of its main functions.

A prototype crane was built and given the designation 15/50, but the decision came to cease manufacture of Tower Cranes, and it never reached the production stage.

Design model of the proposed Ruston-Bucyrus 15/50 Tower Crane.

Summary - Ruston-Bucyrus
Tower Cranes

For many products which reach the end of their production life, in supermarket or in factory, their passing is marked by the sad picture of the last few of their number lying unsold on shelf or factory yard. So it was with the last three Ruston-Bucyrus Tower Cranes rusting away at the Excavator Works, the chemicals leaching from their concrete ballast boxes and solidifying to hang like stalactites in some ancient cave.

Inevitably the question arises why were the Tower Cranes in production for such a relatively short time and the numbers built so few? Certainly the times were right for their introduction, a time of great activity in the development of new towns fuelled by new building techniques using pre-fabricated panels, etc. for which Tower Cranes were ideally suited. However, they were not the success the company had hoped for and it is worth considering that whatever advantages the Tower Cranes might have in construction work over the ever increasing numbers of conventional crawler cranes, they also have their disadvantages;

1. On machines such as the 12/52 with electric motors driving the propel machinery problems emerged with the way in which the electrical feed to the lower works affected the slewing action of the machine. In order to avoid breaking the electrical connections, operation of the machine had to be restricted to slewing one way and then slewing back the way it had come. However this problem was resolved with the eventual incorporation of hydraulic drive.

2. Serious problems were experienced with the 'Wylie' safe load indicator with which the Tower Cranes were fitted. They could not be relied upon to give accurate readings and it was said of them that on a particular setting the alarm would be triggered by a shoe box yet that same setting on another occasion would take several tons. (Evincing wry smiles when received at the Excavator Works was the report of an RB 12/52 on a building site directly outside the office windows of the Health and Safety Executive; due to the problem the overload warning bells were sounding continuously throughout the whole time the machine was working on the contract.) Like the electrical problems, it was only a matter of a little more development work to overcome it.

3. Much more damaging to sales of the Tower Cranes, and possibly the reason for their lack of success were inherent drawbacks to the machines compared with RB's similar sized conventional crawler cranes. Road regulations at the time stipulated that machines up to a certain width over their crawlers could be transported on public roads without the need for police escort, and Ruston-Bucyrus crawler cranes up to the 22-RB fell into this category. However, the Tower Cranes exceeded this limit which meant that a police escort was required, and documentation concerning load and route had to be submitted with so many days notice each time the crane was moved from one site to another. All of which was not good for the busy contractor.

Yet the Tower Cranes did have some unforeseen uses - both the 12/52 and the 34/80 generated their own power and when the miner's strike was on and the nation suffered electricity cuts, someone had the bright idea of using spare Tower Crane generators drawn from the parts warehouse to power the Ruston-Bucyrus office lighting.

LINCOLN'S EXCAVATORS

HYDRAULIC EXCAVATORS
PART ONE - THE 3-RB

Ruston-Bucyrus 3-RB Hydraulic Excavator at the factory

3-RB HYDRAULIC EXCAVATOR

Although hydraulic excavators and excavators with partial hydraulic digging equipments had been in America and on the continent of Europe for several years this had not seriously affected the Ruston-Bucyrus production of rope operated machines. However, by 1960 the trend in the U.K. towards tractor based hydraulic digging equipment and shovel loaders was beginning to have a noticeable effect on the R.B. sales of their smaller range excavators, particularly the 10-RB. Although in the past R-B has produced a range of tractor equipments, it was felt that what was needed was not a tractor based hydraulic digger but an efficient and practical design for an all-hydraulic crawler based excavator of the 10-RB size and capability.

The company's first action was to employ a design engineer with experience of hydraulic excavators to head a special team within the Ruston-Bucyrus Engineering Department whose task it was to design and develop the first Ruston-Bucyrus hydraulic excavator. This person was John Willcock, who was recruited from Aveling Barford Co. in 1961 and he began working on a design, reporting to the Chief Engineer Philip Durand.

There were two over-riding factors to the project; (a) there was a limit to the development budget and (b) it was wanted in a hurry. These factors together determined that there should be a minimum of bought-in components, and as far as possible everything on the new excavator should be built 'in house'. John duly produced a design for a hydraulic hoe excavator mounted on 10-RB crawlers which met their needs and an experimental machine designated the 2-RB was authorized, (it was not given the title 1-RB because in the trade this is the nick-name for a spade).

Willcock decided that the new machine would have a high pressure system of hydraulics, (unlike the low pressure system of the later American 'H' series excavators) and the team developed the hydraulics for the prototype 2-RB using Lucas pumps capable of working at pressure up to 3,000 p.s.i. Operation would be through Lockheed valves which worked as a remote control servo-system and Dobson hydraulic rams.

2-RB Prototype hydraulic excavator with house removed on the test ground at the Excavator Works - September 1963.

3-RB Series 1 Hydraulic Excavator

The 2-RB experimental prototype built in the end of number 3 Bay was completed by the end of 1962 and put on test in the works yard. As a result of the tests they found that the operation of the machine using the Lockheed servo type remote control valves was not satisfactory as they were not really suitable for excavator work and these were replaced by standard type direct hand operated valves. The Lucas pumps were retained and in all other respects the hydraulic equipment seemed to work satisfactory. An extra safety lock valve was added into the system, but this gave trouble and was later removed.

With the necessary modifications the re-built 2-RB prototype could now go into production as the 3-RB Series I and a production line was set up in No.2 Stores of the Excavator Works. By this time Peter Wyatt had joined the Hydraulic Design team in the Engineering department, being appointed as Project Engineer assisting John Wilcock, and a further development of the 3-RB was begun.

Peter Wyatt, Ruston-Bucyrus Project Engineer (formerly Design Draughtsman with B.S.P. Ipswich).

3-RB Series 1 Hydraulic Hoe Excavator;
the first production model at the Excavator
Works awaiting final inspection.

The 3-RB Lower Works in the Lincoln factory comprising a 10-RB crawler mounting to which is attached a fabricated Truck Frame designed to carry the hydraulic propel equipment and on to which is mounted the ball-bearing swing assembly taken from the 11-RB Transit Crane.

Basic Design

The design brief for the 3-RB specified a fully hydraulic excavator mounted upon the existing crawler base developed for the 10-RB, but with the propel motion driven by two independent hydraulic propel motors through double reduction spur gears. A fabricated revolving frame carried the machinery units and operator's cab. The truck frame was also fabricated; between these was mounted the fully rotating ball-bearing swing circle as used on the 11-RB. The swing machinery comprised an epicyclic gear assembly with an independent hydraulic motor drive. The operator's control cubicle was also taken from the 11-RB.

The Hydraulics

From the outset it was decided to incorporate on the 3-RB the most advanced hydraulic system available - going for a high pressure system using axial swash plate piston pumps. It was a high efficiency closed circuit system in which two variable stroke Lucas piston pumps supply oil at 2,500 lbs. per sq. in. to the two stroke propel motors, cam-motors, cam rotor swing motor and three operating rams, via two independent control valve banks. The simultaneous operation of swing and propel motions was achieved via a manually interconnection between the fluid feed pipes of the propel motors.

Hydraulic Rams;
  Boom Hoist 6" Dia. Cylinder with 3" Dia. Rod
  Digging 4½" Dia. Cylinder with 2½" Dia. Rod
  Wrist Action 4" Dia. Cylinder with 2" Dia. Rod

Power Unit

This was provided by a 3YDAN Mk.II 4 stroke air-cooled compression ignition engine rated for intermittent duty, 55 hp. at 1800 r.p.m., with electric starting. Alternative power unit was available with the option of a Sutton/Ford diesel engine, water cooled and rated for intermittent duty, 55 hp. at 2000 r.p.m., again electric starting.

Above: Factory photo of a 3-RB Truck Frame with propel gears and hydraulic propel motors assembled.

Below: Factory photo of the same Truck Frame with the hydraulic piping to the propel motors connected up and the propel gear cases fitted.

Above: Production line of 3-RB Series I Hydraulic Excavators at the Lincoln factory.
For strength the booms on the 3-RB were built by welding two channel sections together rather
than by the traditional method of fabricating the box section from separate plates.

Left: 3-RB Series I Operator's Controls.

With the exception of the last of the Series II machines, all the 3-RB hydraulic hoe type excavators had what was described as 'four-lever' control. The detail on the left shows standard operating and ancillary controls
these are;

 A. Left Hand Track Drive
 B. Swing Control
 C. Digging Ram
   (interconnected to R.H. foot treadle)
 D. Right Hand Track Drive
 E. Boom Ram and Dipper Wrist Ram
 G. Left Hand Pump
 H. Right Hand Pump
 J. Swing Lock
 K. Engine Governor Control

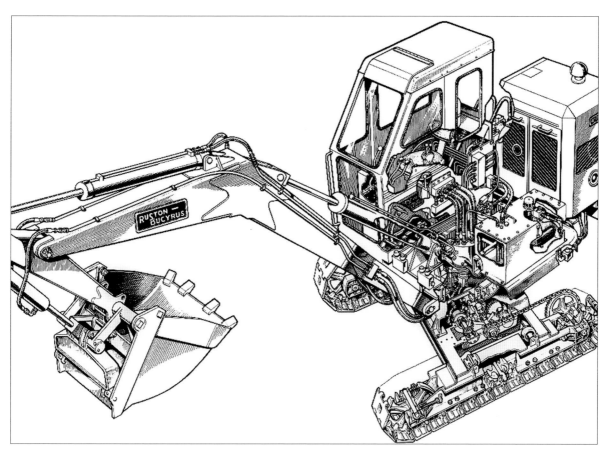

Above: Cut-away diagram of the 3-RB Series I Hydraulic Excavator.

Below: 3-RB Series I Hoe on the test ground at the Excavator Works.

WORKING DIMENSIONS - 3-RB SERIES ONE HYDRAULIC HOE EXCAVATOR

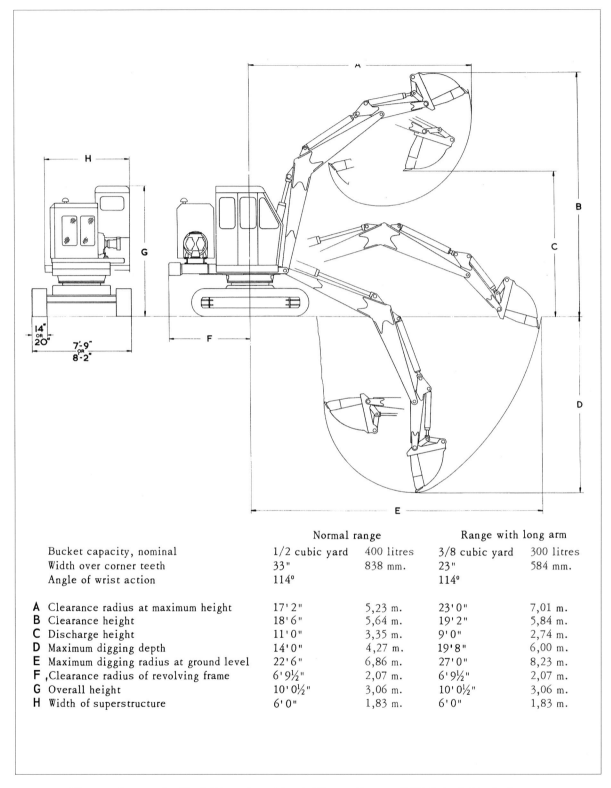

		Normal range		Range with long arm	
Bucket capacity, nominal		1/2 cubic yard	400 litres	3/8 cubic yard	300 litres
Width over corner teeth		33"	838 mm.	23"	584 mm.
Angle of wrist action		114°		114°	
A	Clearance radius at maximum height	17'2"	5,23 m.	23'0"	7,01 m.
B	Clearance height	18'6"	5,64 m.	19'2"	5,84 m.
C	Discharge height	11'0"	3,35 m.	9'0"	2,74 m.
D	Maximum digging depth	14'0"	4,27 m.	19'8"	6,00 m.
E	Maximum digging radius at ground level	22'6"	6,86 m.	27'0"	8,23 m.
F	Clearance radius of revolving frame	6'9½"	2,07 m.	6'9½"	2,07 m.
G	Overall height	10'0½"	3,06 m.	10'0½"	3,06 m.
H	Width of superstructure	6'0"	1,83 m.	6'0"	1,83 m.

Photographs opposite: The 3-RB on show. (above) A Ruston-Bucyrus 3-RB Series 1 Standard
Hoe at the Dublin Show, May 1965. The second picture (below) reveals a Ruston-Bucyrus 3-RB
Series I Standard Hoe on the proving ground at the International Construction Equipment
Exhibition at Crystal Palace in June 1965.

Above: The standard 3-RB Hoe was available fitted with an optional long dipper arm as seen here on the test ground at the Excavator Works. Giving an extra 4' 6" of reach, and fitted with a ³/₈ cu.yd. dipper, this equipment was suited to excavation in soft ground and several were supplied for drainage work.

Below: A variation of the 3-RB was the Scoop Loading Shovel seen here on the test ground; the ½ cu.yd. Shovel Dipper was fitted to the standard-hoe dipper handle providing a horizontal travel of dipper at ground level of 5' 3", and a maximum dumping height of 12' 4". Tests of this machine proved successful within the limits of its capacity and speed of loading and it offered a simple and cheap conversion from the standard hoe.

These two photographs show the prototype for a 3-RB Shovel Loader; based on the standard 3-RB Excavator, the design for the front end equipment was contracted out and the experimental model as seen here was built and assembled in the Lincoln factory. After lengthy testing, the machine was seen to perform well enough within the limitation of a loader mounted on crawlers and depending upon the forward travel of the excavator to fill the dipper. However it is not clear from the records how many were sold, nor indeed if it ever went into full production.

3-RB Clamshell Grab Equipment

The hoe dipper on the standard 3-RB can be removed and a hydraulic grab equipment fitted in its place. The grab is powered by two hydraulic cylinders, each supplying the closing and opening force for one shell, the two being synchronized by spur gears at the pivot points. The grab is designed to give a jaw opening of 85 degrees and this is arranged so that the full force of the piston is available to exert the maximum closing pressure. A pin-connected head assembly joins the bucket to the digging arm of the excavator which allows the grab to swing in any direction and rotate about its vertical axis.

Often used for loose material such as sand and gravel, the grab is also useful for removing building foundations on sites where there is no room for a dragline to operate. There are a number of different types of grab buckets (with or without teeth, depending on application) - the nominal capacity of the standard 3-RB grab bucket is 3/8 cu.yd.

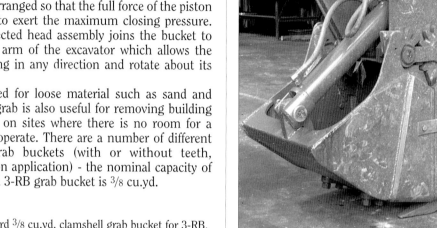

Right: Standard 3/8 cu.yd. clamshell grab bucket for 3-RB.

3-RB Series I with ½ cu.yd. clamshell bucket on demolition work off Lincoln High Street, April 1964.

Another photograph taken in April 1964 of the 3-RB Series I
hydraulic excavator with clamshell attachment at work in the
centre of Lincoln clearing old buildings as part of an inner city
re-development scheme. Not the best timing in the middle of
what appears to be Lincoln's Shakespeare Festival.

3-RB Wheel Mounted 1965

With the production line for the standard 3-RB Crawler Excavator established, the decision was made to develop a wheel mounted version based upon the 3-RB Series I Hoe. A four wheel self-propelled 3-RB was designed by the RB team; the main hydraulic system was the same as that of the standard machine, with an additional hydraulic gear pump fitted to the engine to provide an independent hydraulic supply for steering. Control of the steering was by a simple tiller in place of the more usual wheel, this was dictated by lack of space due to the four-lever operator's controls.

Each twin-tyred rear wheel was powered by an independent motor through a two-speed reduction drive enclosed in a single gearbox. Its two-speed independent gearbox was designed by Peter Wyatt as was the hydraulic control system in which the two propel motors had individual hydrostatic drives from their respective pumps and the speed of the machine could be controlled, both up and down gradients, by adjusting the pump flow controls. A manually controlled inter-connection between the motor feed pipes provided a different action at the wheels when traveling on the highway. This control also allowed for simultaneous dog and propel to be selected for maneuvering on difficult ground conditions.

The wheel mounted 3-RB was equipped with the standard crawler Hoe front end equipment and like the crawler version a range of grab buckets were available. The two propelling speeds were around 10 m.p.h. (low speed) and 12 m.p.h. (high speed).

The prototype machine was built in 1965 and as well as being tested under the usual quarry conditions at Greetwell was road tested on the roads of Lincoln, with hill tests carried out on Lincoln's Harmston Hill in quieter conditions than could be found today. With the test successful, the wheel mounted 3-RB went into production and a first batch of four machines were built.

Of these four machines, one was purchased by Lincoln contractor Charles Coleshaw and another went to work on the construction of the Beattock Bypass, on the Carlisle to Glasgow motorway, where its travelling qualities proved especially valuable. Because it had individual drives to the wheels, dispensing with a differential, there was no 'slip' which meant that the machine could work in the muddiest conditions when a normal machine could not. So effective was this machine that, in addition to its excavating duties it was also used as a tow-tractor, towing compressors around the construction site.

The remaining two wheeled-mounted 3-RBs, rather misguidedly were purchased for work in the icy mountainous regions of Switzerland where they had difficulty operating, (though they could go up 1 in 6 hills on a test at home despite their two-wheel drive). These two machines were returned to the factory and the production of the 3-RB came to an end before any more of the wheel-mounted versions could be built.

Ruston-Bucyrus 3-RB Wheel Mounted Hydraulic Excavator.

Above: 3-RB Wheel Mounted Excavator; view of the special double two-speed propel transmission designed by Peter Wyatt and built in the Ruston Bucyrus workshops.

Below: 3-RB Wheel Mounted Excavator on test at the Excavator Works.

WORKING DIMENSIONS OF THE 3-RB WHEEL MOUNTED EXCAVATOR

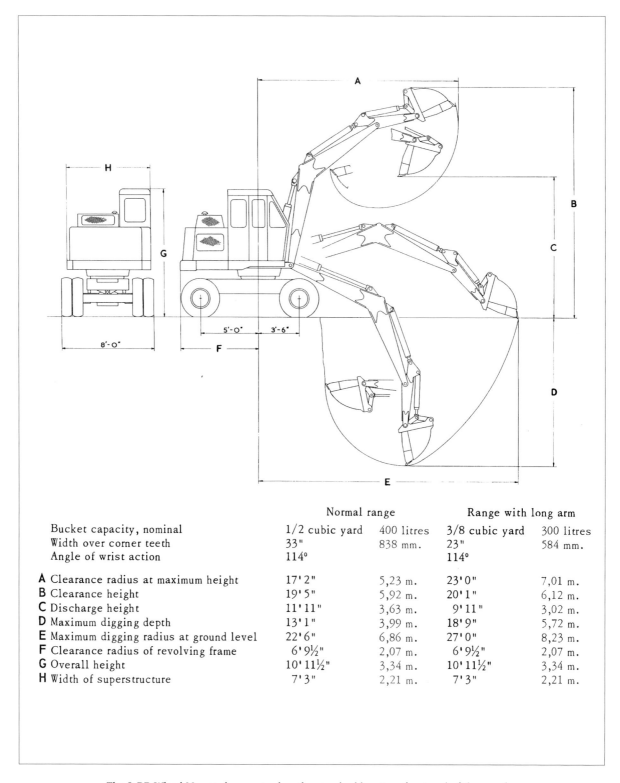

	Normal range		Range with long arm	
Bucket capacity, nominal	1/2 cubic yard	400 litres	3/8 cubic yard	300 litres
Width over corner teeth	33"	838 mm.	23"	584 mm.
Angle of wrist action	114°		114°	
A Clearance radius at maximum height	17'2"	5,23 m.	23'0"	7,01 m.
B Clearance height	19'5"	5,92 m.	20'1"	6,12 m.
C Discharge height	11'11"	3,63 m.	9'11"	3,02 m.
D Maximum digging depth	13'1"	3,99 m.	18'9"	5,72 m.
E Maximum digging radius at ground level	22'6"	6,86 m.	27'0"	8,23 m.
F Clearance radius of revolving frame	6'9½"	2,07 m.	6'9½"	2,07 m.
G Overall height	10'11½"	3,34 m.	10'11½"	3,34 m.
H Width of superstructure	7'3"	2,21 m.	7'3"	2,21 m.

The 3-RB Wheel Mounted excavator has the standard hoe type front end of the crawler machine for which a long arm version is available. Alternative dippers include a hoe-type 16" wide over corner and a 60" wide ditching dipper. Side cutters, applicable to all three standard type dippers, are available to give additional width of 3". Like the crawler machine, a range of grab equipment is available for use with standard and long arm hoe equipment.

Ruston-Bucyrus prototype 3-RB Wheel Mounted Hydraulic Hoe Excavator in 1965 working
on the construction of the Beattock Bypass section of the Carlisle to Glasgow motorway.
The conditions proved a severe test for such an excavator and accounts indicate that it
performed satisfactorily, with its twin-tyred independent-driven rear wheels coping well with
the rugged nature of the terrain.

3-RB Series II (Intermediate Stage)

Conscious of the poor appearance of the first 3-RBs, the design team worked on improving the general look of the machine. Though retaining the 11-RB operator's cubicle, the large box-like engine housing was removed and the engine and pump assemblies were enclosed in a newly designed housing. In all other respects the machine remained the same and this 'new look' version was designated the 3-RB Series II. (The final version of the 3-RB Series II was given a completely new cab.)

The intermediate version of the 3-RB Series II with its improved cab working on a building site; it was on this type of work that the 3-RB proved most successful but it was also the field of the greatest competition from other manufacturers.

3-RB Series II (Final Version)

In 1965 the final version of the 3-RB Series II appeared, the changes involved a newly designed operator's cab and machinery housing, together with a two-lever operator's control system in place of the previous four-lever controls. The photographs featured below shows the last version of the 3-RB Series II working on an urban housing site in Lincolnshire.

275

The machine here being tested at the factory by Ernie Hopcroft, Ruston-Bucyrus Test Fitter/Driver, is an example of the final version of the 3-RB Series II and the two-lever operator controls which replaced the original four-lever controls can be seen in the photograph. This version, which came in at Lot 8 on the Ruston-Bucyrus production schedule in 1965, marked the end of the development of the 3-RB. Out of a total number of seventy 3-RB excavators built and allocated a Sales Order No. between 1964 and 1967, fifty were sold and delivered to customers - this does not include those machines which remained at the factory after production of this model had cease and were offered cheap to local contractors.

Above: A Ruston-Bucyrus Series II Hydraulic Hoe at the works after completion of its final tests.

Despite the optimism with which the RB sales force presented the greatly improved 3-RB Series II and good reports from some early customers, the general response to RB's first venture into hydraulic excavators was not encouraging. There were growing doubts that the 3-RB could fulfil the requirements for a hydraulic excavator which could compete against other manufacture's models in domestic and continental markets.

By 1967, this was sufficient to persuade the Lincoln management, under pressure from the American parent company, to cease its production of the 3-RB and all development of Ruston-Bucyrus hydraulic excavators. The last batch of machines and all remaining spare parts were sold off at a 'knock down' price to a local contractor for the depressing job of digging pits to bury rotting animal carcasses that had resulted from the Foot and Mouth epidemic that was sweeping the country at the time.

Left: 3-RB Series II on show at the Public Works Exhibition at Olympia in November, 1966. At the controls is the Rt. Hon. Anthony Wedgwood Benn, Minister of Technology, being instructed by N.A.Webster (RB Director and General Sales Manager.)

The Ruston-Bucyrus 3-RB; 'A Missed Opportunity'

The timing of Ruston-Bucyrus's entry into hydraulic excavator manufacture was right, certainly so far as the domestic market was concerned, and all the research showed that there was a demand for a small crawler mounted hydraulic machine equivalent in performance to the 10-RB Dragshovel. So the question has to be asked 'why wasn't this first attempt by the Lincoln company to produce a hydraulic excavator successful?'

The design team within the Engineering Department that had been constituted specifically for the 3-RB project had been recruited for their knowledge and experience on hydraulic excavators and was led by R-B's Chief Engineer so it was more than capable of producing a successful design.

A further positive factor towards achieving a successful design was the decision from the beginning to use high pressure hydraulics and positive displacement swash plate friction pumps which were mechanically more efficient than the gear pump design that would be used on the Bucyrus-Erie 20-H hydraulic excavator that succeeded the 3-RB. So we are led to seek the cause of the problems experienced with the 3-RB in the financial constraints imposed upon the project, which in turn led to initial decisions that lie at the root of its subsequent failure;

1. Many of the problems experienced with the 3-RB resulted from the use of the 10-RB Crawler base; the choice of hydraulics system proved successful but any efficiency and advantage gained from the extra power of the hydraulics tended to be dissipated in the cumbersome basic machinery of the excavator. The use of the 10-RB base was dictated by the tight limits imposed on the amount of development money available for the 3-RB Project.

2. Though the choice of high pressure hydraulics proved to be the right way to go enabling lighter, smaller cylinders, it also meant higher build quality and specialized methods of engineering within a clean environment. However, the 3-RB was developed and built within the heavy engineering environment of the Excavator Works when what was needed was a separate purpose-built workshop equipped and offering the working conditions needed for the production of hydraulic equipment. Some of the problem could be traced back to the manufacturing process.

3. Finally it has to be said that, though the 3-RB proved itself in terms of its digging capabilities, it didn't 'look good'. For reasons of economy the new machines were fitted with a cab taken from the 11-RB Transit Crane and an engine house that resembled a rabbit hutch; only at the end when it was too late was thought given to the machine's appearance.

All of the above factors stem from an initial lack of investment and one is led to believe as the RB design team themselves believed, that had they been able to 'start from scratch' with a completely new design the outcome might have been different. John Willcock was already working on an entirely new design for a mobile hydraulic excavator with 180 degree swing and four-wheeled drive to be called the 4-RB when orders came to cease all further development of the 3-RB.

P.H.R. Durand (seated) with, left to right; H. Auger (Chief Draughtsman), G.A. Scott (Asst. Chief Engineer) and R.C. Chevassut (Mr. Durand's successor as Chief Engineer).

LINCOLN'S EXCAVATORS

CHANGES AT
THE EXCAVATOR WORKS

Aerial View of the Excavator Works, 1968

CHANGES AT THE EXCAVATOR WORKS

Change to the Company's Articles of Association

At a meeting of the Board of Directors of Ruston-Bucyrus in the beginning of May 1965, Chairman Eugene Berg placed before the Board a resolution proposing the following changes to the Company's Articles of Association;

Resolution

1. That pursuant to Article 85, the Chairman of the Board, subject to the control of the Board of Directors, shall in addition to his powers and duties under the Articles of Association, have active management of the business of the Company.
2. That pursuant to article 94, the Managing Director, subject to the control of the Board of Directors and to the general supervision of the Chairman of the Board, shall in addition to his powers and duties under the Articles of the Association have active management of the business of the Company.
3. That all resolutions and documents hitherto in force with respect to the powers and duties of the Managing Director shall be deemed superseded by these resolutions.

Mr. Berg's resolution was accepted by the Board in its entirety by a majority vote. In a subsequent memo explaining (and justifying) the changes to the Articles, Mr. Berg wrote;

(a) The resolution is a clarification and specific expression of powers that have actually in the past been exercised albeit informally, by Mr. Coleman as Chairman of Ruston-Bucyrus.

(b) A principal object of the resolution, is not only to strengthen the Ruston-Bucyrus Executive team, but also to foster a close family relationship between the companies that will permit Bucyrus-Erie to render effective assistance to Ruston-Bucyrus to strengthen the competitive position and productivity of RB.

Resignations Follow

Respecting Berg's motives in the interest of Ruston-Bucyrus Ltd., the above resolution nevertheless had the effect of increasing the Chairman's (and ipso facto Bucyrus-Erie's) powers in respect of the management of the Lincoln company. Certainly, Managing Director Everitt thought this when, on the 18th May 1965, he offered his resignation in the belief that Berg's proposed changes would;

"Increase the Chairman's powers compared with the practice of the last 35 years; decrease the powers of the Managing Director; and lead to loss of identity as an Associated Co."

Everitt's resignation was officially accepted on the 18th October 1965, to be followed by Chief Engineer Phillip Durand's resignation in December of the same year. The position of Managing Director was filled by F.T. Hartland and Durand's successor as Chief Engineer was R.C. Chevassut.

The resignation of other key figures in the Ruston-Bucyrus management soon followed; in the spring of 1966, John Austin, General Sales Manager and Sales Director of RB, resigned from the company; James Page, Technical Director of RB for 13 years, resigned in May 1966; and John Edwards, RB Works Manager resigned in July 1967.

The shared motivation for this mass departure of top executives and highly skilled engineers from the Lincoln company is expressed in the newspaper report of Page's resignation quoting him as saying -

"I must go! My function has become superfluous - the situation has now changed and the company is becoming one more subsidiary of a large American Corporation."

J. Austin

R.J. Edwards

J.H. Page

Bucyrus-Erie Co. increases its control

The dramatic effects in 1965 at the top level of the Ruston-Bucyrus company occasioned by Mr Berg's wish for greater direct involvement by the Bucyrus-Erie Co. in its management were further fuelled by events which were occurring at this same time involving RB's English parent company - Ruston & Hornsby.

In the 1960s Ruston & Hornsby Ltd., equal shareholders with the Bucyrus Erie Co. in Ruston-Bucyrus Ltd., were experiencing financial difficulties and J. Mallabar was brought in to act as 'company doctor' to sort things out; he rescued R&H from the financial mess they were in and created a saleable package. A consequence of this was that in November 1966, Ruston & Hornsby Ltd. was taken over by the English Electric Co.

This was a change that the Bucyrus Erie Company had anticipated, for the Articles of Association drawn up at the creation of Ruston-Bucyrus Ltd. on the 29th November 1929 stated that should the ownership of the Ruston partner change, then the B.E. Company would have the option of taking up a controlling interest in Ruston-Bucyrus Ltd. This was duly implemented in 1966 by three shares being transferred over from the former Ruston, now E.E.C., holdings in RB to their American partner. (Fifteen million shares were involved of which the Ruston and BE companies had each held 7½ million, the transfer of these three shares was sufficient to give Bucyrus-Erie the controlling interest in Ruston-Bucyrus Ltd. by six votes.) Though still a jointly owned company, RB's American parent was now in effect its major shareholder.

"The future has never been brighter"

Speaking at a Ruston-Bucyrus Domestic Sales Conference in February 1967, the Company's Chairman Eugene Berg said that RB/BE were about to enter the most successful period in their history -

"The future has never been brighter", he said, "particularly when you realise that our proposed new hydraulic hoes, cranes and other developments, will beat any competition in the world."

Mr. Hartland, RB's recently appointed Managing Director, at the same meeting echoed his Chairman's optimism naming 1966 as the "miserable year" and 1967 as the "hopeful year" and he welcomed the closer liaison between RB and BE.

The replacement of Everitt with Mr. Hartland, a Chartered Accountant, as Managing Director, the appointment of F. Wildmore from the commercial side as his assistant, and the further resignation of Page, the company's highly qualified Technical Director, changed the emphasis of the Lincoln management from Engineering to Commercial, which was only partially restored by Chief Engineer Chevassut's appointment to the Board in 1972.

It was in this climate of optimism that Ruston-Bucyrus embarked upon an expansion of their manufacturing facilities in Lincoln by buying up two old factories - Ruston Spike Island foundry and the old Foster foundry and works on Firth Road.

Above: F.T. Hartland, RB Managing Director 1965-71.

Below: Chairman Eugene Berg addressing RB staff at their Domestic Sales Conference, February 1967.

Expansion of the Ruston-Bucyrus Plant

In the Summer of 1968, Ruston-Bucyrus announced its plans for a massive expansion of its manufacturing and corporate facilities to which there were three distinct components -

(a) The development of the former 13 acre Spike Island foundry complex adjacent to the Excavator Works which Ruston-Bucyrus had purchased from Ruston & Hornsby when the latter transferred their foundry work to their modern plant further along Beevor Street.

(b) the conversion of the former Ruston canteen block into a company recreation centre.

(c) The acquisition and development of the Allen Gwynne workshops and foundry (the old Foster & Co. Wellington Works) situated on Firth Road to the east of the Excavator Works.

The Spike Island Foundry Development

The Ruston & Hornsby Spike Island Foundry was created just before the first World War and was followed, just after the war, by the same company's purpose-built Navvy Works which adjoined it on the Spike Island site. Though the new Ruston-Bucyrus company took over the Navvy Works in 1930 and developed it into the Excavator Works, the foundry complex which included the old Ruston canteen block on Beevor Street remained in R & H ownership. Ruston-Bucyrus's declared aim for the development of the numerous foundry buildings was to provide the extra workshop space to "group associated processes and so cut down material movement."

The main focus of the development was the transformation of the moulding shop, the largest of the foundry buildings, into a specialised plant for the construction of the new B.E. designed 20-H and 30-H hydraulic excavators that were soon to go into full production at Lincoln; this would become new Bays 44-48 of the Excavator Works. The fettling shop would be converted into a bucket and bucket teeth shop, (later to become the company's Experimental and Machine Development Dept.), and several other foundry buildings were transformed into equipment stores. Another part of the foundry development was the conversion of the former heavy core shop into a Ruston-Bucyrus Company Training Centre in which both the training of adults and the basic training of apprentices was to take place, provided for by the "finest training facilities in Lincoln."

Photograph of the rear of the Excavator works taken on the occasion of the visit to the works by Edward, Prince of Wales, in 1927. Just in picture on the left is the corner of No.1 Bay of the Excavator Works, the two large Bays opposite are the main foundry buildings of Ruston's Spike Island foundry complex which also included core shops, fettling shops and pattern shops.

During the war it was used for the construction of aero engines for aircraft built at the nearby R & H Boultham Works, reverting back to foundry work after the war in 1918.

In RB's expansion plans the Bays of this former moulding shop (designated Bays 44 - 48 in the new works plan) were transformed into specialised workshops for the new range of hydraulic excavators. The aim was that the processes of fabrication, machining and assembly for one type of product (hydraulic excavators and cranes) should all take place in the same area. The same principle was applied to

The moulding shop was the main building of the Ruston & Hornsby Spike Island Foundry which was built just prior to the first World War.

another of the foundry buildings, the former Fettling Shop, by converting this into a specialist plant for all bucket and teeth work.

Above: 20-H hydraulic excavators being assembled in Bay 47 of the converted Ruston & Hornsby moulding shop.

This converted moulding shop was not the obvious choice of environment for such work, the first use of the overhead cranes brought cascades of dust everywhere and though the building was thoroughly cleaned, dust was always a potential problem. It is recorded that one customer of a 20-H

claimed warranty for replacement of pumps and cleaning of the complete hydraulic system, a possible consequence of the manufacturing environment maybe, but the machine's hydraulic oil tank sent back with the claim also contained a half-eaten egg sandwich. The booms seen in the picture are the early box plated ones which were replaced on the later 20-RBH by booms constructed from two channel sections.

Aerial view taken in April 1970 of the Ruston-Bucyrus Excavator Works
and Spike Island Foundry.

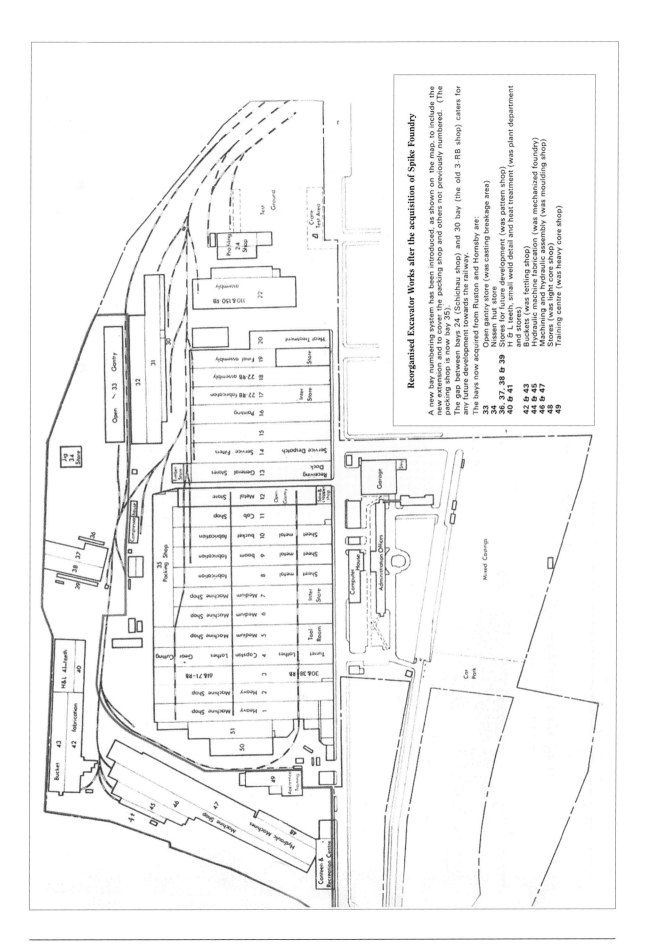

Reorganised Excavator Works after the acquisition of Spike Foundry

A new bay numbering system has been introduced, as shown on the map, to include the new extension and to cover the packing shop and others not previously numbered. (The packing shop is now bay 35).

The gap between bays 24 (Schichau shop) and 30 bay (the old 3-RB shop) caters for any future development towards the railway.

The bays now acquired from Ruston and Hornsby are:

33	Open gantry store (was casting breakage area)
34	Nissen hut store
36, 37, 38 & 39	Stores for future development (was pattern shop)
40 & 41	H & L teeth, small weld detail and heat treatment (was plant department and stores)
42 & 43	Buckets (was fettling shop)
44 & 45	Hydraulic machine fabrication (was mechanized foundry)
46 & 47	Machining and hydraulic assembly (was moulding shop)
48	Stores (was light core shop)
49	Training centre (was heavy core shop)

In the Ruston Spike Island foundry complex purchased by RB was the fettling shop and this was converted by the new owners into specialised bucket and teeth workshops.

Equipped with specialised plant and designated bay 40-43, it provided the location for all the processes related to the development of the 'Lincoln' range of dragline buckets and H & L two-part bucket teeth; highly profitable sections of the excavator works production. Later, in 1971 RB converted the same building into their experimental and development workshop for hydraulic excavators.

Left: Radiographic examination of a bucket lip casting being carried out at the bucket workshops.

Below: This photo shows the new RB Training Centre, Bay 49, created from another part of the old Ruston Spike Island Foundry; the heavy core shop. Later the company's training facilities were further expanded by the creation in 1973 of an Adult Training annex in the former light core shop, Bay 48 on the plan on page 285.

"You Shall Go To The Ball"

The most spectacular of the developments by Ruston-Bucyrus in 1968 was the conversion of the former Ruston & Hornsby canteen block on Beevor Street into the company's new Amenities Centre. Built just before the first World War as a two-storey canteen for workers from the Ruston Foundry and Navvy Works, its upper floor was rented by Ruston-Bucyrus in 1930 to serve as their admin.

offices and drawing office until they were re-located in their own new building (Becor House).

The building continued to serve as canteen for both Ruston and Ruston-Bucyrus employees up to this acquisition by Ruston-Bucyrus. With the purchase of the Ruston foundry complex plans could now be drawn up for its re-development. The project was designed by architects, John Roberts, and no expense was spared in transforming this old building not only into excellent staff catering facilities but one of the finest amenities blocks in U.K. industry.

With its deluxe theatre, well-appointed bars and the finest sprung dance floor in the county, the 'Beevor Rooms' as it was called, opened in June 1969 as the best equipped entertainment centre in Lincoln. Regrettably the Beevor Rooms were never used to their full potential and when in 1977 all social functions ceased and the ballroom became temporary accommodation for the RB Parts Sales Department before being demolished, there was brought to an end a glorious but expensive 'white elephant'.

Left: Ruston Canteen Block on Beevor Street in 1932.

Below: Artist's impression of the proposed new Ruston-Bucyrus 'Beevor Rooms'.

Aerial photograph of Lincoln's Spike Island and Firth Road Engineering Works in the mid 1960s -
several conurbations of world renowned engineering works and worker's houses similiar to this
existed in the downhill part of Lincoln at the time.

The Firth Road Factory Development

In August 1968 it was officially announced that the Ruston-Bucyrus company had purchased the Lincoln works of Allen Gwynnes Pumps Ltd. on Firth Road originally known as the Wellington Works.

This was the foundry and workshops established in 1899 by William Foster & Co. for the manufacture of traction engines and other heavy machinery, though it is best remembered for its association with the first tanks in World War I and in particular Sir William Tritton, the company's Managing Director who was largely responsible for their development.

The acquisition of this extra 23 acre foundry and workshop space by RB allowed for the production of small castings and fabrication work previously sub-contracted out. In addition to this, it was decided to transfer all low-volume assembly to this Firth Road site, which included well drills and tower cranes, as well as the 10-RB which by this time was coming towards the end of its production life.

Above: Photograph showing the foundry and workshops on Firth Road purchased by RB from Allen Gwynnes Pumps Ltd. that were originally Foster's Wellington Works; the foundry section is in the centre of the works by the foundry chimney.

Key to picture of Spike Island and Firth Road Engineering Works opposite:

A. Ruston-Bucyrus Ltd. Excavator Works (Formerly R & H Navvy Works 1918-1930, R-B Excavator Works 1930-1985).

B. Spike Island Foundry (R & H Ltd. 1914 - 1968) (Ruston-Bucyrus Ltd. 1968 - 1985)
Products: R&H castings for Ruston engines and navvies, W.W.I aeroplane engines. R-B excavator production.

C. James Dawson & Sons Ltd. (Built 1889)
Production of 'Balata' and rubber belting for use in agriculture and industry, later 'V' belting for automotive industry, one of the first companies to make silicone rubber belting, and hoses.

D. The Wellington Works (William Foster & Co. 1899-1927, Foster Gwynnes 1927-1960, Allen Gwynnes 1960-1968, R.B. Ltd. 1968-1984, demolished 1984)
Products; traction & portable engines, W.W.I tanks; Gwynnes pumps; excavators.

E. The Boiler Works (Ruston Proctor & Co. 1905-1918, R & H Ltd. 1918-1972, Ruston-Bucyrus Ltd. 1973-1984 then demolished for the Tritton Rd. development).
Products; boilers, pressure vessels, Ruston steam navvies; excavators.

F. The R & H Boultham Works (originally called the Motor Works built by Ruston Proctor for storage, the factory was established in 1915)
Products; R&H motor car, diesel engines, diesel loco-motives, W.W.I aircraft (Sopwith Camel) & their engines.

G1 & G2. The R & H Sheaf Woodworks (Anchor Works) (Built by Ruston Proctor & Co. in the late 1800s, became known as the R & H Anchor Street Works in 1950s, the Anchor Street part was demolished in the mid 1960s)
Products; Threshing machines, farm wagons; diesel engine fuel pumps & injection equipment (Anchor Street)

H. The R & H New Beevor Iron Foundry (opened Jan. 1950) Products; iron castings for Ruston oil engines, diesel locos, etc.

The Firth Road foundry purchased from Allen Gwynnes Ltd. was extensively updated by RB to incorporate modern techniques and equipment. These photographs of the part of the foundry designated as Bay 76 in the overall plan of the Excavator Works show (above) the transfer of molten metal, and (below) the large moulding section.

LINCOLN'S EXCAVATORS

HYDRAULIC EXCAVATORS
THE 'H' RANGE

A Ruston-Bucyrus 20-H Hydraulic Excavator on test at Greetwell Quarry, Lincoln

The European Surves

With the 3-RB in production at Lincoln and the new B.E. 20-H hydraulic excavator in America, and fuelled by RB's concerns to meet the requirements of their European markets, a joint BE / RB team was set up in the autumn of 1964 to conduct a market survey of the E.E.C. countries (at this time roughly one in every four machines produced by Ruston-Bucyrus was destined for Europe). This was followed in the summer of 1965 with a more specific survey of the German market carried out by a second joint RB / BE team; a large part of this survey was focused on hydraulic excavators and the extent to which the options of the 3-RB or the new B.E. 20-H hydraulic excavator would meet the requirements of the German market.

German Market Survey - 1965

The team looked at the excavators and cranes that were being sold in Germany by each of the principal makers, the merchandising methods employed and customer requirements. With regard to hydraulic excavators, the team concluded that in order to satisfy the German market they would have to meet the following requirements;

1) The provision of alternative wheel mounting (all hydraulic excavators sold in Germany were offered with this).
2) Germans require a universal machine and substantial changes in front end design would be needed to permit installation of a range of optional equipments.
3) The design targets as to range, front end feature and crawler tracks on the machines sold in volume in Germany are substantially different from those on which the 3-RB and the new B.E. line of hydraulic machines are based.
(4) The crawler widths need to be reduced to meet continental transport regulations, either permanently, or as a temporary measure for transportation only.

Conclusion; With reference to the 3-RB or 20-H, only the first of the above requirements was met (with the 3-RB wheel mounted).

Report by J.H. Page and R.C. Chevassut on visit to Bucyrus-Erie Co. Nov. 1965

As the possibility of Ruston-Bucyrus production of the Bucyrus-Erie hydraulic excavators gained momentum, RB's Technical Director Page and Assistant Chief Engineer Chevassut on the 15th November 1965 visited the Bucyrus Erie Co. to look at that company's hydraulic excavator programme, and in particular to assess the suitability of the 20-H for the European markets.

Report Results

The report on their visit was submitted to Mr. Berg before they left the States; it echoes the concerns arising from the surveys and suggests certain actions if the 20-H is to be successful in the U.K. and German markets.

Area of Concern:
1) The size of crawler mounting and the method of propel.
2) The heavy fixed dimension front end.
3) As replacement for the 22-RB it is not a universal machine.
4) Price (in the German market).
5) The requirement of wheel mounting.

Action needed on the 20-H for U.K. market:
1) B.E. have now arranged for 20-H mounting to be retractable to 9'-0", method of propel to be resolved.
2) A variable length boom to be developed - the front end is associated with the crawler dimension because of stability. (JCB and Liebherr, etc. have a variable boom and there are signs that this is popular).
3) This to us is the most important factor in the U.K., but there appears to be little done about it at present.
4) This needs checking but if the machine is cheaper than the 22-RB, it will probably be acceptable.
5) This is provided for by the 3-RB wheel mounted.

Actions needed on the 20-H for German market:
1) The machine must be able to reduce 8'-2" in some form.
2) A two-piece boom with different lengths and quick change is essential.
3) Probably not important
4) This seems to be crucial. If we cannot reach a satisfactory price, it is not worth going ahead.
5) This is provided for on the 3-RB.

Page's conclusions:
Mr. Page's report on this trip concluded;
"It seemed clear from their response that Bucyrus-Erie do not intend any necessary alterations such as those we have recommended for the 20-H to meet our own markets."

Opposite page: The Ruston-Bucyrus 20-H Hydraulic Excavator went into production at the Excavator Works in 1967 and the machine was officially launched at the International Construction Equipment Exhibition, Crystal Palace, London in October 1967.

THE B.E. 'H' RANGE OF HYDRAULIC EXCAVATORS

With the decision to end all production and development of the 3-RB, notice came that Ruston-Bucyrus's need for hydraulic excavators was to be met in future by models from the new B.E. 'H' range of hydraulic machines, the first of which, the 20-H, was already in production in the States. Of this range, the models to go into production at the Excavator Works were to be the 15-H, 20-H, and 30-H, with nominal dipper capacities of ½ cu.yd., ⅞ cu.yd., and 1½ cu.yd. respectively.

Bucyrus-Erie's experience of hydraulics began when the company acquired the Milwaukee Hydraulics Corporation in 1948 and began building that company's truck-mounted combined hydraulic and cable operated H2 Hydrocrane. Both RB and BE had built part hydraulic wrist-action dragshovels but the 20-H in 1966 marked the American company's first production of a fully hydraulic excavator.

In respect of the decision to adopt the B.E. hydraulic machines Mr. Hartland, RB's recently appointed Managing Director is quoted as saying -

"Our association with Bucyrus-Erie is probably our greatest asset, since it makes available to us their design engineering and product development. From this close association will stem the introduction of a new range of hydraulic excavators into our product line. These machines will be complimentary to our existing range of excavators and will continue to further our reputation."

Unfortunately, Hartland's confidence in his company's adoption of the new B.E. range of hydraulic excavators would prove to be misplaced, for if the 3-RB was a failure, the B.E. 'H' range was little short of a disaster for the Lincoln company. The problems associated with these machines in the field had the effect of damaging RB's reputation with its U.K. customers rather than enhancing it.

Above: The newly converted R&H Spike Island Foundry moulding shop, now the Ruston-Bucyrus hydraulic machine assembly and machine shop, with the first of the 20-H machines nearing completion. Designated Bay 47 of the Excavator Works, this was a surprising choice for hydraulic production, with cascades of dust falling with each passing of the overhead gantry cranes.

Below: The first prototype 20-H, Lot 1/1 in the production line, was quickly prepared for exhibition at the I.C.E. Exhibition at Crystal Palace and is seen here mounted on a low-loader ready for its journey to the show.

Two more photographs taken in October 1967 of the Lot 1/1 20-H show machine leaving the Excavator Works via the Rope Walk on the first stage of its journey to London and the Crystal Palace exhibition hall. Here it would join two other new products on the Ruston-Bucyrus stand - the new 61-RB and 38-RB Series Two.

Above: The first Ruston-Bucyrus 20-H, Lot 1/1, was allocated RB machine number 32168 and returned from the show to the Excavator Works for final inspection and preliminary tests.

Below: In November 1967, machine number 32168 was moved to the Ruston-Bucyrus performance testing grounds at Lincoln's Greetwell Quarry, where this first Ruston-Bucyrus built 20-H underwent rigorous tests. Never intended for sale, Mc.No.32168 was written off to product development, though it was later purchased cheaply by local contractor Charles Coleshaw for spares.

Above: Ruston-Bucyrus 20-H Hydraulic Hoe, Mc.No.32449, the first of the Lot 2 production machines at the Excavator Works, awaiting delivery to customer W.H. Bridges Ltd. It was supplied fitted with a Cummins engine on April 4th 1968.

The B.E. designed 20-H was a $7/8$ cu.yd. hoe-type hydraulic excavator using low pressure hydraulics (220 p.s.i.). It had a 32ft. reach, 20ft. digging depth, and 17ft. 5in. dumping height. Ruston-Bucyrus set up a production programme after building two test machines (Lot 1) and though, like the 15-H and 30-H that followed, it was said to have been 're-engineered' in the States for the British market, this meant little more than the changes necessary to meet British Standards of manufacture. Apart from a modification to meet the U.K. road transport regulations, none of the recommendations in the 1965 European Survey were adopted - they were effectively the American machines.

Cut-away illustration 20-H Hoe Hydraulic Excavator.

Diesel engine drives the hydraulic pumps via an air operated plate type clutch and the low pressure hydraulic system of the 20-H comprised two constant flow gear type pump units to tandem and four spool type hydraulic control valve assemblies, three directional control and one diverting valve to increase speed. Four double acting cylinders power the boom hoist, dig and wrist functions, and fixed displacement gear type motors mounted on the deck are used for the independent swing and propel function. The swing motor drives the swing pinion and gear, and the propel motor drives through a system of gears down the centre of the machine to the propelling machinery in the lower works with final chain drive to the crawler drive tumblers.

Left: Ruston-Bucyrus 20-H under construction in the factory showing the deck layout. A Cummins V6 engine is mounted at the rear of the revolving frame and a compressor for the air controls is mounted on top of the engine and gear driven from the camshaft. A General Motors 4-cyl. engine was offered as an alternative power unit. The fabricated hydraulic oil tanks mounted on each side integral with the revolving frame and linked by a cross-feed pipe present a large surface area for cooling.

Below: The 20-H standard crawler mounting in the works with fabricated truck frame, axles and crawler side frames. This shows the standard excavator tracks, but tractor type crawler tracks were available as an option. The width over the crawlers when working was 9'-10" but to meet U.K. regulations they could be retracted to 9'-0" for transportation on the roads.

Above: Ruston-Bucyrus 20-H on heavy rock duty.

Below: 20-H on demonstration at Waterhall Farm, Hertford in October 1968.
Equipments demonstrated were a standard grab with 30" shells and a 40" light duty dipper
with blade type side cutters.

Above: Photograph taken in April 1969 of the 20-H final assembly line in 47-Bay of the Excavator Works. (Note the distinctive grille at the rear of the cabs of the 'H' range of hydraulic excavators is part of their 'wing tunnel' cooling system. This is effected by a cooling fan drawing air through grilles in the sides and underside, over the hydraulic components and piping, and out through the radiator and rear grille.)

Below: Ruston-Bucyrus 20-H fitted with Norton Mk.II ¾ cu.yd. grab.

'A Strange Animal' - Hydraulic Hoe with Rotating Boom

Around the time the 20-RBH Hydraulic Hoe was being developed at Lincoln, this unusual looking B.E. designed backhoe rotating boom was shipped from America for tests by Ruston-Bucyrus. Fitted to a 20-RBH base machine and carrying the 20-RBH newly designed dipper handle, it is pictured below in the Excavator Works yard.

Driven by a single hydraulic ram the cylindrical upper portion of the boom was free to rotate sideways in either direction allowing the hoe-type dragshovel to dig at an angle thus creating a concave trench. It is not known for what special application this equipment was designed but RB were not impressed and the idea was not pursued beyond this one test.

Problems with the 20-H

The testing and subsequent performance of the Ruston-Bucyrus built 20-H in the field showed that, though its digging capabilities were good, there were fundamental problems associated with the excavator - as detailed below - which resulted in a large number of dissatisfied customers and machines returned to the factory.

Propel; Unfortunately the propelling qualities of the 20-H did not match its digging performance. Because it had a completely mechanical propel system driven through the centre post from hydraulic propel motors mounted on the deck it lacked propelling power and the machine was inclined to stall - customers were complaining that "it couldn't climb the curb."

Steering; Also resulting from its design of propel was the machine's inadequate steering. The sales catalogue made much of the fact that the machines were equipped with two propel motors and one could be forgiven for assuming this meant one for each set of crawlers, thus greatly improving the crawlers turning capabilities. But this was not so, the two motors drove a big gear on the central shaft down through the middle of the machine to operate the propel machinery (the need for two motors was dictated by the fact that a single motor could not be found in the States big enough for the job). This meant that the 20-H, like traditional mechanical excavators, could only be turned by 'spragging' the crawlers.

The net result of this was that while competitors' machines could do a spin turn with independent motors driving contra-rotating tracks, the 20-H clanked round like a dinosaur. (Later B.E. 20-H machines were fitted with individual propel motors.)

Noise Level; The 'wind tunnel cooling' installed on the 20-H, already mentioned, was effective in its intended purpose of cooling the hydraulics but the noise as the cooling fan drew air through the housing and out through the rear grille was excessive. Added to the normal operating sound, this resulted in a very noisy excavator.

Structural Failures; The first batch of ten 20-H Hydraulic Excavators left the Lincoln factory during April to June of 1968, and there were already signs which became more apparent as each subsequent machine left the assembly line that the company had a serious problem on their hands. Machines were breaking down as a result of certain structural failures, resulting in large numbers being returned to the factory to be replaced by a new machine. The main problem seemed to lie in the basic design of the 'H' machines; they had a fabricated revolving frame, fabricated truck frame, to which was bolted fabricated crawler side frames and fabricated axles. A consequence of this lack of base castings was that it was impossible to achieve a tight, rigid structure and in heavy digging these main units would flex and wear resulting in structural damage. The flexing also resulted in excessive and abnormal wear on the propel machinery. Further structural problems appeared with the front end equipment; the fabricated dipper handles suffered from metal fatigue and breakages occurred on many of the machines.

Perhaps the most expensive structural failure which occurred on more than one occasion was the breaking away of the boom foot near the operator's cab which allowed the hydraulic rams to push the boom sideways towards an alarmed and frightened operator. Since this was the result of failure within the revolving frame, repairs required the machine to be returned to the factory and the whole front end stripped down, with possible expensive warranty claims to follow.

20-RBH

Attempts were made by Ruston-Bucyrus to solve some of these problems - nothing could be done about the basic design but where possible the machine was strengthened up where the breakages occurred and a new stronger dipper handle was designed.

The American dipper handle was a box structure created by welding separate plates to form the sides top, bottom and end, thus involving maximum welding. This was replaced by a box section handle which, like the 3-RB, was built by welding together two folded channel pieces which eliminated much of the welding and increased its strength. With these improvements and other modifications the Ruston-Bucyrus 20-H was re-launched as the 20-RBH to disassociate it from the B.E. original, a marketing strategy in the face of increasing loss of confidence in the 20-H among RB customers.

One such customer was Tornborg & Lundberg of Sweden who were eagerly awaiting RB's new hydraulic machine in the traditional belief that if you bought a Ruston-Bucyrus excavator you could 'knock hell out of it' and it would keep going. Production of the 20-H / 20-RBH ended in 1972, by which time forty 20-H machines and 102 of the improved 20-RBH had been built.

Above: 20-RBH Hoe, Mc.No.32807, equipped with ⁷/₈ cu.yd. rock dipper excavating sewage trench at Heighington, Lincoln. The machine was supplied to local company Lindum Construction Ltd. in September 1971 and, like the one in the photograph below, is equipped with the revised dipper handle.

Below: 20-RBH Hoe, Mc.No.35078, was delivered to J.W. Pearson in March 1971 and is seen here laying North Sea Gas piping at Caenby Corner near Lincoln.

20-RBH Hoe with Two-Piece Pin Connected Boom 1969

From the beginning, there had been concern that the B.E 'H' range of hydraulic machines did not fully answer the needs of R.B.'s domestic and continental markets as suggested in the several surveys; in particular the need for a machine with the capability of altering the length of its boom to suit various digging applications, and different types of front end equipments.

By 1969, the main work of the hydraulic section of the Ruston-Bucyrus Engineering Dept. was focused on the development of the 20-RBH and Peter Wyatt raised the possibility with his boss, Chief Engineer Bob Chevassut, of developing a two-piece boom for it similar to other European makes of hydraulic hoe-type excavators.

This would be straight forward exercise of maintaining the same geometry as the existing 20-RBH machine but replacing its standard one-piece boom with a two-part boom which had alternative connecting pin positions that enabled the reach to be extended. Its advantage over the standard equipment was that with this type of boom and the further option of two different lengths of dipper handle, the front end could be adjusted to suit different digging depths and conditions. A further advantage was that it also offered the opportunity of interchangeable front end equipments.

This idea was directly in line with Chevassut's own recommendations made to B.E. on his 1965 visit, and he directed Peter to develop such an equipment. Designs were drawn up and a prototype built which was tested and proved to be successful. The 20-RBH Two-Piece Boom Hydraulic Hoe eventually went into production at the Lincoln factory in 1971 as an alternative to the standard one-piece hoe, and was soon also adopted on the Bucyrus-Erie 20-H. So successful was it that the two-piece boom became standard on subsequent RB and BE hydraulic hoe excavators.

A 20-RBH on tractor-type crawlers fitted with the Ruston-Bucyrus designed two-piece hoe equipment.

The connection of the upper boom is made using two of its four connecting pin positions and this allows for three alternative working ranges - Maximum Range (pin position 1 & 2) effective length 11' 6"; Intermediate Range (pin position 2 & 3) effective length 9' 3"; Minimum Range (pin positions 3 & 4) effective length 7' 0". (Note the above photograph shows the Intermediate Range position.)

To these options was added a choice of two lengths of dipper handle - Standard 7' 0" or Long 11' 0".

From these variables the following comparison can be made of the 20-RBH maximum digging radii;
Maximum range boom, Standard 7' 0" handle
    Maximum Digging Radius 27' 3"
Maximum range boom, Long 11' 0" handle
    Maximum Digging Radius 36' 0"
Choice of Dipper
    Standard - 1 cu.yd.
    Wide (used with standard handle only)
        - 1¼ cu.yd. or 1½ cu.yd.

20-RBH Parallel Action Loading Shovel 1970 / 1971

The Lincoln management had always felt strongly that when it came to hydraulic excavators there was a need in their domestic and European markets for a hydraulic shovel type excavator. This was identified in all the surveys yet the development of the 3-RB and the subsequent adoption of the B.E. 'H' range of machines had not addressed this need.

With the RB's development of the two-part boom hoe they now had a machine convertible to shovel equipment and Chevassut began drawing up proposals for a hydraulic quarry shovel based upon the 20-RBH. Peter Wyatt drew up the specifications (which included both toothed rock dipper of 1¼ cu.yd. and coal dipper of 1½ cu.yd.), drawings were prepared and a model was built.

Of particular note was the fact that it was designed with parallel action, and though other european manufacturers were building this type of shovel, it was the first U.K. built machine of this type. (Not all quarry shovels had parallel action front ends; its advantage in providing forward movement of the dipper parallel to the ground was particularly useful for selective digging in narrow coal seams with flat floors where you only wanted the coal, or in excavating china clay where the seams are quite thin and you must not mix the sand with the clay.)

The Ruston-Bucyrus engineering department with Bob Chevassut discussing with his chief draughtsman, Harold Auger, the design model for the 20-RBH Parallel-action Hydraulic Shovel Loader.

Robert C. Chevassut was one of a small group of graduate trainees recruited in the early 1950s by James H. Page, Ruston-Bucyrus's brilliant Technical Director. This was a rare departure from the company's traditional practice of training potential managers through their established apprentice scheme. Chevassut, a civil engineering graduate from Manchester University had a brilliant engineering mind and his rise within the company was both justified and understandable. He succeeded Philip Durand as RB's Chief Engineer in 1965 and was appointed Director of Ruston-Bucyrus Ltd. in 1972.

Chevassut's work on RB's specialist lifting cranes is described in Vol. IV of Lincoln's Excavators, though his wider engineering application made him an invaluable asset to the Lincoln company.

On one of his regular visits to B.E., Chevassut, accompanied by Peter Wyatt, took the drawings and model of the proposed parallel-action hydraulic loading shovel for the parent company's approval and was given the go-ahead to build a prototype of his design. (While there Peter was required to visit B.E.'s Evansville Plant on a different matter and there saw the prototype for the special 60S, a large hydraulic shovel which also had parallel action front end, but of a more complicated design. This machine did not prove successful and never went into full production.)

The prototype 20-RBH Shovel Loader was built and the machine was put through several months of rigorous testing in the Greetwell quarries. The machine performed well, in fact too well for Greetwell quarry because it was excavating rocks too large to go through the crushing plant. Despite its success in digging, the machine wasn't dumping fast enough; most parallel action shovels had bottom opening dippers which enabled much quicker dumping but the prototype was too small a machine for such to be fitted easily.

This was only one factor in the general conclusion by the Ruston-Bucyrus design team that the 20-RBH, the only machine available to them at the time, was not really big enough for conversion to a quarry loading shovel.

Proposals were drawn up and drawings made in the RB Engineering Department to produce a two-piece and parallel shovel equipment for the 15-RBH and 30-RBH but nothing further was done and the idea was shelved. (Several years later, Bob Chevassut's idea of a hydraulic parallel front loading shovel would resurface when the final phase of Ruston-Bucyrus hydraulic excavator development saw the successful production of the 375-RS Hydraulic Quarry Shovel.)

The prototype of RB's design for a parallel action loading shovel based on the 20-RBH is seen here on test; there is no record of what became of it after the project was dropped and only the wooden scale model exists as evidence of this first attempt by the Lincoln Company to produce a purpose-built hydraulic quarry shovel.

15-H / 15-RBH Hydraulic Excavator

The 20-H had its problems, but the next of the B.E. designed hydraulic excavators to go into production at the Excavator Works can only be described as a complete failure, this was the ½ cu.yd. 15-H. The first production batch of four 15-H excavators (Lot 1/1-4) which left the factory in June 1971 were all eventually scrapped and in the ensuing climate of returned machines and cancelled orders, a further batch of six was produced. After attempts by RB to correct some of the faults with the 15-RBH, a final batch of ten were produced; with the last 15-RBH leaving the factory in April 1974.

The standard 15-H was a hoe-type hydraulic excavator mounted on tractor type crawlers; the power unit on the first batch was a 3-cyl. General Motors diesel engine, but the final batch was supplied with a 6-cyl. Perkins. The hydraulic system comprised three constant flow gear-type pumps, three double acting cylinders for boom hoist, dig and wrist actions, and fixed displacement gear-type motors to operate the independent swing and propel functions.

One of the declared reasons for RB's adoption of the 'H' machines was that here we had a range of different size excavators all using the same hydraulic systems, allowing for interchange of components. However, this did not turn out to be the case, possibly because B.E. at that stage were unsure which basic design was the best. They 'played their options' with the result that, though the 20-H and 30-H had similar propel systems with a hydraulic propel motor on the deck driving a completely mechanical lower works, the 15-H had its propel motors mounted on the crawler side frames driving the crawlers directly through an enclosed gear system.

This should have resulted in better propel performance, but it gave rise to serious problems. The use of gear motors with slow speed, high torque, meant that a long gear case was needed along each crawler side frame containing several reduction gears driven off the motor to achieve the torque and speed required to drive the machine on rough ground. This system inevitably put a strain on the crawler side frames causing twisting and flexing that resulted in both structural failures and damage to the gears. (This problem was avoided later on the successful Ruston-Bucyrus designed RH1 with the choice of high pressure hydraulics, epicyclic gear boxes and oil-operated disc brakes instead of lorry type brakes.)

Like the 20-H, Ruston-Bucyrus attempted to minimise some of the faults by introducing the 15-RBH which incorporated certain improvements, but aside from its mechanical problems, the 15-H was never a popular machine with U.K. operators; the feeling was that it too small to meet their requirements, and of the twenty produced by RB many were scrapped or sold off cheaply.

A 15-H lower works in the Lincoln factory with tractor-type crawler mounting that was standard on these machines. One of the hydraulic motors can be seen mounted on the crawler frame with its enclosed gearing to the drive tumbler. This lower works was simply not strong enough to take the propelling loads.

Above: Ruston-Bucyrus 15-H Hoe with L.P.H. tractor-type crawlers.

Below: 15-RBH Hoe on D2 type crawlers waiting to be collected from the works.
This is Mc.No.35867 which was Lot 2/3 in the RB production schedule and was never
sold but went out on hire to T. Johnson on 8th March 1973.

Ruston-Bucyrus 30-H / 30-RBH

The third and last model in the B.E. 'H' range of hydraulic excavators to be built by Ruston-Bucyrus was the 30-H and as an enlarged version of the 20-H Hydraulic Hoe it was the most successful of the three models. Physically larger and with a correspondingly larger engine, it had standard dipper capacity of 1½ cu.yd. though a range of dippers were available up to 2⅛ cu.yd. Its hydraulic system was basically the same as the 20-H, and like the 20-H its propel comprised two hydraulic motors mounted on the deck driving centrally through gearing to the lower works propelling machinery. The power unit on the Ruston-Bucyrus machines was a General Motors Type 6V-71N and the net weight of the machine (with hoe equipment) was around 27 tons.

The Ruston-Bucyrus 30-H went into production in 1969 with test machine No.33585 (which was later scrapped) and full production followed. A number of improvements were made during the course of its manufacture, including strengthening up the crawler mounting, and reinforcing the boom and handle, resulting in its re-launch as the 30-RBH. From the first test machine a total of 48 30-H and 30-RBH were built, until production ended in 1975.

The first 30-H Hoe produced by Ruston-Bucyrus following the test prototype was purchased by J.H. Peck & Sons Ltd. of Ardwick and delivered to the customer in July 1969; it is seen below working on the Princess Road extension for the Manchester Corporation.

In its job trenching for 48in. concrete pipes and back filling in hard clay the machine proved very satisfactory and the only problem, common to hydraulic excavators in general, was the excessive wear to its dipper. After only two months, this machine was already on its second set of RB's specially hardened H&L dipper teeth.

The first 30-H Hoe at work for J.H. Peck & Sons Ltd of Ardwick.

A Change of Direction and Success at Last

It was clear to the Lincoln management that the B.E. designed 'H' range of hydraulic excavators did not answer the needs of their domestic and overseas markets for a Ruston-Bucyrus hydraulic excavator that could compete successfully against the foreign makes (mainly German) that were affecting the sales of their smaller rope excavators.

Constant modifications to the B.E. designs was not the answer to the situation and by 1970 the decision had been made that Ruston-Bucyrus would design and build their own range of hydraulic excavators.

LINCOLN'S EXCAVATORS

HYDRAULIC EXCAVATORS
SUCCESS AT LAST

Ruston-Bucyrus 375-RS Hydraulic Shovel, Ribblesdale Cement Company

A NEW RANGE OF RB HYDRAULIC EXCAVATORS

The production of the B.E. designed 'H' range of hydraulic excavators, despite many modifications, was not proving the hoped for success with the Ruston-Bucyrus U.K. and European customers and within the Lincoln company there was a growing belief that the only solution was the development of an entirely new hydraulic excavator to their own design and specification. From their experience with the 3-RB and the American machines RB's Chief Engineer Bob Chevassut and his team felt confident that they could produce a successful design from scratch and in 1971 the Lincoln Engineering Department began work on designs for a completely new Ruston-Bucyrus hydraulic excavator.

Aware that the key to a successful machine was its hydraulic system, the RB design team decided that with the new machine they would return to high pressure hydraulics and piston type pumps rather than the low pressure, gear pump system of the American machines. By this time John Willcock had left the company and Peter Wyatt was given the task of preparing proposals for a design.

In the last days of the 3-RB, Willcock had the idea of fitting it with constant horse-power control which meant that instead of 'swashing' the pumps manually you connected the system through the pumps so that as you load the pumps they swash back automatically. Wyatt picked up on this idea and using Linde pumps developed a constant horse-power, variable flow hydraulic system which provided automatic balance of pressure and flow for all working conditions; the principle was, 'high pressure, low flow, less power needed, greater efficiency'. To solve any travelling problems a new propel system was designed which had two independent sets of hydraulic motor and gear box, one for each track, mounted in a fork of the truck frame.

Happy with the proposals and plans for the new machine, a confident Chevassut suggested to Bucyrus-Erie that the Lincoln company could build a complete new hydraulic excavator that was efficient, of less power, but with a faster performance than any produced up to that point. Eugene Berg, President of B.E. wrote back saying - "Prove it! Build a mock-up and show me it works".

The test mock-up for the proposed RBH-1 photographed during a
hill test in Lincoln's Greetwell Quarry.

RBH-1 Hydraulic Excavator (The Test Mock-up)

The specifications were drawn up and the design work completed in the Engineering Dept. with Peter Wyatt design engineer (hydraulics) and Eric Wadsworth design engineer for the structural side, and it was decided to build a 'test bed' version of the proposed new Ruston-Bucyrus hydraulic excavator which by now had been given the working title of the RBH-1.

Ruston-Bucyrus had recently acquired the Foster Gwynnes foundry and workshops on Firth Road in Lincoln and it was here in the unlikely setting of the old Foster's Tank Shop where the first World War 1 tanks were built, that an experimental mock-up was built to test the proposed new hydraulic system before building a full prototype.

The test-bed machine used the 15-H revolving frame, operator's cab and front end equipment, everything else was stripped off and replaced by the new hydraulic system and a complete new lower works incorporating a new hydraulic propel. Construction of this test machine was carried out by a small team of engineers under the supervision of Peter Bateman reporting to the Engineering Dept. The completed mock-up went to Greetwell Quarries for extensive testing and its performance was measured against a 15-H doing the same work under the exact same conditions. The tests proved that the mock-up would out-dig the 15-H, producing with the same size equipment 25% more output.

The RBH-1 Prototype Hydraulic Excavator 1971 / 1972

Following the success of the test mock-up, a prototype for a completely new hydraulic excavator could now be built from scratch embodying the hydraulic principals of the test machine. The new prototype would be called the RBH-1 and it would feature constant horsepower, variable-flow hydraulics, two-lever control, independent hydraulic propel with epicyclic gear boxes and multi-position two-piece boom.

With Peter Bateman as engineer in charge of a small group of platers and fitters, the full prototype of the new hydraulic excavator was built in the No. 2 Stores of the Excavator Works where the production line of the earlier 3-RB had taken place.

The production team, with Peter Bateman on the left, posed in front of the completed RBH-1 Prototype machine.

RBH-1 Success at Last!

The first prototype RBH-1 was completed and ready for testing on 28th March 1972 and after preliminary tests in the works yard, it began a series of field tests in Lincoln's Greetwell Quarry. At this point a note of encouragement was received from Mr. Berg, President B.E. Co., in a letter to Bill Winter, RB Managing Director, on 16th May 1972, saying:

> "I have had an opportunity to review the material you sent on the subject machine (Model RBH-1) and have had a number of discussions with Don Barber and Bob Meyer (B.E. Engineering Manager). They were highly in praise for the design and hydraulic circuitry and feel that it should be a real winner. In their opinion your test results are quite satisfactory and the number of changes should be minimal. Bob Chevassut and his staff are to be highly complimented on their development. I understand you are building a prototype of the new machine and suggest you build two and send one over here."

Cordially, E.P. Berg, President B.E. Co.

Despite Berg's confidence, the problems experienced by Bucyrus-Erie with the travelling of their own crawler mounted 15-H Excavator prompted the President's added directive to the RB Engineering Dept. that

> "the RBH-1 travelling performance must be proved by undergoing a 600 mile continuous travelling test in quarry conditions."

A course was duly set up in Greetwell quarries and the test carried out day and night in a period of very wet and muddy conditions. At times the water was up to the side platforms with the entire crawlers and truck frame carrying the propel drives entirely submerged, yet the machine came through the test to everyone's satisfaction. (Not a small part of this success may be attributed to the cleverly chosen wet conditions which ensured the machine's mechanical parts were well lubricated.)

The success of the RBH-1 Prototype in all its field tests meant that plans could be made for full production of this new excavator which, in order to distinguish it from the B.E. 'H' Range of hydraulic excavators, would be called the 150-RH.

RBH-1 Prototype on tests in the Works yard.

RB Engineering Dept's Hydraulic Excavator team with the RBH-1 Prototype at the works, 28th March 1972.
Left to Right: Frank Auger, Eng. in Charge - Hyd. Cranes/Exc.; Peter Batemen, Eng. in Charge - Exp. Shop;
Peter Odam - Fitter, Exp. Shop; Peter Wyatt, Design Eng. - Hydraulics; J. Sorby-Grice, Fitter; Bob Chevassut,
Chief Engineer; Tom Sims, Plater; Eric Wadsworth, Design Eng. - Cranes; Alfred Brown, Plater - Exp. Shop;
John Harrison (seated in cab), Fitter/Test Driver.

A Sudden Departure

There was now every sign that the hopes for a new range of hydraulic excavators based upon the RBH-1 would be fulfilled but regrettably Bob Chevassut, the person within the Lincoln company's management most responsible for this promising new line, would not see the conclusion of his project.

In June, 1973, Berg called an international marketing meeting at B.E. headquarters; the week long meeting involved representatives from Bucyrus-Erie Co., Ruston-Bucyrus Ltd., and Komatsu-Bucyrus K.K. The purpose of the meeting was to,

"further co-ordinate engineering, manufacturing and marketing efforts of BE, RB and KB to offer Bucyrus machines that will best satisfy diverse construction machine requirements throughout the world."

Representing Ruston-Bucyrus at the meeting were recent American appointees W.B. Winter (Managing Director) and J.H. Wilcox (Director and General Sales Manager), together with Bob Chevassut (Director and Chief Engineer).

The nature of the meeting and its significance for Chevassut is unclear but three months later he resigned as Director and Chief Engineer from the company to which he had devoted the whole of his working life. His function as Chief Engineer was filled in October 1973 by American R.E. Meyer, brought over from the B.E. company and appointed Manager of Engineering of Ruston-Bucyrus Ltd.

Chevassut's going marked the last of a long line of talented and dedicated professionals within the Ruston-Bucyrus management who found it difficult to work under what they felt were constraints resulting from the ever increasing control by the American parent company.

The Ruston-Bucyrus 150-RH

Under Meyer work continued in the Engineering Department on the development of the 150-RH and in February 1974, Robert E. Meyer was appointed Director of Ruston-Bucyrus Ltd. Unfortunately, within a few months for health reasons he had to return to the States and the Engineering Department continued under the twin control of Lyle Grider as Manager, Design & Development and G. A. Scott, as Manager, Product Engineer. Peter Wyatt was transferred to the Experimental Dept. and a new design team was set up in the Engineering Dept.

Peter Bateman and his small team of platers, fitters etc. carried out the few minor changes to the RBH-1 necessary to prepare it for full production as the 150-RH - the hydraulic circuitry was slightly different and different pumps were used; the oil cooler was relocated; the original cylinders which had been designed in house were replaced by bought-in units; and mainly for appearance the operator's cab was re-designed. The first 150-RHs retained the 4 cyl. Ford engine that was used on the RBH-1 prototype, but from the start this was found to lack the necessary power and subsequent models were fitted with either Perkins 6-cyl. water-cooled or Deutz 5-cyl. air cooled diesel engines.

The first Ruston-Bucyrus 150-RH came off the Lincoln production line in the Spring of 1976 and in November of that year it was proudly exhibited on the Ruston-Bucyrus stand at the Public Works Exhibition held in the National Exhibition Centre, Birmingham.

The pre-production 150-RH with Perkins engine on test; this was Mc.No. 36166 which was subsequently purchased by A & V Squires and delivered to them in March 1977.

Above: 150-RH Hydraulic Hoe excavator equipped with 24" Bofors rock dipper, excavating limestone rock in Kirton Lindsay quarries near Lincoln. This early model was on lease to Ready Mixed Concrete for test purposes.

Below: 150-RH Hoe on lease to A. Barker. Scunthorpe, excavating a drainage ditch at Broughton near Brigg.

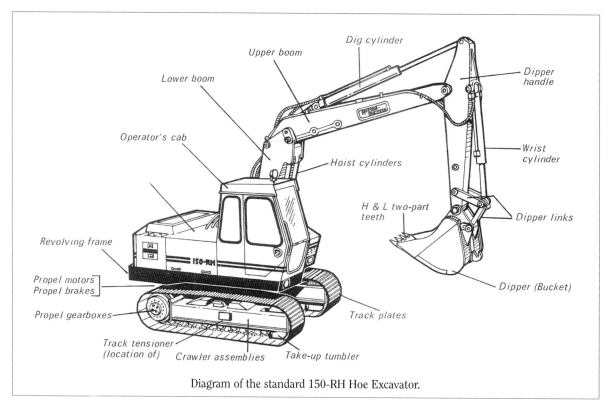

Diagram of the standard 150-RH Hoe Excavator.

A feature of the 150-RH Hydraulic Hoe excavator was its adaptability to particular working conditions and different applications; the former was achieved by the combination of a two-piece multi-position boom and a choice of three different lengths of dipper handle, and the latter by the wide range of dippers and optional equipments such as grabs, grapples, hammers, etc. that could be easily and quickly attached to the basic machine. For certain equipments such as hydraulically operated grabs the hydraulic cylinder on the dipper handle is removed and replaced by a hydraulic pack.

150-RH (Mc.No.36170) fitted with Cactus Grab scrap handling at Smith-Clayton Forge, Lincoln, October 1976.

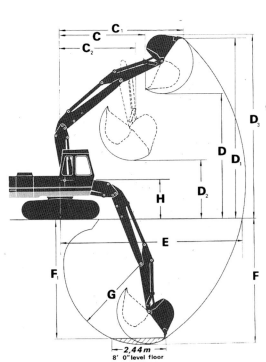

Multi-position variable-geometry boom

The two-piece multi-position boom gives variable geometry for a wide range of operation. The upper boom has four pin-connecting holes which are located in the lower boom in six positions, as required, giving varying boom lengths and boom-angles.

The two boom-angle positions are for maximum working height or maximum digging depth.

G   Sweep radius 3,43 m 11' 3"

H   Height of boom-foot pin above ground level 1,24 m 4' 1"

Upper boom section: arrangement and position		Maximum range (Pin positions 1 & 2) Fully extended		Minimum range (Pin positions 3 & 4) Fully retracted	
		Low angle	High angle	Low angle	High angle
C	Radius at beginning of dump	3,88 m 12' 9"	3,12 m 10' 3"	3,20 m 10' 6"	2,82 m 9' 0"
C1	Radius at end of dump	5,56 m 18' 3"	4,04 m 13' 3"	5,03 m 16' 6"	3,81 m 12' 6"
C2	Clearance radius (minimum)	3,35 m 11' 0"	2,44 m 8' 0"	2,66 m 8' 9"	2,05 m 6' 9"
D	Dumping height	5,33 m 17' 6"	6,63 m 21' 9"	4,42 m 14' 6"	5,56 m 18' 3"
D1	Clearance under dipper—end of dump	7,77 m 25' 6"	9,30 m 30' 3"	6,78 m 22' 3"	8,23 m 27' 0"
D2	Dumping clearance under dipper	2,44 m 8' 0"	3,43 m 11' 3"	1,67 m 5' 6"	2,44 m 8' 0"
D3	Clearance height—end of dump	7,85 m 25' 9"	9,22 m 30' 3"	6,93 m 22' 9"	8,15 m 26' 9"
E	Digging radius (maximum)	8,08 m 26' 6"	8,54 m 28' 0"	7,01 m 23' 0"	7,39 m 24' 6"
F	Digging depth (over front, side or corner of mounting)	5,33 m 17' 6"	4,72 m 15' 9"	4,49 m 14' 9"	4,11 m 13' 6"
F1	Depth of 2,44 m (8' 0") level floor	5,10 m 16' 9"	4,57 m 15' 0"	4,19 m 13' 9"	3,96 m 13' 0"

Maximum weight of dipper and contents		1490 kg 3290 lb		1910 kg 4205 lb		
Dipper capacities generally available	litres cu. yd	480 $\frac{5}{8}$	575 $\frac{3}{4}$	480 $\frac{5}{8}$	575 $\frac{3}{4}$	670 $\frac{7}{8}$ 770 1

Working Range Diagram for 150-RH Hoe with Standard 6'-9" Dipper Handle.

Above and below: 150-RH on loan to Anglian River Authority cleaning
out a river bed in Grantham, Lincs.

Above: The keys of the first Ruston-Bucyrus hydraulic excavator to be purchased by the Upper Witham Internal Drainage Board are being officially received at the Excavator Works in Spring 1978 by the Board's representatives - Mr. P. Wright, Vice Chairman, (left); Councillor S.A. Campbell, Vice Chairman, (second left); Mr. J. Barnatt, Clerk / Chief Engineer (fourth from right); Mr. J.T. Hollis, Chairman (third from right); Mr. A. Houlder, Asst. Engineer (right). Presenting the keys of the new 150-RH is P.R. Baynham, RB Area Manager, east Midlands, with G. Brammer, Manager Sales Admin. (third left).

Below: A clear measure of the success of the Ruston-Bucyrus 150-RH was in the fact that a large proportion of the Lincoln company's production was exported to the U.S.A. where they were preferred by B.E. customers to the American equivalent. This photo shows some of a U.S.A. order in Spring 1979, waiting to be dispatched to the States.

Expanding the Range -
150-RW / 175-RH / 220-RH

The 150-RH proved an immediate success and went on to sell in large numbers, so it was not surprising that Ruston-Bucyrus considered the possibility of other models of hydraulic excavators based upon this successful basic design.

For some time there had been signs that a large version of the 150-RH would be popular with the U.K. markets and two years later, in 1978, the first 220-RH left the production line. This 21.8 ton hydraulic excavator, which could be equipped with a $2\frac{5}{8}$ cu.yd. dipper, was available with a range of equipments and like the 150-RH had the adaptable multi-position boom, choice of handles and crawlers. The 220-RH design was the same as the 150-RH but it was a larger machine overall with bigger engine, bigger pumps, etc. and it proved as popular with U.K. and European customers as its smaller brother.

Concerned at the fact that they were losing out to other makes of hydraulic excavators in the lucrative coal handling work in open-cast mines, Ruston-

Bucyrus developed a shovel version of the 220-RH designated the 220-RS. Primarily considered as a coal-loading shovel, it had a specially designed boom and handle, and could be fitted with a 2 cu.yd. dipper with hydraulically-operated bottom-dumping door. At this time it was the largest British-built hydraulic shovel.

Market research also indicated a need for a hydraulic excavator in size between the 150-RH and 220-RH and by the 1980s this was answered with the development of the 175-RH which was essentially the 155-RH on the 220-RH crawler mounting; this extra stability resulted in an economical machine with the capability of operating up to 2 cu.yd. dipper, though it never had a chance to prove itself before production of all RB hydraulic excavators ceased in 1983.

Also at this time, a wheel version of the 150-RH was developed and introduced on to the market as the 150-RW; this proved an outright success in terms of sales and one customer (the National Coal Board) purchased the whole of its first year's production in 1980. The same year, saw an improved and up-dated 150-RH introduced as the 155-RH.

The twenty-ton 220-RH Hoe hydraulic excavator feeding quarry trucks via a hopper.

The 220-RH had the basic RB designed high pressure hydraulic system similar to the 150-RH, using Linde variable displacement pumps and constant horsepower control which had proven so successful. It also had a similar propel system in which each track was driven independently by a high

speed fixed displacement hydraulic motor through an epicyclic gearbox. Both the 220-RH and the 150-RH proved popular machines with U.K. customers, and by the time production of all hydraulic excavators ceased in 1983, 59 units of the 220-RH/RS had been sold and 333 units of the 150-RH / 155-RH.

Above: An early test prototype of the 220-RH at the Excavator Works equipped with the coal-loading shovel front end which would later go into full production as the 220-RS.

Below: 175-RH Hoe excavator on display in front of the Ruston-Bucyrus Admin. Offices; powered by a Deutz 5 cyl. air-cooled diesel, it offered dipper sizes up to 2 cu.yds.

375-RS Hydraulic Quarry Shovel

In 1978 Lyle Grider was appointed Manager of Engineering and by that time there was every indication that Ruston-Bucyrus had a successful range of small to medium hydraulic excavators, but there remained the unanswered matter of a purpose-built heavy duty hydraulic shovel. The 54-RB rope shovels used in the quarries were getting 'old in the tooth' and as hydraulic machines were becoming an alternative, the quarry managers were asking RB for a heavy hydraulic rock shovel/loader that could replace them.

Eight years earlier Chevassut had developed the 20-RBH parallel-action loading shovel which never got beyond the prototype stage and Bucyrus-Erie the abortive 60S, so it was now time for another look, and the Ruston-Bucyrus Engineering Department under Lyle began the development of a completely new parallel-action heavy duty hydraulic quarry shovel to be called the Ruston-Bucyrus 375-RS. Attention was first focused on the front end equipment and with a design developed and drawings prepared in the Engineering Dept., model testing was carried out.

A new Experimental Workshop had been set up at the Excavator Works in the old former Ruston foundry fettling shop, (in more recent times occupied by a pine furniture maker), with Peter Bateman in charge of Prototype machine build and Peter Wyatt in charge of Hydraulic Testing. Here the latter had a test rig built with which to identify and measure loads and stresses in the proposed design for the new front end. The rig consisted of a Perspex scale model of the equipment, and because hydraulics were not being tested, the model was actuated by a temporary low-pressure system using cylinders made from spare tubing. The principle of the test rig was that;

The strength modulus and physical properties of the Perspex material used for the model was known, and also the comparative stress scale factors for Perspex to steel. This information, together with the scaling up factor from model to full size, could be interpreted in a formula which could be used to interpret loads and stresses in the Perspex model to the real thing. All that was needed was a way of identifying and measuring stresses in the model at different working loads and positions.

This was achieved in a temperature controlled cubicle by first spraying the model with a coating of Tenslac; after a critical curing period, loads could be applied to the structure and any stress points, ('hot spots') would appear as cracks in the coating which could be identified and their positions marked on the model. (Different grades of Tenslac were available to match the applied loading on the model.) As a separate exercise, once the stress points were located, subsequent strain gauging of the model could take place to measure the stress factors.

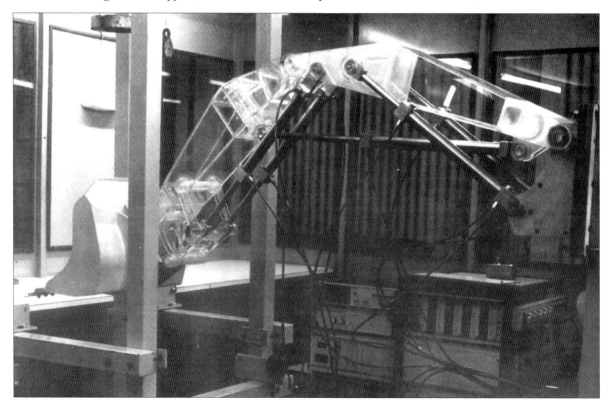

Perspex test rig of the proposed 375-RS parallel-action shovel front end equipment.

Ruston-Bucyrus Experimental (Prototype) Shop.

A s the development of Ruston-Bucyrus hydraulic excavators progressed it was decided to establish a fully equipped experimental workshop separate from the main production areas where prototypes of the proposed new range of hydraulic machines could be built and equipment tested. This was created out of the former Ruston and Hornsby fettling shop, part of the old Spike Island Foundry, which was completely re-furbished and fitted out with the necessary specialised equipment.

Once the design for the proposed new 375-RS had been worked out, the time came for the building of a prototype; to save time a Bucyrus-Erie 350-H base machine was shipped in from the States to use as test bed upon which the various aspects of the new design could be tested out in heavy duty working conditions. Although retaining its glass fibre cab, inadequate for heavy duty quarry work, the 350-H upper works was stripped of all but the American G.M. engine, mounted on a complete new quarry lower works developed for the 375-RS, installed with a complete new hydraulic system, and equipped with the new parallel-action shovel front-end also developed specially for the 375-RS.

The test-bed for the 375-RS prototype using the B.E. 350-H base machine on trials at Kirton Lindsey quarries near Lincoln. With a dipper capacity of up to 4 tons and a range of heavy duty front-tip and bottom-dump dippers the test machine proved its abilities in the heaviest digging.

After sufficient tests with the prototype, the RB team were ready to build the new 375-RS from scratch. It had a newly designed entire lower works equipped with special quarry tracks, RB's well proven high-pressure constant horse power variable-flow hydraulic system, a metal cab complete with rock guard which, unlike the glass fibre cab of the BE 350-H could withstand the rigours of heavy quarry work and a specially designed heavy-duty rock shovel front-end with dipper wrist cylinders mounted on a single piece boom. Parallel wrist-action of the dipper enabled level crowding action to be achieved using hoist and crowd functions only and hydraulically operated bottom-dump dippers were available. Powered by the same 274 H.P. 8-cyl. G.M. diesel engine that was used on the B.E. 350-H, the Ruston-Bucyrus 375-RS, at 51 tons was the largest British built hydraulic excavator at that time.

Both R-B and B.E. agreed that in performance the 375-RS was a successful machine. After prolonged field testing, it was put into production at the Lincoln factory with a first batch of five machines.

The first of a batch of five RB 375-RS Hydraulic Quarry Shovels assembled in the factory.

A.   Linde Constant Horsepower Variable Piston Pumps
B.   Servo Pump
C.   Power Unit GM. 8V-71N (304 hp. at 2100 rpm)
D.   Double Filtration Return Filters Protect Pump / Pressure Filters Protect Circuit
E.   Fuel Tank (Capacity 150 galls).
F.   Hydraulic Oil Tank (System Capacity 137 galls. / Tank Capacity 81 galls).
G.   Crowd and Auxiliary Valve
H.   Closed Loop Swing System
J.   Hoist and Wrist Valve

A Ruston-Bucyrus 375-RS operated by the Ribblesdale Cement Co.
at work in Lindum Quarry in the 1980s.

The 375-RH, with its large diameter sealed heavy duty cross-roller swing circle and purpose designed wide mounting rock shovel lower works, was ideally suited to hard quarry conditions. The high performance front end with boom mounted wrist cylinders provided maximum crowd force and the parallel-action ensured good clean up. This enabled the 375-RS, with either rock bucket or on re-handling work, to out-perform all other equivalent machines supplied by its competitors.

The success of the current new range of Ruston-Bucyrus hydraulic excavators after earlier 'blind alleys' generated confidence at the Excavator Works and a second batch of 375-RS machines was scheduled, with plans for the development at Lincoln of further models, when matters came to an abrupt halt. In 1983 a directive came down from the B.E. parent company that all production of Bucyrus Erie and Ruston-Bucyrus hydraulic excavators should cease forthwith.

Ruston-Bucyrus 375-RS Quarry Shovel with operator's rock-guard at work for the Ribblesdale
Cement Co. This company employed two 375-RS Shovels in their Lanehead Quarry in the early
1980s loading limestone into Terex dump-trucks for processing at their nearby cement works.

A Summary of Ruston-Bucyrus Hydraulic Excavators

The lack of investment in the early years of the Lincoln company's attempts to produce a crawler mounted hydraulic excavator resulted in compromises and decisions which almost guaranteed a failure. It was felt in three main areas -

(a) lack of adequate production facilities demanded of this entry into the new field of hydraulic engineering,

(b) compromises in design resulting from the constant need to minimise capital expenditure,

(c) excessive use of 'bought in' component parts which were 'fixed price' items on which you couldn't cut production costs.

(The much smaller company of JCB., like RB had no hydraulic experience nor special manufacturing facility at the outset, but they did the clever thing of buying up hydraulic excavator manufacturers Whitlock, so gaining all the design experience and production facility they required for their own proposed models.)

The failure of the Ruston-Bucyrus 3-RB led to the introduction of the American designed 'H' range of hydraulic excavators which in performance and specification failed to compete against the European hydraulic excavators that posed a threat to the Lincoln company's smaller construction size excavators.

From the start the parent Bucyrus-Erie Co. had shown little enthusiasm for hydraulic excavators such as were being developed in Europe and this lack of incentive and their whole-hearted embrace of cable excavators may be explained by the fact that the American company's main interest, and its most important and lucrative markets, lay in mining machinery which at that time was less threatened by the inroads of the European hydraulic 'invasion'. (At the time few could foresee the giant hydraulic mining shovels of the future which one day would offer serious competition to the medium sized cable mining shovels.)

With the introduction of the RB designed RBH-1 and its derivatives, 150-RH, 220-RH, 375-RS etc., there was every sign that Managing Director Everitt's concerns of ten years earlier had at last been addressed and the Lincoln company had achieved a successful range of hydraulic excavators to meet the demands of their own domestic and overseas markets.

In a climate of great optimism, plans were made at the Excavator Works for the development of further hydraulic excavators, but these plans were short-lived for serious financial problems in America forced the BE Company in 1983 to close down all production of hydraulic excavators in the States and at the Lincoln factory, just when it seemed that Ruston-Bucyrus had a line of successful and competitive machines.

Whatever the circumstances of their end, we can look back on hydraulic excavators as an opportunity lost and an interesting, if frustrating, chapter in the history of Lincoln's Excavators.

Ruston-Bucyrus 375-RS Hydraulic Shovel ready to be dispatched from the Excavator Works; described as the "First All-British Hydraulic Shovel Excavator", the Ruston-Bucyrus 375-RS had its first public showing at the National Exhibition Centre, Birmingham in February 1981.

LOOKING AHEAD

This photograph entitled 'Looking Ahead' from the R-B archives is an apt choice for both the closing of this volume and leading the reader forward to the publication of the fourth and final edition of 'Lincoln's Excavators' which charts the progress of Ruston-Bucyrus Ltd and the expansion of the works to an unprecedented scale to meet the large range of additional new products. In answer to the expanding U.K. open-cast coal industry, large mining shovels and massive walking draglines were added to the product range and the demands of the construction industry led to the development of telescopic transit cranes and large crawler-mounted supercranes.

Types of Excavators

The development of the mechanical digger to replace manual labour in mines, construction sites, and waterways has resulted in a variety of different types, each suited to a particular kind of excavation work. Though this has led on the larger machines to specialisation, for example Mining Shovels and Draglines, the principle of a small to medium excavator that could be adapted to different work by simply changing its equipment had become well established by the time the Ruston-Bucyrus company began manufacturing.

The 'Universal Excavator' as it was called, was a basic machine which could be easily and quickly converted from one type of excavator to another by replacing its front end equipment with a different type and the necessary exchange or addition of certain machinery components. The different types are shown below and a fully 'Universal' machine would be capable of conversion to all the equipments here illustrated.

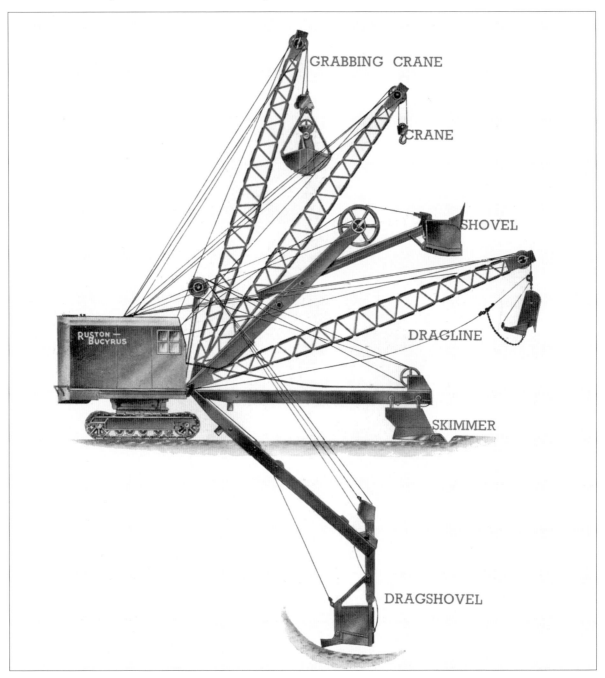

Excavator Terminology

The language that describes Cranes and Excavators and their operation has changed over the years as the machines themselves have changed.

In the early years the terminology was more descriptive of the Steam Navvies but by the 1930s developments in both the design of the machines and their application produced a new language that had its roots in America; it is this language and its conventions that are now generally accepted worldwide and that are used throughout this third Volume in the story of Lincoln's Excavators.

The following illustration identifies by name the main components of three types of Excavator - the Shovel, Dragline, and Grabbing Crane.

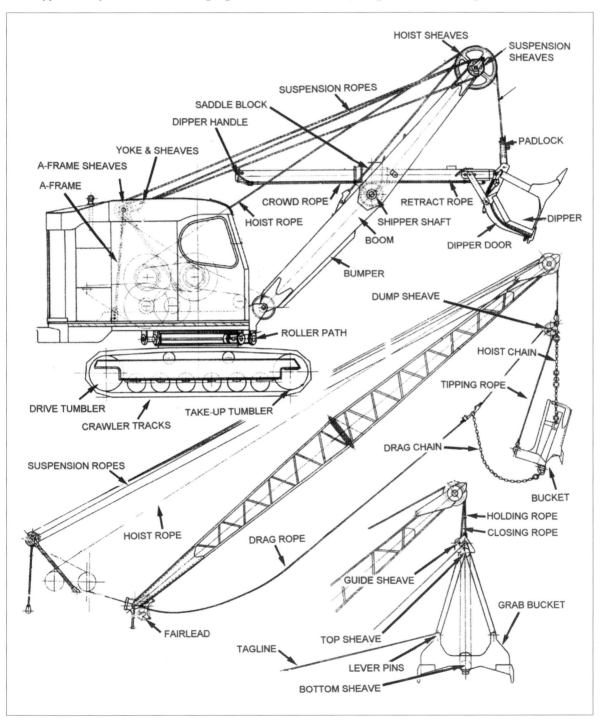

Machinery & Drawing Index

Ruston-Bucyrus 19-RB Dragshovel 21
Ruston-Bucyrus 19-RB Shovel 22,62
Ruston-Bucyrus 19-RB Dragline 24,25
Ruston-Bucyrus 10-RB Dragline 25,48,49
Ruston-Bucyrus 10-RB Shovel 28,50
Ruston-Bucyrus 10-RB Dragshovel 51
Ruston-Bucyrus 24-RB Shovel 46
Ruston-Bucyrus 24-RB Dragline 47
Ruston-Bucyrus 33-RB Electric Shovel 47
Ruston-Bucyrus 54-RB Shovel 54,59,60
   Truck Frame & Revolving Frame 55
   Main Machinery - Diesel / Single Motor Electric 56-58
Ruston-Bucyrus 54-RB Dragline 22,61-65
   Folding A-Frame 66,67
Ruston-Bucyrus 54-RB Long-Boom Stripping Shovel 68
   Working Ranges 69
Ruston-Bucyrus 54-RB Ward-Leonard Electric Shovel .. 70,72-74
   Ward-Leonard System 70
   Ward-Leonard Deck Machinery & Electrical Equipment 71
Ruston-Bucyrus 54-RB Ward-Leonard Tunnel Shovel 73
Ruston-Bucyrus 38-RB Shovel 76-79
   Main Machinery 80,81
   Single Motor Electric 82
Ruston-Bucyrus 38-RB Dragline 83
Ruston-Bucyrus 38-RB Series Two Shovel 84,88-93
   Main Machinery 84-87
Ruston-Bucyrus 38-RB Series Two Standard & Heavy Duty
   Crane / Dragline 94
Ruston-Bucyrus 22-RB Shovel 23,96,97,103,104,105
   Main Machinery 98,99
   Equipments available 102
Ruston-Bucyrus 22-RB Single Motor Electric 100
   Main Machinery 100,101
Ruston-Bucyrus 22-RB Skimmer 106
Ruston-Bucyrus 22-RB Dragshovel 107
Ruston-Bucyrus 22-RB Crane, Grabbing Crane/Dragline..108,109
Ruston-Bucyrus 22-RB Two-in-One 110,111
Ruston-Bucyrus 22-RB Wrist-action Dragshovel . 112,113,116,118
   Working Range Dimensions 114
Ruston-Bucyrus 22-RB Improved Wrist-action Dragshovel....115
Ruston-Bucyrus 22-RB with Air Control 119,122
   Air-Assist Control System 120,121
Ruston-Bucyrus 110-RB Mining Shovel..... 124-126,132,133,136
   Working Dimensions 125
   Crawler Mounting 127
   Front End Equipment 126
   Pressurised Cabs - 110/150/195 Series 135
   Static Control - 110/150/195 Series 148,149
Ruston-Bucyrus 110-RB Dragline 124,131
Ruston-Bucyrus 110-RB Long Range Mining Shovel 129
Ruston-Bucyrus 110-RB Diesel-Electric Shovel 134
Ruston-Bucyrus 110-RB Diesel-Electric Dragline 134
   Diesel-Electric Dragline Machinery 134
Ruston-Bucyrus 150-RB Ward-Leonard
   Electric Shovel 38,139,141,144,152,161
   Live Boom Suspension 144,145
   Working Dimensions 146
   Uprating 150,151
   Dipper Assembly & Transportation 162,163
Ruston-Bucyrus 150-RB Ward-Leonard
   Electric Dragline 138,139,140,147
Ruston-Bucyrus Excavator Engine Range 157,158
Ruston-Bucyrus 30-RB Shovel 166,169
   Full Air Controls 172,173
   Involute Splines & Cut-Hardened Gears 174,175

   Crawler Mounting 176
   Swing Brake 177
   Truck Frame & Main Machinery 167-170
Ruston-Bucyrus Series One Dragshovel 171
Ruston-Bucyrus 30-RB Series II Logging Cranes 178,179
Ruston-Bucyrus 30-RB Dragline 180
Piling & Special Applications 181-198
   Drop Hammer Pile Driving 181,185
   Power Hammer Application 181
   Boom Suspended Piling Rig 183-186,190
   Direct Mounted Piling Rig 183,188,189
   Bored (None-displacement) Piling 191-194
   Continuous Flight Auger (CFA) 195
   Types of Piling 196
   Diaphragm Walling 197
Ruston-Bucyrus 3-RB Hydraulic Excavator 230
Ruston-Bucyrus 12/60 Tower Crane 230,234-240
   Working Heights 235
Ruston-Bucyrus 12/52 Tower Crane 240-245,248
   AEC Matador Towing Unit 242
   Road Towing dimensions 243
   Operating Machinery 246,247
Ruston-Bucyrus 34/80 Tower Crane 240,249-252
   Road Towing & Working dimensions 251,255
   Hydraulic System 253
   Ratings 254
Ruston-Bucyrus 15/50 Tower Crane Prototype 256
Ruston-Bucyrus 2-RB Prototype Hydraulic Excavator 258
Ruston-Bucyrus 3-RB Series I Hydraulic Excavator 257-263,265
   Design, Hydraulics, Power Unit 260,261
   Working Dimensions 264
   Operating & Ancillary Controls 262
   Shovel Loader prototype 267
   Scoop Loading Shovel variation 266
   Long Dipper Arm variation 266
   Clamshell Grab equipment 268,269
Ruston-Bucyrus 3-RB Wheel Mounted
   Hydraulic Excavator 270, 271,273
   Working Dimensions 272
Ruston-Bucyrus Series II Hydraulic Excavator (interim) ... 274
Ruston-Bucyrus Series II Hydraulic Excavator (Final) 275,276,277
Bucyrus-Erie 'H' Range of Hydraulic Excavators 291-293
Ruston-Bucyrus 20-H Hydraulic Excavator..294,297,300,301,303
   Cut-away Illustration 298
   Deck Layout & Crawler Mounting 299
   Hydraulic Hoe with Rotating Boom 302
Ruston-Bucyrus 20-RBH Excavator 303,304
   Two-Piece Pin Connected Boom 305
Ruston-Bucyrus 20-RBH Parallel Action Loading Shovel . 306,307
Ruston-Bucyrus 15-H / 15-RBH Hydraulic Excavator ...308,309
Ruston-Bucyrus 30-H / 30-RBH Hydraulic Excavator 310
Ruston-Bucyrus RBH-1 prototype Hydraulic Excavator ..312-315
Ruston-Bucyrus 150-RH Hydraulic Excavator . 316-318,320,321
   Working Range Diagram 319
Ruston-Bucyrus 150-RW Wheeled Hydraulic Excavator 322
Ruston-Bucyrus 175-RH Hydraulic Excavator 322,323
Ruston-Bucyrus 220-RH Hydraulic Excavator 322,323
Ruston-Bucyrus 375-RS Hydraulic Quarry Shovel 324-330

General Index

Ableson & Co. 234
Adult Training Annex 286
Amalgamated Roadstone Co. 91
Allen, R.G. 44/230/231
Amey Group Ltd. 180
Anglian River Authority 320
Auger, H. 278/306
Austin J. 280
Ash, Ted. 119
Associated Electrical Industries Ltd. 148
Avon & Somerset River Board 47
A. Barker Crane Hire 192/193/317
Bateman, P. 313/316/324
Bauma Exhibition 1965. 169
Beattock By-pass 273
Becor House. 19
B.E. Executive Committee. 231
Beever Rooms. 287
Berg, E.P. 44/231/232/280/281/314/315
Bird, Philip 119
Bradley, R (West Piling) 182
Bradshaw, Keith 155/156
British Gypsum 214
Brown, Douglas. 178/179
Cerro Colorado Copper Mine 152
Chevassut, R.C. 94/278/280/292/305/306/307/315
Chinnor Cement Co. 46
Clawson, D.A. 176
Clugston Cawood 77
Coldrife O.C.C.S. 210
Coleman, W.W. 11/30/231
Coleshaw, C. 270
Concrete Industries 135
Deeping Fen, Lincs. 48
Dowsett Piling 188/189
Drax Power Station 181/186/187
Dublin Show 1965 264
Durand, P.H.R. 31/146/278/280
East Midland Municipal Engineers 139
Edwards. R.J. 280
English Electric Co. 281
Everitt, E.S. 7/11/21/44/141/166/231/232/280
Excavator Works 1955 38
Experimental Prototype Works 325
Falmouth Dock Construction 78
Farr 'Dynavane' System 135
Fen Drains & Excavations Ltd. 49
W & C French Ltd. 116/117
Frodingham Ironstone Mines 125
Frodingham Iron & Steel Co. 74
Gazeway Plant Hire Ltd. 245
Greetwell Quarry 270/296/312
Grider, Lyle 316/324
Hartland, F.T. 30/281
H&L Teeth 150/196
Holcombe Quarries 169
Hopcroft, E. 276
Hoveringham Stone Ltd. 93
Hyde-Truch, C.J. 11
Hydraulic Machine Development Machine 315
I.C.E. Exhibition 1961 110
I.C.E. Exhibition 1963 112
I.C.E. Exhibition 1965 (Crystal Palace) 264/265
I.C.E. Exhibition 1965 (Olympia) 240/241
I.C.E. Exhibition 1967 112

International Building Exhibition 1963 . . . . 229/230
W. Kendrick & Sons Ltd. 246
Ketton Portland Cement 68
Kirton Lindsey Quarry 317/326
Lehane, Mackenzie & Shand Ltd. 212
Lian Hup Granit Co. 50
E. Light & Sons Ltd 171
Lincoln Engineering Society 139
Linley, Sir Arnold 36
Litle, W.L. 30/44
Walter Llewellyn & Sons Ltd. 21
Longwood Quarries. 104/105
Mallabar, J. 281
Marlow, D. 37
Marston Valley Brick Works. 124
Martin & Co. Ltd. 118
Meanwell, P. 182
Meyer, R.E. 315/316
M.S. "Skagen" 222/225
Nigg Bay Oil Project 183/184
O.S.H.A. 122
Oxfordshire Ironstone Company. 59/60
Page, J.H. 31/119/137/141/280/281/292/306
J.H. Peck & Sons Ltd. 310
Poligkeit, Bert 37
Pontoon Dredger "Perak" 65
Product Range 1956. 52
Production Chart 1950 20
Production Team (Hydraulic Prototype) 313
Public Works Exhibition 1956 166
Public Works Exhibition 1976 316
R.A.F. Scampton 28
Restrictive Trades Practices Act 1958 158
Ribblesdale Cement Company 328/329
Rowlinson Construction Ltd 245
Rugby Cement Ltd 130-133
Savage, W. 11/30/31
Scott, G.A. 278/316
Seymour Plant 202
Shanks & MacEwen 109
Shepherd Hill & Co. 61
Slag Reduction Co. Ltd. 215
Smith-Clayton Forge 318
Star Cranes Ltd 234
Stevenson, P. 104
Stirlingshire C.C. 97
Strauss, Rt. Hon. G.R. 19
Tarmac Roadstone Co. 122
Tornberg & Lundberg 222/303
United & General Engineering Co. 154
Upper Witham Drainage Board 321
Wadsworth, E. 313
Walker, C. 33
Webster, N.E. 277
Wellington Works 288/289/290
Wests Piling. 182/185/190/198
Wilcock, J. 258
Willment Bros. 62/63
G. Wimpey & Co. 78/79/184/226/227
Works Re-organization Chart. 31
Wyatt, P. 46/259/270/271/305/317/324

RUSTON — BUCYRUS